S0-AVY-990

CURRENT TOPICS IN

DEVELOPMENTAL BIOLOGY

VOLUME 11

CONTRIBUTORS

J. BRACHET
MARGARET E. BUCKINGHAM
ROBERT CLELAND
ALFRED GIERER
JOHN PAUL MERLIE
P. D. NIEUWKOOP
STEVEN B. OPPENHEIMER
DAVID L. RAYLE
ROBERT G. WHALEN

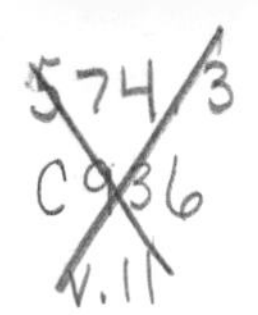

CURRENT TOPICS IN DEVELOPMENTAL BIOLOGY

EDITED BY

A. A. MOSCONA

DEPARTMENTS OF BIOLOGY AND PATHOLOGY
THE UNIVERSITY OF CHICAGO
CHICAGO, ILLINOIS

ALBERTO MONROY

C.N.R. LABORATORY OF MOLECULAR EMBRYOLOGY
ARCO FELICE (NAPLES), ITALY

VOLUME 11
Pattern Development

1977

ACADEMIC PRESS New York · San Francisco · London

A Subsidiary of Harcourt Brace Jovanovich, Publishers

ACADEMIC PRESS, INC.
111 Fifth Avenue, New York, New York 10003

United Kingdom Edition published by
ACADEMIC PRESS, INC. (LONDON) LTD.
24/28 Oval Road, London NW1

LIBRARY OF CONGRESS CATALOG CARD NUMBER: 66-28604

ISBN 0-12-153111-2

PRINTED IN THE UNITED STATES OF AMERICA

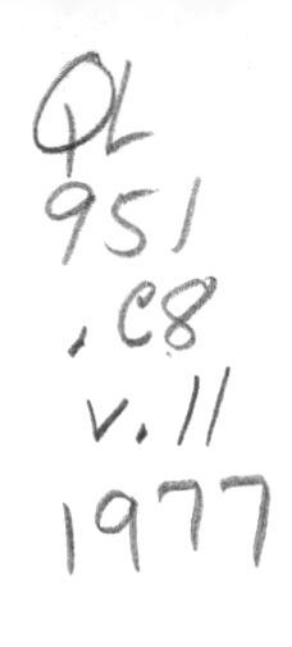

CONTENTS

CHAPTER 4. Origin and Establishment of Embryonic Polar Axes in Amphibian Development

P. D. NIEUWKOOP

CHAPTER 5. An Old Enigma: The Gray Crescent of Amphibian Eggs

J. BRACHET

CHAPTER 6. Control of Plant Cell Enlargement by Hydrogen Ions

DAVID L. RAYLE AND ROBERT CLELAND

LIST OF CONTRIBUTORS

Numbers in parentheses indicate the pages on which the authors' contributions begin.

J. BRACHET, *Laboratoire de Cytologie et Embryologie Moléculaires, Département de Biologie Moléculaire, Université Libre de Bruxelles, Bruxelles, Belgium and Laboratorio di Embriologia Molecolare, C.N.R. Arco Felice, Napoli, Italy* (133)

MARGARET E. BUCKINGHAM, *Service de Biochimie, Département de Biologie Moléculaire, Institut Pasteur, Paris, France* (61)

ROBERT CLELAND, *Department of Botany, University of Washington, Seattle, Washington* (187)

ALFRED GIERER, *Max-Planck-Institut für Virusforschung, Tübingen, West Germany* (17)

JOHN PAUL MERLIE, *Service de Biochimie, Département de Biologie Moléculaire, Institut Pasteur, Paris, France* (61)

P. D. NIEUWKOOP, *Hubrecht Laboratory, Uppsalalaan 8, Utrecht, The Netherlands* (115)

STEVEN B. OPPENHEIMER, *Department of Biology, California State University, Northridge, California* (1)

DAVID L. RAYLE, *Department of Botany, San Diego State University, San Diego, California* (187)

ROBERT G. WHALEN, *Service de Biochimie, Département de Biologie Moléculaire, Institut Pasteur, Paris, France* (61)

PREFACE

Volume 11 of Current Topics in Developmental Biology continues the editorial policy of including in the same volume diverse approaches and experimental systems related to a common theme. We thank the contributors for their cooperation in the preparation of this volume, and the staff of Academic Press for their efforts to expedite publication.

A. Monroy
A. A. Moscona

CURRENT TOPICS IN

DEVELOPMENTAL BIOLOGY

VOLUME 11

CHAPTER 1

INTERACTIONS OF LECTINS WITH EMBRYONIC CELL SURFACES

Steven B. Oppenheimer

DEPARTMENT OF BIOLOGY
CALIFORNIA STATE UNIVERSITY, NORTHRIDGE
NORTHRIDGE, CALIFORNIA

I. Introduction

The cell surface plays an important role in morphogenesis and malignancy. During morphogenesis cells make and break surface contacts, and surfaces of one type of cell move over surfaces of similar or different cells. The surfaces of cells, because they are involved in initiating cell interactions, must contain information that, in part, controls morphogenesis of developing individuals. In a similar sense, cells in primary tumors contact each other and surrounding cells at their surfaces. When surface contacts between cells in a tumor dissociate, tumor spread occurs. Cells are released from tumors and crawl or are transported by the bloodstream to distant sites in the body. New surface contacts are then made between tumor cells and normal cells, and secondary tumors develop.

Carbohydrate-containing molecules make up a part of the surface of cells. The oligosaccharide chains of glycoproteins, glycolipids, and polysaccharides reach away from the cell surface. These sugar chains, therefore, are likely candidates for mediating initial cell–cell surface interactions. Lectins, which are proteins or glycoproteins, usually isolated from the seeds of plants and other material, bind to cell surface sugar chains. Each lectin preferentially binds to certain terminal sugars or groups of sugars on these chains. Lectins, therefore, are useful tools for studying the surfaces of adult, embryonic, and malignant cells.

The literature on interactions of lectins with tumor cell surfaces is extensive and will not be dealt with in detail here. Instead, the present account focuses upon the interactions of lectins with embryonic cell surfaces. The first section of this report will briefly summarize information on various lectins and their sugar-binding specificity. The next section will deal with information gained through study of the interactions of lectins with gametes. Finally, it will be shown how lectins are being used to examine cell surface changes which occur during development in a variety of systems.

II. Characteristics of Lectin Interactions

A. Lectin–Cell Interactions

Numerous papers and reviews have appeared in recent years that provide detailed information about lectin biochemistry and interactions of lectins with cell surfaces and specific saccharides (for reviews, see Nicolson, 1974; Sharon and Lis, 1972; Lis and Sharon, 1973). A general picture has emerged regarding interactions of lectins with cell surfaces. Although many exceptions exist, it appears that many lectin receptor sites are more mobile in the membranes of tumor cells and embryonic cells than in a variety of untransformed cell lines. Lectins induce a clustering or capping of receptor sites in the membranes of transformed or embryonic cells but not in the surfaces of many nontransformed cell lines (review by Nicholson, 1974). Numbers of exposed cell surface lectin receptor sites may vary among cell types (Noonan and Burger, 1973) or at different stages in the cell cycle (Fox *et al.*, 1971). In general, the difference between heterogeneous populations of transformed and embryonic cells versus nontransformed cells appears to be a mobility of receptor sites rather than in numbers of surface sites (Nicolson, 1974). Such information has been obtained by measuring amount of bound radioactive (Cline and Livingston, 1971; Ozanne and Sambrook, 1971) or fluorescent lectin (Neri *et al.*, 1975, 1976) to cells and examining cells treated with ferritin or fluorescent-tagged lectins before and after fixation for patterns of receptor site distributions at the cell surface (Nicolson, 1974; Roberson *et al.*, 1975). Recent studies suggest that cytoskeletal elements such as microtubules and microfilaments help control mobility and distribution of cell surface lectin receptor sites (Nicolson, 1974; Yin *et al.,* 1972; Berlin and Ukena, 1972). Cytoskeletal element-disrupting drugs such as cytochalasin B, colchicine, vinblastine, and a variety of local anesthetics dramatically alter the mobility and distribution of cell surface lectin receptor sites in a variety of cell types (Nicolson, 1974; Kaneko *et al.,* 1973; Roberson and Oppenheimer, 1975; Poste *et al.,* 1975).

B. Lectin Specificities

Lectins may bind to the terminal sugars of cell surface oligosaccharides or with groups of sugars within oligosaccharide chains (So and Goldstein, 1967; Goldstein *et al.,* 1973). Concanavalin A (Con A) binds to α-D-mannose, D-glucose, or β-D-fructofuronosyl groups (So and Goldstein, 1967). Wheat germ agglutinin (WGA) binds *N*-acetyl-D-glucosamine-like residues (Burger, 1969). *Ricinus communis* agglutinin (RCA) binds β-D-galactose-like groups (RCA_I) (Nicolson *et al.,* 1973) or α- or β-D-galactose or *N*-acetyl-D-galactosamine-like residues (RCA_{II}) (Nicolson *et al.,* 1973). Soybean agglutinin (SBA) binds *N*-acetyl-D-galactosamine and D-galactose-like residues (Lis *et al.,* 1970). Numerous other lectins with preferential binding affinity toward given sugars or groups of sugars have been isolated and are reviewed in detail elsewhere (Nicolson, 1974; Mäkelä, 1957; Lis and Sharon, 1973; Boyd, 1963; Toms and Western, 1971). Some of these lectins and those saccharides to which they preferentially bind (in parentheses) follow: *Dolichos biflorus* (*N*-acetyl-D-galactosamine); *Lens culinaris* (α-D-mannose, α-D-glucose); *Ulex europaeus* (L-fucose); *Phaseolus vulgaris* (*N*-acetyl-D-galactosamine); *Lotus tetragonolobus* (α-L-fucose); *Robina pseudoacacia* (D-mannose, *N*-acetyl-D-glucosamine); *Helix pomatia* (*N*-acetyl-D-galactosamine); *Limulus polyphemus* (sialic acid); *Wisteria floribunda* (*N*-acetylgalactosamine).

C. Concanavalin A

Concanavalin A (Con A), isolated from the jackbean in 1936 by Sumner and Howell, has been extensively studied. Since this lectin has been used in many of the studies with embryonic cells that will be discussed here, a brief description of its properties is in order. Con A can be purified on Sephadex gels by affinity chromatography using sucrose or glucose in the elution buffer (Agrawal and Goldstein, 1967). Con A is composed of 25,500 molecular weight subunits. At a pH above 5.6, Con A protomers form tetramers of about 112,000 MW or larger aggregates (Agrawal and Goldstein, 1968; Becker *et al.,* 1971).

Edelman's group (Edelman *et al.*, 1972) has determined that Con A is a polypeptide chain containing 238 amino acid residues, and this group has provided a tentative primary sequence for the Con A molecule. Each Con A protomer has one carbohydrate binding site and two metal-binding sites (Edelman *et al.*, 1972). X-Ray crystallographic findings suggest that the Con A protomer is a globular protein of overall dimensions 42 Å × 40 Å × 39 Å (Edelman *et al.*, 1972).

III. Interactions of Lectins with Gametes

A. Sperm

The interactions of lectins with male gametes have been studied during the past 11 years in a number of laboratories. Kashiwabara *et al.* (1965) found that bull sperm were agglutinated tail-to-tail with soybean agglutinin. Head-to-head agglutination of sperm from clams (*Venus mercenaria* and *Mytilus mytilus*) was observed by Badel and Brilliantine (1969) using extracts from 23 different plant seeds. Other studies were completed by Uhlenbruck and Hermann (1972).

Nicolson and Yanagimachi (1974), using ferritin-conjugated RCA_I, found that the relative mobility of lectin receptors was higher on post-acrosomal regions of rabbit sperm than on acrosomal and tail regions. Lectin-induced clustering was not demonstrated in the acrosomal and tail regions, indicating the existence of localized restraints on the mobilities of lectin receptors.

Edelman and Millette (1971) cleaved rodent sperm at the junction of the heads and tails by treatment with proteases. The components were isolated by density-gradient centrifugation. Mouse sperm contained about 10^7 Con A receptor sites per cell using ^{125}I-labeled Con A. Sperm heads contained about 75% of the total numbers of Con A receptor sites. Using fluorescent-labeled Con A, these workers found that the Con A-binding sites on the head appeared to be concentrated in the acrosomal region. The carbohydrate-containing receptor sites on the sperm cell surface may play a role in the capacitation reaction or in the interactions of sperm with eggs. Nicolson *et al.* (1973) found that WGA and RCA mediated agglutination of rabbit sperm decreased during sperm maturation. Using ferritin-conjugated lectins, this group found that numbers of WGA and RCA binding sites decreased during maturation of these sperm, and this change in binding site number may relate to the increasing fertilizability of rabbit sperm during maturation. Nicolson (1974) pointed out that such studies provide important information about the surfaces of maturing spermatozoa and may eventually lead to the development of a contraceptive.

B. EGGS

Extensive investigations of egg surfaces have been made using lectins. Sea urchin fertilization could be prevented by treating eggs with Con A at 100 μg/ml (Lallier, 1972). In an interesting study by Oikawa *et al.* (1974), hamster fertilization was effectively inhibited by treatment of eggs with *Ricinus communis* agglutinin at 100 μg/ml, which binds terminal D-galactose-like residues on the cell surface. Wheat germ agglutinin and *Dolichos biflorus* agglutinin at similar concentrations also blocked fertilization. Con A was least effective. It was proposed by these workers that the agglutinins bind to specific oligosaccharides of the zona pellucida and induce cross-linking of adjacent saccharide chains in such a way to prevent enzymic penetration of the zona by the sperm. Here, too, development of effective contraceptives may be feasible by utilizing lectins which bind to cell surface saccharides potentially involved in fertilization or which may be linked in such a way to prevent sperm penetration as suggested above.

Monroy's group has investigated lectin receptor sites on ascidian eggs. Trypsin treatment enhanced agglutinability of unfertilized ascidian eggs *(Ascidia malaca)* after removal of chorions while untrypsinized eggs showed little agglutinability or fluorescence when treated with fluorescent-Con A (Monroy *et al.*, 1973). After fertilization (after elimination of polar bodies), Con A-mediated agglutination increased, fluorescence became pronounced after labeling with fluorescent-Con A, and binding of ^{125}I-labeled Con A also markedly increased (O-Dell *et al.*, 1973; Monroy *et al.*, 1973).

Con A binding to rabbit eggs also increased after fertilization (Gordon *et al.*, 1975). In mouse eggs, no increase in ^{125}I-labeled Con A (Pienkowski, 1974) or fluorescent-labeled Con A (Yanagimachi and Nicolson, 1974) binding occurred after fertilization but agglutinability of fertilized mouse eggs and parthenogenetically activated mouse eggs increased compared with unfertilized eggs (Pienkowski, 1974). Eggs therefore appear to possess lectin receptor sites and the characteristics of these sites change after fertilization.

Rodent eggs show species-specific differences in lectin-induced agglutination when treated with RCA_I (Oikawa *et al.*, 1975). Hamster eggs required only 3 μg of RCA_I per milliliter for maximal agglutination while mouse eggs required 10 μg/ml and rat eggs required 30 μg/ml of the lectin for maximal agglutination (Oikawa *et al.*, 1975). Thus, the zona pellucida of different rodent eggs is different with respect to oligosaccharide chain characteristics. Specific surface receptors for RCA_I, Con A, and WGA were localized on the zonae pellucidae and plasma membranes of hamster, mouse, and rat eggs with ferritin-labeled lectins. Intact eggs showed most dense concentrations of RCA_I and WGA receptors in the outermost regions of the zonae pellucidae of these eggs and sparse distributions of Con A receptors throughout the zonae (Nicolson *et al.*, 1975). Zona free eggs labeled with ferritin-RCA_I showed dense uniform labeling of their plasma membranes. Plasma membrane WGA and Con A binding sites were present in small clusters when eggs were incubated at 25°C. At low temperatures (near 0°C) or if eggs were fixed before addition of labeled lectin, these receptors appeared more randomly distributed. Thus, at 25°C lectin receptor sites can move in the plane of the plasma membrane. Nicolson *et al.* (1975) report that WGA bound to the zona blocks sperm binding to the zona. WGA does not block fertilization, however, in zona free eggs. Thus, the blocking or cross-linking of lectin receptors of the zona pellucida appears to be the primary mechanism by which WGA blocks fertilization. WGA receptors on the zona may be structurally related or sterically close to the sperm receptor sites.

Johnson *et al.* (1975) found that the plasma membrane of the unfertilized mouse egg contained areas which bound fluorescein isothiocyanate Con A (FITC-Con A) in different amounts. The area where the second polar body becomes extruded only slightly bound FITC-Con A. The rest of the surface bound this lectin intensely. In the hamster egg, FITC-Con A, RCA, and WGA bound well to the entire surface (Yanagimachi and Nicolson, 1976). In certain species, therefore, surface differentiations may exist at the egg surface prior to fertilization.

IV. Interactions of Lectins with Embryonic Cells: Cell Surface Changes during Development

A. Vertebrate Embryos

In pioneering studies, Moscona (1971) found that chick embryo neural retina and liver cells, dissociated with EDTA or trypsin, agglutinated with Con A. WGA did not cause these cells to agglutinate unless the cells were trypsinized prior to WGA treatment. These results suggested that WGA sites were present in untrypsinized cells, but in a state which precluded agglutination.

Kleinschuster and Moscona (1972), in their comprehensive follow-up study to Moscona's 1971 investigation, carefully examined the interactions of lectins with chick neural retina cells during different development stages. RCA agglutinated cells of all developmental stages to the same degree on matter whether the cells were obtained by EDTA treatment or trypsinization. These results suggest an abundance of RCA receptor sites throughout the surface of the cells at all developmental stages. WGA agglutinated only trypsinized cells from the various developmental stages (8-, 12-, 16-, and 20-day embryonic retinas) again suggesting that WGA surface receptor sites are present on untrypsinized cells of all stages but in a state that precludes agglutination. Con A receptor sites, however, appeared to change from an agglutinable to a nonagglutinable state during differentiation and aging of retina cells. Con A easily agglutinated EGTA-separated retina cells from earlier embryos but was markedly less effective on EGTA-separated cells from the later (fetal) stages. Trypsin treatment of the older cells facilitated increased agglutinability. These results (Kleinschuster and Moscona, 1972) show that embryonic cell surfaces change with differentiation and maturation. Such changes could involve changes in numbers of exposed surface lectin receptor sites or in distribution or mobility of these sites at the cell surface (Nicolson, 1974). It is clear, however, that young embryonic cells have similar characteristics of surface lectin receptor sites compared with transformed cells. Such information adds to the notion that cancer cells are adult cells which have regressed back to the embryonic state in terms of certain surface characteristics.

Other vertebrate developmental systems have been probed with lectins. K. E. Johnson and E. P. Smith (unpublished observations, 1976) found that blastula and gastrula stage cells of *Xenopus laevis* and *Xenopus mulleri* embryos dissociated with EDTA bind fluorescent-labeled Con A and soybean agglutinin. Only gastrula stage cells show clustered or capped lectin binding sites while blastula cells show a more random or even distribution of these binding sites. The bound lectins become restricted to portions of the cell surface in gastrula stage cells during incubation with lectin. There seems to be an increased mobility of Con A receptor sites in gastrula stage cells compared with blastula stage cells, which may reflect changes in membrane fluidity during development. There was a striking correlation between the onset of receptor site capping and clustering and the beginning of active cell movements. Other investigators have examined fluorescent-Con A binding to intact *Xenopus* embryos and report regional differences of binding patterns in these embryos (O'Dell *et al.*, 1974).

Nicolson and Yanagimachi (1974) found that FITC-Con A binding decreased as the early hamster embryo approached the blastocyst stage, and Nilsson *et al.* (1973) found that surface negative charge on rabbit blastocysts decreased prior to implantation in the uterus. These results may reflect changes in the biochemical structure of embryonic cell surfaces that prepare the embryo for implantation and further development (Yanagimachi and Nicolson, 1976).

In studies on mouse embryos (Rowinski *et al.,* 1976), 1-, 2-, 4-, and 8-cell stage embryos were agglutinable with Con A (10–100 μg/ml). Morulae agglutinated at concentrations of 100 μg/ml and higher while blastocysts did not agglutinate at all even at 5000 μg of Con A per milliliter. Inner cell masses isolated from blastocysts, however, were readily agglutinable at 10 μg of Con A per milliliter. Thus, significant membrane differences between agglutinable inner cell mass cells and outer, nonagglutinable, trophoblastic cells must exist.

B. Invertebrates

Lectins have helped reveal major differences in the surfaces of specific populations of developing sea urchin embryo cells. Using a quantitative electronic particle counter assay to measure lectin-mediated agglutination (Oppenheimer and Odencrantz, 1972), it was shown that *Strongylocentrotus purpuratus* and *Lytechinus pictus* embryo cells dissociated by removal of calcium and magnesium were 25 ± 5% more agglutinable with Con A at early developmental stages (day 1) than at later ones, with a marked decline in agglutinability between day 2 and day 3 (Fig. 1). Agglutinability with RCA also decreased gradually from days 1 to 7 of development (Fig. 1). RCA_{II} was more active in agglutinating these cells, suggesting involvement of *N*-acetyl-D-galactosamine-like groups. WGA-mediated agglutination remained very low at all developmental stages studied (Fig. 1), unless the cells were trypsinized (Krach *et al.,* 1973, 1974). In these studies agglutination was measured by electronically counting the number of single cells which form aggregates over time in a rotating suspension in a gyratory shaker (Moscona, 1961) with a large diameter of gyration (Henkart and Humphreys, 1970). This assay (Oppenheimer and Odencrantz, 1972; Oppenheimer, 1976) facilitates measuring agglutination quantitatively, utilizing very small sample sizes.

In the sea urchin embryo system it therefore appears that changes in specific carbohydrate-containing cell surface receptor sites occur with differentiation. It remained to be seen if these changes reflected changes in all cell populations or if specific cell populations differed in lectin receptor site characteristics.

The sea urchin embryo lends itself well to studies of specific embryonic cell populations because at the 16-cell stage very unequal cytoplasmic cleavage occurs that results in the formation of small cells (micromeres) that become motile mesenchyme cells and other larger cells (macromeres and mesomeres) that differentiate into a variety of tissues. Using Ficoll gradients (Hynes and Gross, 1970) to separate micromeres from macromeres and mesomeres, it was shown that only the micromeres were agglutinable with Con A whereas the other popu-

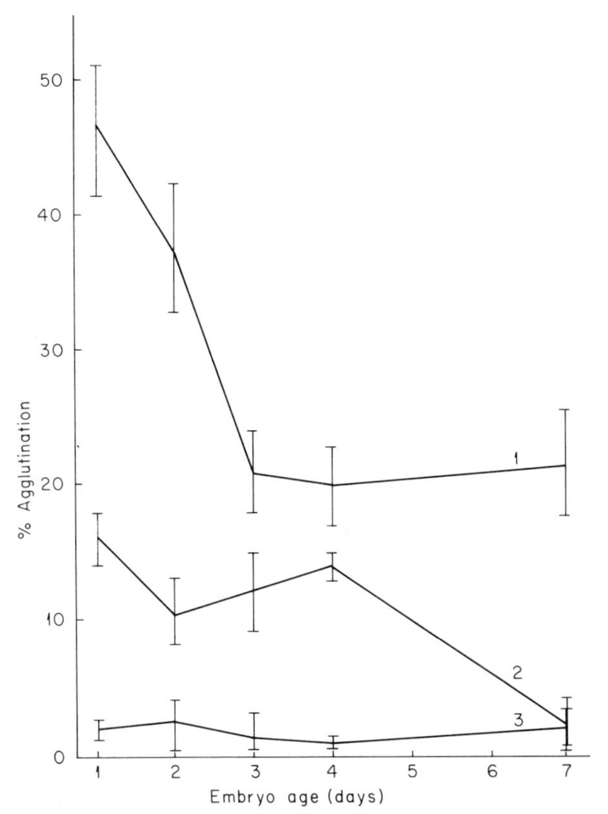

FIG. 1. Summary of age-dependent agglutination of sea urchin embryo cells with lectins. (1) Con A, 20 μg/ml; (2) RCA, 20 μg/ml; (3) WGA, 20 μg/ml. Embryos were dissociated in calcium-magnesium-free sea water and rotated; percent agglutination was determined after 60 minutes as described by Krach *et al.* (1974). Each point gives the range of values obtained in 3 repeated experiments. In each experiment, duplicate vials were used for each time point. Values have been corrected for background aggregation occurring in lectin-free controls.

lations were not (Roberson and Oppenheimer, 1975) (Fig. 2). Preliminary experiments (Sternburg and S. B. Oppenheimer, unpublished observations) suggest that it is at the 16-cell stage, at the stage at which micromeres, mesomeres, and macromeres are formed, that a major differentiation in lectin receptor site characteristics occur between the newly formed cell types.

Fluorescent-tagged Con A was utilized to determine the nature of the surface differences between micromeres, mesomeres, and macromeres (Roberson *et al.*, 1975).

When the sea urchin embryo cells were fixed before addition of

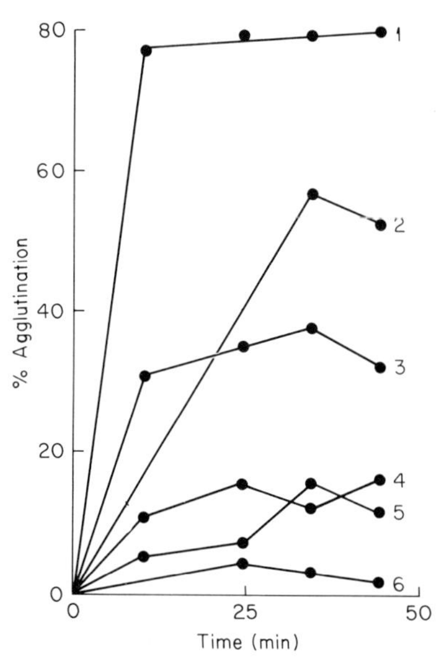

FIG. 2. Kinetics of Con A agglutinability of specific sea urchin cell populations. (1) micromeres; (2) 50% micromeres, 50% mesomeres and macromeres; (3) mesomeres and macromeres; (1, 2, 3) Con A 1 mg/ml; (4) mesomeres and macromeres; (5) 50% micromeres, 50% mesomeres and macromeres; (6) micromeres; (4, 5, 6) without Con A. Embryos were dissociated, separated and rotated as described in Roberson and Oppenheimer (1975), and the percent agglutination was determined as the percentage of single cells that have agglutinated under the standard conditions of the assay.

fluorescent-Con A (750 μg/ml) all three cell populations displayed random receptor site distributions. However, if the cells were treated with fluorescent-Con A prior to fixation, the receptor sites on the micromeres were capped or highly clustered, while macromeres and mesomeres displayed random site distributions (Fig. 3) (Roberson *et al.*, 1975). Con A, therefore, induced clustering and capping of receptor sites only on the micromeres, suggesting that the lateral mobility of Con A receptor sites on these cells is greater than on the other cell types. The greater lateral mobility of Con A receptor sites on specific embryonic cells, malignant cells, and other migratory or motile cell types may be due to (1) greater intrinsic fluidity of the lipid bilayer, (2) structural modification of Con A receptor sites, or (3) alterations in the structure of microtubules and microfilaments attached to the inner membrane surface which might affect the mobility of membrane proteins and glycoproteins. These possibilities and others have been discussed by Nicolson (1974).

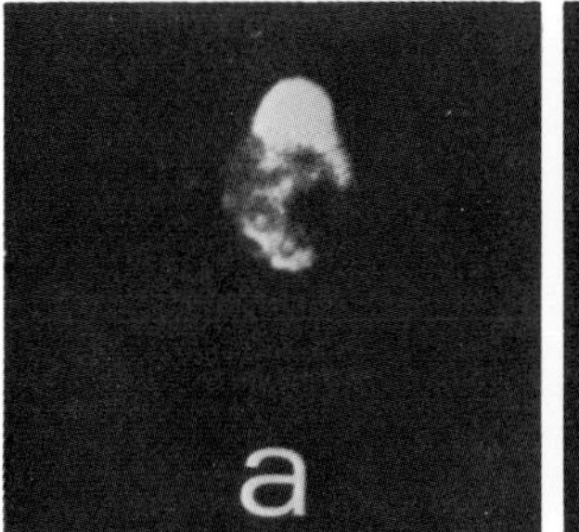

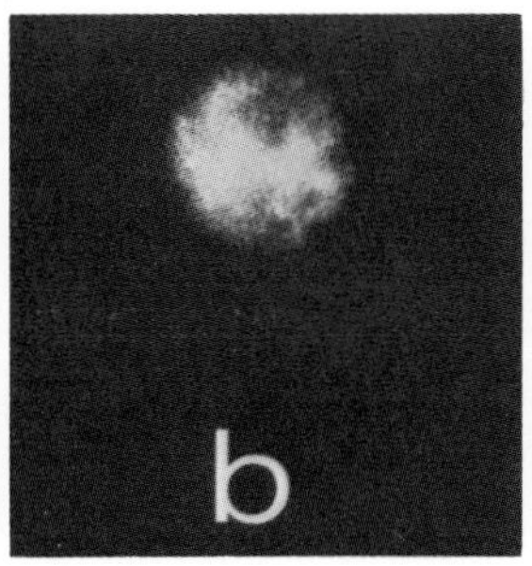

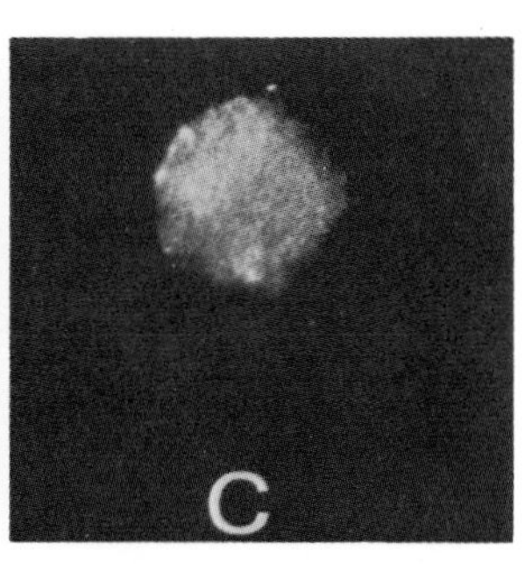

FIG. 3. Concanavalin A receptor site distribution on the surface of a micromere, mesomere, and macromere. Gametes of the sea urchin *Strongylocentrotus purpuratus* were obtained by injection of 0.55 *M* KCl. The egg suspensions were treated and fertilized as described by Roberson and Oppenheimer (1975). The zygotes were distributed into beakers and allowed to develop at 17°C until the 32- to 64-cell stage was reached. Zygotes were collected and washed 3 times in CMF-SW with 1% Ficoll. Each 3 ml of packed cells was incubated for 10 minutes in 2 ml of 0.01 *M* EGTA in CMF-SW with 1% Ficoll and gently aspirated to complete dissociation. This cell suspension was diluted with 10 ml of CMF-SW with 1% Ficoll and layered over a 5 to 15% discontinuous Ficoll gradient made in a beaker. The beaker was placed in a 17°C incubator for 3 hours in order to separate out any debris, unfertilized eggs, or undissociated embryos. Cells were treated with FITC-Con A (750 μg/ml, Miles-Yeda) for 10 minutes in rotating suspension at 17°C and washed in CMF-SW with 1% Ficoll. The cells were fixed in 4% formaldehyde in CMF-SW with 1% Ficoll for 20 minutes, washed twice, and mounted on slides. (a) Micromere; (b) mesomere; (c) macromere. From Roberson *et al.* (1975). Copyright 1975 by the American Association for the Advancement of Science.

A method has been developed to quantitatively determine topographic distributions of lectin receptor sites on the surfaces of specific single cells (Neri *et al.*, 1976). This method utilizes a photometer attached to a fluorescence microscope and an adjustable measuring field diaphragm that only permits light from the specific field under study to reach the photomultiplier (Fig. 4). This technique permits simultaneous examination of bound lectin qualitatively and quantitatively, allows study of lectin binding to the surface of a single cell or part of a single cell, and is more rapid and less costly than radioactivity methods that require large numbers of cells.

This method has been utilized to quantitatively determine lectin receptor site distributions on sea urchin micromeres, mesomeres, and macromeres before and after fixation (Neri *et al.*, 1975). Figure 5 and Table I quantitatively show that: (1) the micromeres do not bind significantly more fluorescent Con A per unit area than the macromeres; and (2) Con A-induced clustering or capping is significantly higher in the micromeres as judged by the higher variation in fluorescence intensity of four areas measured on each individual cell and by the fact that

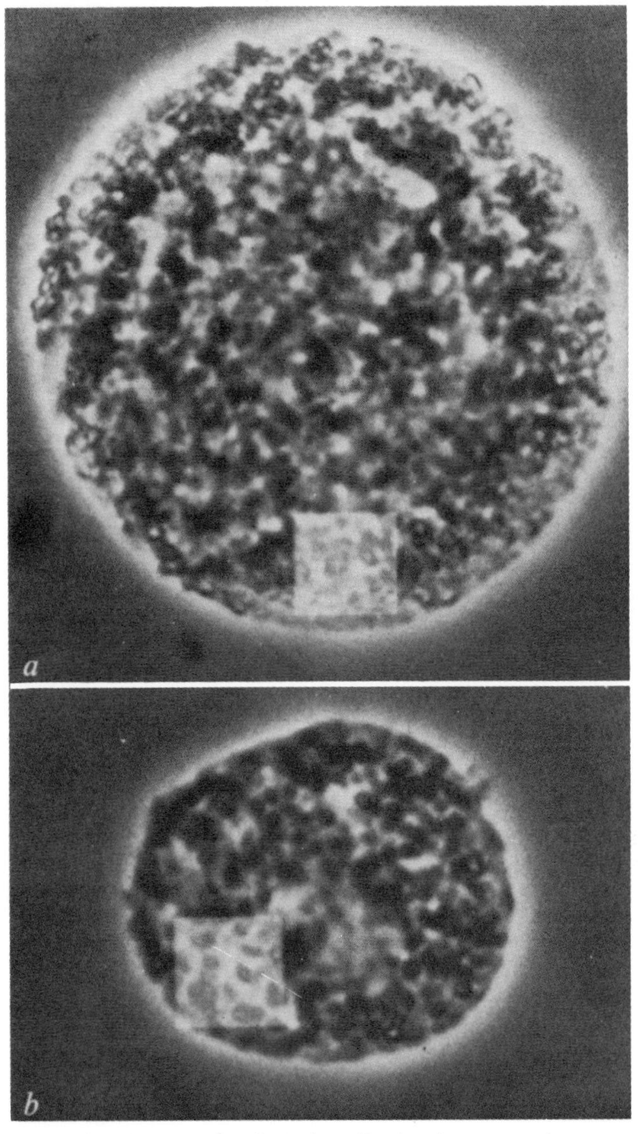

FIG. 4. Specific populations of embryonic cells showing measuring area. A sample containing cells of both populations that have been treated with FITC-Con A (750 μg/ml) and fixed in 4% formaldehyde. An individual cell of either type was brought into focus by phase-contrast illumination before photoexcitation to limit fluorescence fading to a minimum. At this time diameter measurements were taken; the surface area was calculated and entered in Table I. The measuring field diaphragm for fluorescence quantitation was then adjusted to cover an area of 56.25 μm^2. Thereafter, the only light reaching

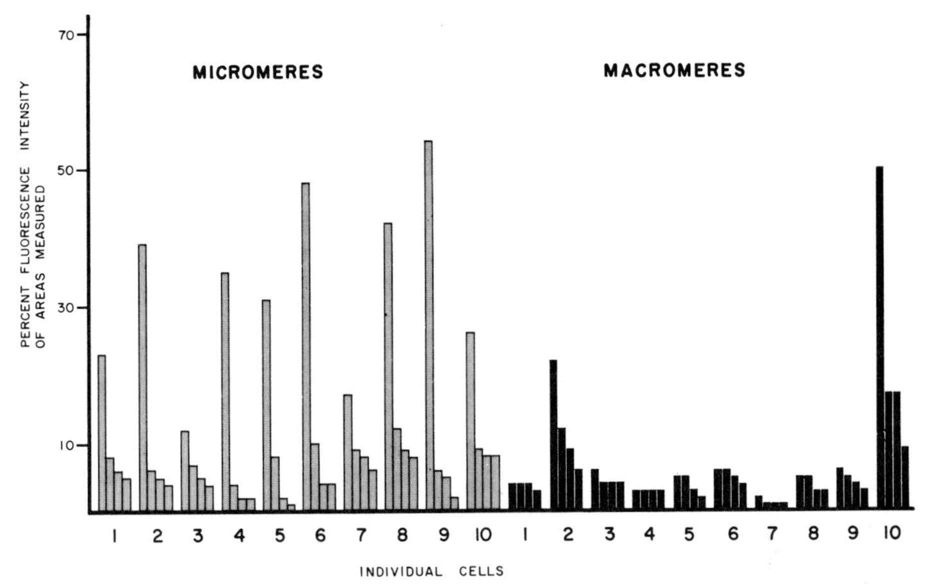

FIG. 5. Fluorescence intensity distribution of four areas measured on ten individual micromeres (shaded columns) and macromeres (solid columns). Abscissa: 10 individual cells of both types. Ordinate: fluorescence intensity (%) of areas measured was derived from:

$$\frac{\text{Intensity of each area measured}}{\text{Fluorescence intensity of individual cell}} \times 100$$

Also see legend to Table I. From Neri *et al.* (1975). Reprinted with permission from *Nature*.

the fluorescence intensity contributions to the mean fluorescence intensity of 10 cells by the capped areas in micromeres was higher than that of macromeres. Therefore, quantitative fluorescence topographical measurements support the previous qualitative observations that

---

the photomultiplier was that which was included by the measuring area only. To determine the topographical distribution of FITC-Con A on the surfaces of individual cells, the fluorescence intensity of 4 distinct areas comprising 56.25 μm^2 were measured. The source for fluorescence excitation was from an XBO 150 W, 20 V Xenon lamp (Osram) powered by a Leitz power supply rated at $\pm 0.1\%$ constant voltage supply. The following light filters were used: excitation filter 5 mm BG12; red suppression filter 4 mm BG 38; and suppression filters K495 and K510. The photomultiplier used was an EMI 9558 with photocathode type S20. The high tension supply unit was set to deliver 1.1 kV to the photomultiplier, the digital picoammeter set at a display rate of 1 s^{-1}. (a) Macromere with measuring area (phase contrast, × 1625). (b) Micromere with measuring area (phase contrast, × 1625). All measurements of fluorescence intensity are given in Table I and Fig. 5. From Neri *et al.* (1975). Reprinted with permission from *Nature*.

TABLE I

A QUANTITATIVE COMPARISON OF FLUORESCENCE TOPOGRAPHY DISPLAYED ON THE SURFACES OF SPECIFIC POPULATIONS OF EMBRYONIC CELLS TREATED WITH FITC-CON A[a]

Cell type	Mean surface area (μm^2)	MFI[b]	MFI/surface area (μm^2)	MFI/area measured	MFI of areas measured excluding cap areas	MFI of cap areas measured only	Fluorescence intensity contribution by cap areas to MFI
Micromere	1,052.35 ± 101.91[d]	55.62 ± 11.64	0.058 ± 0.014	7.23 ± 1.82	3.05 ± 0.44	19.77 ± 5.66	32.2% ± 4.3%
Macromere	3,397.97 ± 307.85	130.32 ± 33.09	0.038 ± 0.008	5.97 ± 0.91	5.00 ± 0.80	8.93 ± 2.64	10.8% ± 4.7%

[a] From Neri *et al.* (1975).

[b] For measuring the mean fluorescence intensity (MFI) of 10 cells of each type, the measuring field diaphragm was adjusted to provide an area which measured the fluorescence of only 1 cell. Corrections for fluorescence contributed by background during these measurements have been made. For fluorescence background measurement, three empty areas adjacent to the cell which had been previously quantified were measured, and the mean was subtracted from the total fluorescence intensity. Units of fluorescence intensity are in terms of 10^{-8} A.

[c] An area measured for each individual cell of both populations was 56.25 μm^2.

[d] Standard error.

specific embryonic cell populations possess lectin receptor sites that differ in mobility characteristics.

V. Concluding Remarks

Cell surface carbohydrate-containing molecules have been implicated in mediating cellular interactions (Oppenheimer *et al.,* 1969; Oppenheimer, 1973, 1976; Hausman and Moscona, 1973; Roseman, 1970; Roth *et al.,* 1971; Chipowsky *et al.,* 1973; McLean and Bosmann, 1975; Weiss, 1967). Oligosaccharide chains from cell surface complex carbohydrates extend from the cell surface and offer a first line of contact with approaching cells and substrates. Lectins, which somewhat specifically bind to these chains, offer useful probes for examining the role of these molecules in mediating contact and migration of cells (Steinberg and Gepner, 1973) in dynamic systems such as developing embryos and tumors.

ACKNOWLEDGMENT

The investigations summarized in this review from the laboratory of the author were supported by DHEW research grant CA 12920 from the National Cancer Institute.

REFERENCES

Agrawal, B. B. L., and Goldstein, I. J. (1967). *Biochim. Biophys. Acta* **147**, 262.
Agrawal, B. B. L., and Goldstein, I. J. (1968). *Arch. Biochem. Biophys.* **124**, 218.
Badel, P., and Brilliantine, L. (1969). *Proc. Soc. Exp. Biol. Med.* **130**, 621.

Becker, J. W., Reeke, G. N., and Edelman, G. M. (1971). *J. Biol. Chem.* **246**, 6123.
Berlin, R. D., and Ukena, T. E. (1972). *Nature (London), New Biol.* **238**, 120.
Boyd, W. C. (1963). *Vox Sang.* **8**, 1.
Burger, M. M. (1969). *Proc. Natl. Acad. Sci. U.S.A.* **62**, 994.
Chipowsky, S., Lee, Y. C., and Roseman, S. (1973). *Proc. Natl. Acad. Sci. U.S.A.* **70**, 2309.
Cline, M. J., and Livingston, D. C. (1971). *Nature (London), New Biol.* **232**, 155.
Edelman, G. M., and Millette, C. F. (1971). *Proc. Natl. Acad. Sci. U.S.A.* **68**, 2436.
Edelman, G. M., Cunningham, B. A., Reeke, G. N., Jr., Becker, J. W., Waxdal, N. J., and Wang, J. L. (1972). *Proc. Natl. Acad. Sci. U.S.A.* **69**, 2580.
Fox, T. O., Sheppard, J. R., and Burger, M. M. (1971). *Proc. Natl. Acad. Sci. U.S.A.* **68**, 244.
Goldstein, I. J., Reichert, C. M., Misaki, A., and Gorin, P. A. J. (1973). *Biochim. Biophys. Acta* **317**, 500.
Gordon, M., Fraser, L. R., and Dandekar, P. V. (1975). *Anat. Rec.* **181**, 95.
Hausman, R. E., and Moscona, A. A. (1973). *Proc. Natl. Acad. Sci. U.S.A.* **70**, 3111.
Henkart, P., and Humphreys, T. (1970). *Exp. Cell Res.* **63**, 224.
Hynes, R. O., and Gross, P. R. (1970). *Dev. Biol.* **21**, 383.
Johnson, M. H., Eager, D., Muggleton-Harris, A., and Grave, H. M. (1975). *Nature (London)* **257**, 321.
Kaneko, I., Satoh, H., and Ukita, T. (1973). *Biochem. Biophys. Res. Commun.* **50**, 1087.
Kashiwabara, T., Tanaka, R., and Matsumoto, T. (1965). *Nature (London)* **207**, 831.
Kleinschuster, S. J., and Moscona, A. A. (1972). *Exp. Cell Res.* **70**, 397.
Krach, S. W., Green, A., Nicolson, G. L., and Oppenheimer, S. B. (1973). *J. Cell Biol.* **59**, 176a.
Krach, S. W., Green, A., Nicolson, G. L., and Oppenheimer, S. B. (1974). *Exp. Cell Res.* **84**, 191.
Lallier, R. (1972). *Exp. Cell Res.* **72**, 157.
Lis, H., and Sharon, N. (1973). *Annu. Rev. Biochem.* **43**, 541.
Lis, H., Sela, B., Sachs, L., and Sharon, N. (1970). *Biochim. Biophys. Acta* **192**, 364.
McLean, R. J., and Bosmann, H. B. (1975). *Proc. Natl. Acad. Sci. U.S.A.* **72**, 310.
Mäkelä, O. (1957). *Ann. Med. Exp. Fenn.* **35**, 1.
Monroy, A., Ortolani, G., O'Dell, D., and Millonig, G. (1973). *Nature (London) New Biol.* **242**, 409.
Moscona, A. A. (1961). *Exp. Cell Res.* **22**, 455.
Moscona, A. A. (1971). *Science* **171**, 905.
Neri, A., Roberson, M., Connolly, D. T., and Oppenheimer, S. B. (1975). *Nature (London)* **258**, 342.
Neri, A., Roberson, M., and Oppenheimer, S. B. (1976). *In* "Concanavalin A as a Tool" (H. Bittiger and H. B. Schnebli, eds.), p. 221. Wiley, Sussex.
Nicolson, G. L. (1974). *Int. Rev. Cytol.* **39**, 89.
Nicolson, G. L., and Yanagimachi, R. (1974). *Science* **184**, 1294.
Nicolson, G. L., Blaustein, J., and Etzler, M. E. (1973). *Biochemistry* **13**, 196.
Nicolson, G. L., Yanagimachi, R., and Yanagimachi, H. (1975). *J. Cell Biol.* **66**, 263.
Nilsson, O., Lindqvist, L., and Ronquist, G. (1973). *Exp. Cell Res.* **83**, 421.
Noonan, K. D., and Burger, M. M. (1973). *J. Biol. Chem.* **248**, 4286.
O'Dell, D. S., Ortolani, G., and Monroy, A. (1973). *Exp. Cell Res.* **83**, 408.
O'Dell, D. S., Tencer, R., Monroy, A., and Brachet, J. (1974). *Cell Differ.* **3**, 193.
Oikawa, T., Nicolson, G. L., and Yanagimachi, R. (1974). *Exp. Cell Res.* **83**, 239.
Oikawa, T., Yanagimachi, R., and Nicolson, G. L. (1975). *J. Reprod. Fertil.* **43**, 137.
Oppenheimer, S. B. (1973). *Exp. Cell Res.* **77**, 175.

Oppenheimer, S. B. (1976). *In* "Tests of Teratogenicity in Vitro," p. 261. North-Holland Publ., Amsterdam.
Oppenheimer, S. B., and Odencrantz, J. (1972). *Exp. Cell Res.* **73**, 475.
Oppenheimer, S. B., Edidin, M., Orr, C. W., and Roseman, S. (1969). *Proc. Natl. Acad. Sci. U.S.A.* **63**, 1395.
Ozanne, B., and Sambrook, J. (1971). *Nature (London), New Biol.* **232**, 156.
Pienkowski, M. (1974). *Proc. Soc. Exp. Biol. Med.* **145**, 464.
Poste, G., Papahadjopoulos, D., and Nicolson, G. L. (1975). *Proc. Natl. Acad. Sci. U.S.A.* **72**, 4430.
Roberson, M., and Oppenheimer, S. B. (1975). *Exp. Cell Res.* **91**, 263.
Roberson, M., Neri, A., Oppenheimer, S. B. (1975). *Science* **189**, 639.
Roseman, S. (1970). *Chem. Phys. Lipids* **5**, 270.
Roth, S., McGuire, E. J., and Roseman, S. (1971). *J. Cell Biol.* **51**, 525.
Rowinski, J., Solter, D., and Koprowski, H. (1976). *Exp. Cell Res.* (in press).
Sharon, N., and Lis, H. (1972). *Science* **177**, 949.
So, L. L., and Goldstein, I. J. (1967). *J. Immunol.* **99**, 158.
Steinberg, M. S., and Gepner, I. A. (1973). *Nature (London), New Biol.* **241**, 249.
Sumner, J. B., and Howell, S. F. (1936). *J. Bacteriol.* **32**, 227.
Toms, G. C., and Western, A. (1971). *In* "Chemotaxonomy of the Leguminosae" (J. B. Harborne, D. Boulter, and B. L. Turner, eds.), p. 367. Academic Press, New York.
Uhlenbruck, G., and Hermann, W. P. (1972). *Vox Sang.* **23**, 444.
Weiss, L. (1967). "The Cell Periphery, Metastasis, and Other Contact Phenomena." North-Holland Publ., Amsterdam.
Yanagimachi, R., and Nicolson, G. L. (1974). *J. Cell Biol.* **63**, 381a.
Yanagimachi, R., and Nicolson, G. L. (1976). *Exp. Cell Res.* (in press).
Yin, H. H., Ukena, T. E., and Berlin, R. D. (1972). *Science* **178**, 866.

CHAPTER 2

BIOLOGICAL FEATURES AND PHYSICAL CONCEPTS OF PATTERN FORMATION EXEMPLIFIED BY HYDRA

Alfred Gierer

MAX-PLANCK-INSTITUT FÜR VIRUSFORSCHUNG,
TÜBINGEN, WEST GERMANY

I. Introduction

Morphogenesis of a higher organism is a complex process that we can hope to understand only as combinations of more elementary mechanisms. Whereas the formation of some subcellular structures such as ribosomes and chromosomes probably involves self-assembly of molecules analogous to crystallization, most multicellular biological patterns cannot be understood merely on this basis. Rather, regulation of cell proliferation and differentiation as well as the interaction of and communication between cells play a major role. Thus, the following processes are expected to contribute to multicellular order:

1. Spatial patterns of differentiated cells may result from the regu-

lation of the time sequences and quantities in which various cell types are produced.

2. Cells may move within a tissue, e.g., attracted by chemotactic substances.

3. Cells may interact by direct contact to form or stabilize specific structures, like single and double cell layers, hollow spheres, and tubes.

4. Local changes in cell interaction, differentiation, mobility, and/or proliferation may cause tissues to evaginate and build a new structure, such as a bud.

5. Initially near-homogeneous structures develop strikingly different parts. Formation of a localized structure is often preceded by "prepatterns," that is, spatial patterns of some physical properties that determine the positions at which, for example, cell differentiation and tissue evagination proceed.*

Insights into these processes have been derived from many different organisms. A suitable one is the freshwater coelenterate hydra, since it exhibits several elementary processes in a relatively simple form. These are the subjects of the first part of the article, where some recent evidence on cell differentiation, cell movement, cell interaction, and morphogenesis in hydra will be discussed with particular emphasis on spatial patterns and prepatterns.

On this basis I will discuss, in a second part, some general concepts of biological pattern formation, with emphasis on physicochemical mechanisms capable of forming reproducible spatial patterns. Readers mainly interested in these physical aspects of biological pattern formation may begin with Section III.

II. Hydra as Model for Elementary Processes in Development

A. Some Properties of Hydra

Hydra is a few millimeters long and has an asymmetrical polar organization with tentacles, hypostome, and the gastric column including the budding zone, peduncle, and basal disk (Fig. 1a). It is made of two cell layers, ectoderm and endoderm, with a mesoglea in between (Fig. 1b). Further, there are mucous cells in the hypostome, gland cells in the endoderm of the gastric column, and secreting basal disc cells in the foot. Embedded mostly in the ectodermal layer of the gastric col-

* This definition of prepatterns, which is somewhat more general as well as more abstract than that in part of the literature, will be used in this article. It implies that the relation between prepatterns and patterns can be obvious or subtle, simple or complex.

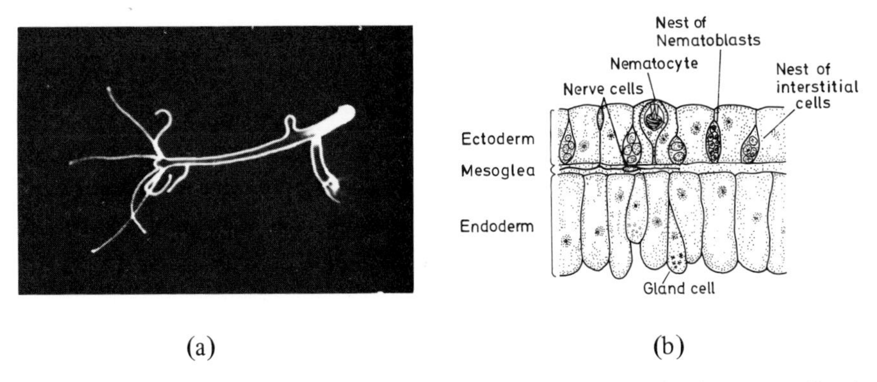

FIG. 1. (a) Hydra has a polar structure with (left to right) tentacles, hypostome (head area), and the gastric column including a budding zone, peduncle, and basal disk. The figure shows an animal with two buds. (b) Schematic drawing of a cross section through the wall of the gastric column, showing the two cell layers with various cell types.

umn are interstitial cells which look undifferentiated and occur singly as well as in nests. Further, one finds—also in nests—large numbers of nematoblasts which are precursors of the nematocytes. The latter are produced in the gastric column, but most nematocytes migrate to the tentacles that catch and kill the prey. There are different types of nematocytes with different spatial distributions in the animal. Further, there are nerve cells occurring all over the animal, but at highest concentrations in the head area.

Well-fed animals proliferate by budding. They can be grown in the laboratory (Loomis and Lenhoff, 1956), doubling once in about 3.5 days. The interstitial cells (i-cells) are stem cells and precursors to nerves and nematocytes in growing and budding hydra. These i-cells are particularly suitable for studying quantitative aspects of cell differentiation and its regulation.

The most interesting feature of hydra is its high power of regeneration. Hydra became one of the earliest model systems in the history of developmental biology when Abraham Trembley, in 1740, discovered that a section of the gastric column regenerates a complete animal with head and foot within a few days. Evidence on regeneration and transplantation shows that prepatterns are involved in directing the positions of new heads and feet. Hydra regeneration thus allows us to study the basic problem of how, within a near-uniform tissue, new structures are formed at predictable positions, and to evaluate general concepts on prepattern formation.

B. Steady-State Analysis of Cell Differentiation

In growing and budding hydra, epithelial cells produce their own type (Campbell, 1967; Clarkson and Wolpert, 1967; David and Campbell, 1972). The origin of minor components, such as mucous and gland cells, is not yet established. Nematocytes and nerves are derived from i-cells (Lentz, 1966; Burnett, 1968), part of which are stem cells capable of reproducing themselves as well as giving rise to differentiated cells. Stem cells are regulated so that, in each round of replication, defined proportions reproduce their own kind and develop into one or several pathways of differentiation, respectively. This "decision" between pathways corresponds to the elementary process that occurs repeatedly in cell lineages of higher organisms leading from the fertilized egg to the system of differentiated cells. In most biological systems each decision is restricted to a limited phase of development. However, some systems are in a steady state, reproducing stem cells and producing differentiated cells continuously. Examples are the bone marrow system with stem cells producing granulocytes and erythrocytes, and well-fed growing and budding hydra with the interstitial cells producing nerves and nematocytes. Such steady states are particularly suitable for quantitative evaluations.

A typical example for the steady-state analysis of i-cells and their products in the body column of hydra is the kinetics of incorporation of DNA precursors into nerve cells (David and Gierer, 1974). Radioactive thymidine is applied to whole animals, and after various time intervals, hydras are disintegrated into cells, and the proportion of nerve cells carrying radioactive label is determined. There is a lag phase of about 18 hours with no label in nerves. Thereafter the proportion of labeled nerve cells increases at a rate of about 18% per day. It follows that 18 hours elapse between the end of the last S phase and the appearance of neural processes. There must be a cell division in between, because the DNA complement of nerve cells is $2n$. The subsequent increase of 18% per day accounts for the maintenance of the density of nerve cells in the expanding tissue. Even after many days, still a considerable part of the nerve cells is unlabeled, showing that nerves have a long life-span in the tissue.

In nematocyte production, interstitial cells produce nests of up to 32 cells by subsequent synchronous divisions (Slautterback and Fawcett, 1959; Lehn, 1951; Rich and Tardent, 1969; David and Challoner, 1974). Interstitial cells are rapidly labeled with no lag phase detectable. From kinetic data the times of replication have been determined (Campbell and David, 1974). After the last division, cells differentiate into nematocytes, passing through a long nematoblast stage. Several days

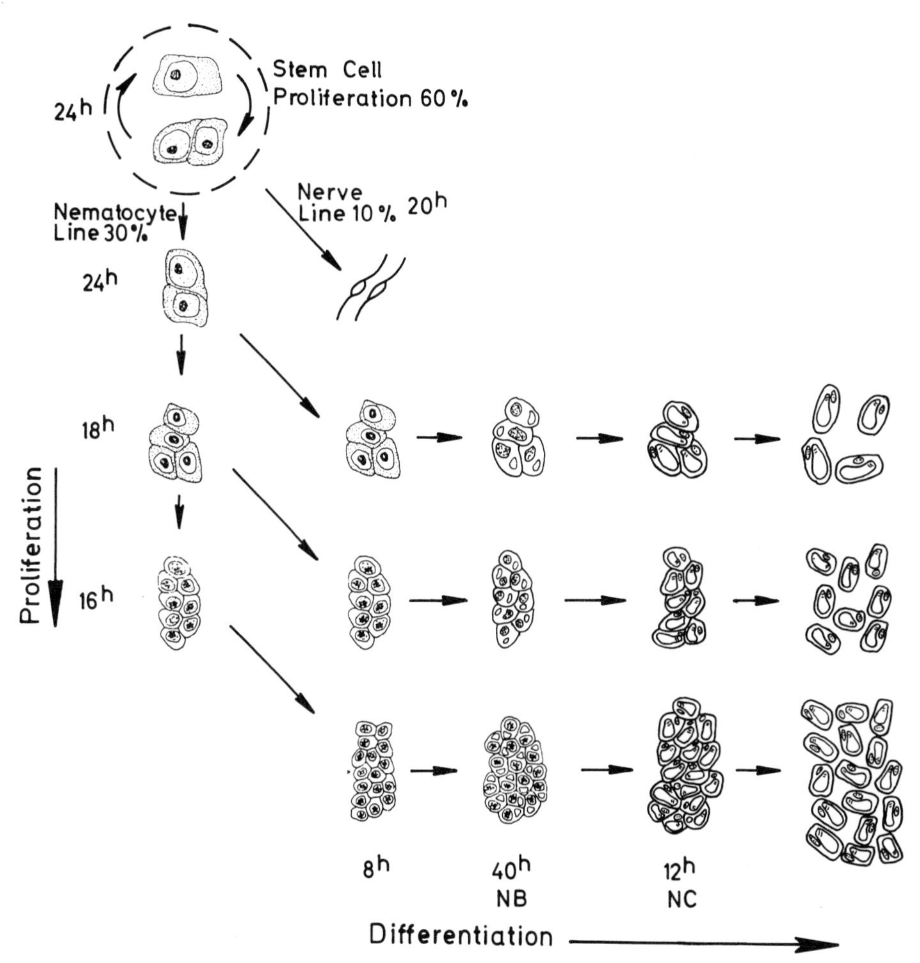

FIG. 2. Cell proliferation and differentiation in the steady state of growing and budding hydra. Nerve cells and nematocytes are produced from interestitial (i-) cells as precursors. Among the i-cells there are some 4000 stem cells reproducing once per day. Of the cells reproduced, 60% are stem cells, 10% lead to nerves, and 30% to nematocytes. Proliferation rates and turnover times of intermediates are indicated in the cell flow diagram. NB, nematoblasts; NC, nematocytes. Adapted from David and Gierer (1974).

elapse from the last round of DNA replication to the completion of the nematocyte capsule (Vögeli, 1972).

The lag phases of labeling and the turnover times of nematoblasts and nematocytes were measured for the steady state. Taking all these measurements together, the time course of production and differentiation of nerves and nematocytes can be reconstructed (David and Gierer, 1974) (Fig. 2).

If the exponential increase of all parts of the cell population with time is taken into account, amounts of various cell types are inversely related to the times of proliferation and transition. Amounts of cell types and nests of interstitial cells of various size calculated on this basis from the kinetic data agree well with the amounts measured directly, showing the consistency of the cell flow diagram (Fig. 2). In particular, the number of interstitial cells occurring singly and in nests of two account for the maintenance of their own concentration in the tissue as well as that of nerve and nematocyte production. Among these interstitial cells are the true stem cells capable of both reproducing their own type and producing differentiated cells. Their number is estimated to be around 4000. They replicate about once per day; 60% of the cells produced are stem cells, 30% are nematocyte precursors, and 10% are nerve precursors. In nematocyte production, each further replication of interstitial cells producing nests takes around 20 hours. Eight hours after the last replication the nematoblast vacuoles appear, and after another 40 hours the capsule of the mature nematocyte is visible. Some 12 hours later, nematocytes separate, and most of them move to the tentacles.

C. Regulatory Processes in Differentiation

1. *Regulation of the Stem Cell Pool*

In the steady state, the relative amount of stem cells in the tissue is maintained indefinitely. This must be due to a regulation in which stem cells or their products feed back negatively on stem cell production. It is conceivable that regulation affects proliferation rates or the proportion of stem cells reproducing their own kind. Bode *et al.* (1976) have partially depleted hydra tissue of interstitial cells by treatment with hydroxyurea and studied the kinetics of replenishment. The data are consistent with the concept that at low i-cell densities the proportion of stem cells which produce differentiated cells upon replication drops below the steady state level of 40%, to increase the production of new stem cells for replenishment.

2. *Regulation of Nematocyte Production*

Different types of nematocytes arise from different average nest sizes (David and Challoner, 1974), and production rates follow different spatial patterns in the gastric column (Lehn, 1951; Tardent *et al.*, 1971). Depletion of nematocytes by excessive discharge in the tentacles affects regulation of nematocyte production in the gastric column (Zumstein, 1973). The regulatory effects appear to be on the determination of stem cells to produce nematocytes of various types, and on average nest size of nematoblasts, which depends on the number of replication of i-cells (see Fig. 2). Thus nematocyte production is controlled by feedback from products to precursors.

3. Spatial Pattern of Nerve Cells

The ratio of 1:3 for nerve cell versus nematocyte determination of stem cells is an average over the body column of mature hydra. The actual cell differentiation follows a spatial pattern with many nerves produced in the small head area and all nematocytes in the gastric column. One may calculate from the cell distribution (Bode *et al.*, 1973) that the ratio of stem cells required for nerve versus nematocyte production in the gastric column is about 1:7, whereas in the head almost exclusively nerve cells are produced. This spatial pattern is regulated, probably by the spatial distribution of substances acting as morphogens. It is conceivable that they act on proliferation, movement and/or determination of i-cells. In the head area, there are only few i-cells, most of them single (David and Challoner, 1974). Since even small nests are virtually absent, low nematocyte production cannot be attributed to a control of proliferation of i-cells, which merely reduces the nest size of the nematoblasts. Migration of i-cells toward the head has been detected to a limited extent (Herlands and Bode, 1974a). On the other hand, there are interstitial cells which are multipotent, as demonstrated by David and Murphy (1977). Using the cell aggregation technique described below in Section II, H, aggregates devoid of interstitial cells were formed. It was found that if a cell sample containing only one stem cell is added, the aggregate can be "repopulated" with nerve cells as well as with nematocytes. The fact that there are multipotent i-cells suggests that the action of morphogens in determining the spatial pattern of differentiation is at least partially on regulating stem cells in or near the head to produce predominantly nerve cells, but a contribution of cell migration is also to be envisaged.

4. Non-Steady States

In a regenerating section of hydra, many new nerve cells already are produced in the future head area 1 day after cutting (Bode *et al.*, 1973). There is a lapse of 18 hours between the end of the last S phase and the differentiation of the nerve cells. It is unlikely that signals determining stem cells to develop nerves act long after S phase. This suggests that the decision where to form a new head is made a few hours after cutting, in agreement with evidence from transplantation experiments (Webster and Wolpert, 1966; MacWilliams, 1977). Determination of new nerve cells for a future head appears to be an early event in regeneration.

5. *Some Open Problems of Determination*

It remains undecided whether one stem cell produces, after replication, two determined cells (e.g., nerve cell precursors) or one determined cell and one stem cell.

Further it is of interest whether the determination of a differentiated cell (e.g., a nerve or a small penetrant) occurs in one single step or in several consecutive steps. If the latter is the case, it would be of interest whether these steps occur in one or in several consecutive rounds of replication. It is thus conceivable that there are stem cells of different potency range (e.g., for nerve and nematocytes, nerves only, nematocytes only, etc.). This would not affect the estimate of the total number of stem cells.

D. Cell Migration

Most nematocytes produced in the gastric column migrate to the tentacles to be incorporated into the battery cells. Two different possibilities are to be envisaged for the origin of the signal that directs migration. A chemotactic substance may be produced in the head and form a gradient by diffusing into the gastric column, or there may be some polar tissue property throughout the gastric column, such as a gradient of chemotactic substances produced locally. A decision can be reached by transplanting the head to the "wrong" end of the gastric column of hydra and studying how this affects the direction of movement of new nematocytes. It is found that both mechanisms mentioned are involved. Local polar tissue properties direct the migration of the main type of nematocytes (desmonemes), whereas others (stenoteles) are directed by a signal extending from the head (Herlands and Bode, 1974b).

E. Tissue Evagination

In budding, head regeneration, and tentacle formation, smooth hydra tissues form defined structures in space. These structures are not formed from a blastema with rapidly proliferating undifferentiated cells; rather they are produced from preexisting tissue, especially from epithelial cells changing their shape and thus altering locally the curvatures of the tissue. The rates of proliferation of epithelial cells are nearly uniform throughout the body column, including the budding zone (Campbell, 1967; Clarkson and Wolpert, 1967), and do not increase in head regeneration (Park *et al.*, 1970). Moreover, depletion of interstitial cells or application of inhibitors of the cell cycle do not inhibit head regeneration (Diehl and Burnett, 1965; Clarkson, 1969). The role of i-cells in budding is not yet resolved, but the most conspicuous morphogenetic effect in this process is the shape change of the epithelial cells. Thus tissue evagination in head and bud formation appears to be relatively independent of proliferation; it seems to be caused primarily by effects on the existing epithelial cells and their interaction with each other, the surfaces and/or the mesoglea.

F. Morphogenetic Substances

In hydra, as in most biological systems, the chemical basis of pattern formation presents a very difficult problem because of the lack of a direct assay for morphogens. Many substances can influence regeneration and morphogenesis without being involved in the natural *in vivo* processes. For instance, treatment of regenerates with LiCl leads to supernumerary tentacles (Ham *et al.*, 1956), whereas incubation with reducing agents often causes two feet to be formed at two ends of a section (Hicklin *et al.*, 1969). Though these substances are not expected to be the real morphogens, further study on their mechanisms of action could nevertheless contribute to our understanding of the actual morphogenetic events with which they interfere. In hydra, there are some metabolic features, such as the rates of oxidation, which are graded in the animal (Child, 1941). However, such gradients cannot provide in themselves an explanation of pattern formation; rather they are one of the features of the pattern, the formation of which is to be explained. It is conceivable that morphogenesis is due to a highly complex system involving hundreds of types of interacting molecules; it is even possible that physical parameters other than substance concentrations, such as electrical properties, are the primary cause. Without completely disregarding such possibilities, however, the most likely solution to morphogenesis involves the formation of spatial concentration patterns of limited sets of morphogenetic substances. On the other hand, it is not to be expected that only one or two substances suffice for the morphogenesis of an animal.

The strategy to find such morphogenetic substances is to search for compounds occurring naturally in the animal which exert morphogenetic effects, and to accumulate indirect evidence as to their possible involvement *in vivo*. In particular, if a specific organic substance exerts morphogenetic effects at very low concentrations, and if its natural occurrence in the animal correlates with morphogenetic activities in time and space, this substance is not unlikely to be involved in *in vivo* morphogenesis.

Lesh and Burnett (1964) as well as Lentz (1965) have found that hydra extracts can induce supernumerary tentacles or heads in regenerating sections of hydra, and Lentz (1965) has produced evidence by electron microscopy that activity resides in neurosecretory granules. A head-activating factor has been partially purified and highly enriched from the crude extract about 10^5-fold (Schaller, 1973). The assay is a statistical one, the active factor causing an increase of about 15% in tentacle number per regenerate. The substance has a molecular weight of about 1000. It is sensitive to Pronase and therefore appears to be or to contain a peptide. It occurs graded in the animal, with the highest concentration found in the head area, and the distribution is correlated with the distribution of nerve cells. Upon regeneration and budding, amounts of factors change locally in a way suggesting involvement in morphogenetic processes.

The factor is active at extremely low concentrations and exerts effects in the "hormone range" of about 10^{-10} M. The concentration at which it still exerts activity is low not only in absolute terms, but also in comparison to the average concentration at which the factor occurs in the animal which is 1000 times higher. Upon careful homogenization of hydra tissue, one finds most of the active substance to be enclosed in vesicular structures from which it can be released by osmotic shock or sonication. It thus appears that most of the active substance is enclosed in vesicles in an inactive form and exerts its activity upon release (Schaller and Gierer, 1973).

There is another naturally occurring factor discovered by Berking (1977) which inhibits budding and regeneration. It has a molecular weight of around 500. It is also active in very low absolute amounts, at concentrations much smaller than the average concentration in the animal, especially as far as bud inhibition is concerned. Upon careful homogenization of the tissue, most of the activity is found in rapidly sedimenting components, but these are not identical with the vesicular structures containing the activator. Distribution in the animal is again graded, the highest concentration occurring in the head area.

The evidence on these activators and inhibitors shows that specific substances can affect the morphogenesis of the organism at extremely low concentrations. It supports the notion that the factors mentioned, probably in conjunction with others still to be discovered, are somehow involved in morphogenetic processes of the animal, although the actual function and mechanism of action are still to be established. Moreover, the findings suggest that in some cases morphogenetic substances are produced not by *de novo* synthesis, but rather by release of preexisting compounds from "storage" compartments.

The maintenance of a spatial distribution of a diffusible substance continuously consumes energy: It is a steady state rather than a thermodynamic equilibrium. However, if a graded diffusible morphogen would be effective at a level of 10^{-10} *M*, a simple calculation shows that the energy consumption required can be neglected in terms of the total metabolism of the tissue.

G. Induction of Secondary Centers by Transplantation

Short-range activation by small transplants inducing a second center is a widespread feature in developmental biology exemplified by Spemann's classical induction experiments on the amphibian gastrula. Long-range inhibition causing similar or like structures to be produced only at distance from each other is also a common biological feature accounting, for instance, for regular spacings of leaves in plants. In hydra, such activating and inhibiting effects can be quantitatively evaluated and experimentally modified to study their involvement in pattern formation.

Early in the century, Browne (1909) discovered that small pieces of heads, transplanted to the gastric column of hydra, induce the formation of a second head there. Bud tips are found to induce buds and parts of feet can induce feet (Browne, 1909; Yao, 1945).

The transplants thus exert a short-range effect on the host tissue, activating it to participate in the formation of a new structure, such as a head. On the other hand, heads inhibit the formation of other heads nearby under certain conditions. If a second head is grafted onto the gastric column and the original head is cut off later, no head will regenerate at the cut in many cases (Rand *et al.*, 1926).

Transplants can induce head formation even if the transplanted piece is derived from the gastric column. This can occur if a piece of tissue derived from an area relatively close to the head is transplanted to an area relatively more distant. The effect is inhibited if a hydra head is too close to the point of transplantation. Wolpert *et al.* (1971) have studied this effect quantitatively by serial transplants, grafting sections of one animal axially onto sections of another one (Fig. 3). Areas of hydra are denoted distal to proximal with H (head) 1234 . . . . For instance, the experiments show that the grafts 12/1234 . . . do, but H 12/1234 . . . do not form second heads at the junctions. However, if the junction is sufficiently far away from the head as in the graft H 123/1234 . . . or H 1234/1234 . . . , a second head can develop. Other transplantation experiments have shown that the inhibitory effect takes time to spread across the tissue, the rate being consistent with molecular diffusion (Wolpert *et al.*, 1972).

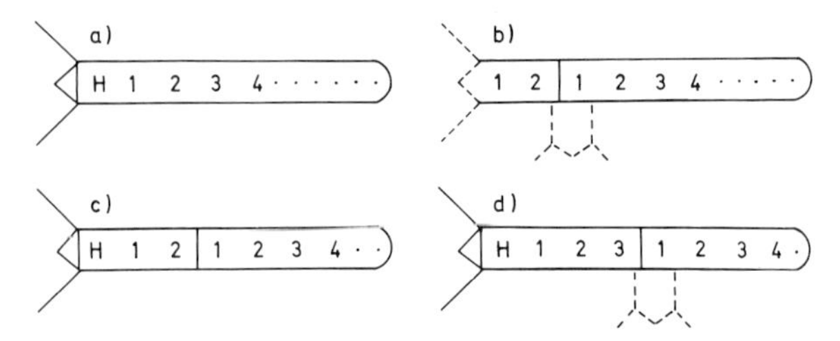

FIG. 3. Examples of axial grafts by Wolpert *et al.* (1971) showing the inhibitory effect of heads on secondary head formation which depends on the distance of the preexisting heads from the junction. [symbol] indicates preexisting heads, [symbol] newly formed heads (and/or feet). (a) Notation of areas of hydra. (b–d) Axial grafts. The effect can be quantitatively simulated on the basis of pattern formation by lateral inhibition [Gierer and Meinhardt, 1972; see Section III].

Thus, the capacity for head formation in transplantation is correlated quantitatively with the position from which the transplant was derived as well as with the distance of the position of the transplant from the head in the host. The results suggest that there is inhibition extending from preexisting heads which counteracts some more local activating effect of the transplanted tissue; switching to initiate secondary head formation occurs if activation locally overcomes inhibition (Wolpert, 1971).

Head and foot formation seem to be determined by separate inhibitory systems. Regeneration of a foot is inhibited if another foot is transplanted nearby (MacWilliams and Kafatos, 1968). The kinetics are consistent with a diffusible inhibitor (MacWilliams and Kafatos, 1974). Buds inhibit other buds as they arise in growing hydra alternatively on opposite sites of the gastric column (see Fig. 1a), similar to the leaf arrangement in many plants.

H. REGENERATION OF HYDRA FROM AGGREGATED CELLS

Cells prepared from embryonic tissues often aggregate and sort out to re-form organlike structures (Weiss and Moscona, 1958; DeLong, 1970), and cells prepared from sponges can even aggregate to form a new animal (Wilson, 1907). Hydra has been long known to regenerate even from very small pieces of tissues centrifuged or grafted together (Rösel von Rosenhof, 1755; Bertalanfry and Rella, 1942; Lehn, 1951) and from tissue pressed through a thin mesh (Aisupiet, 1935). More recently, we found that one may dissociate hydra into cells, form aggregates from these cells, and regenerate complete animals from the aggregate (Gierer *et al.*, 1972) (Fig. 4). A similar finding has been reported by Noda (1971).

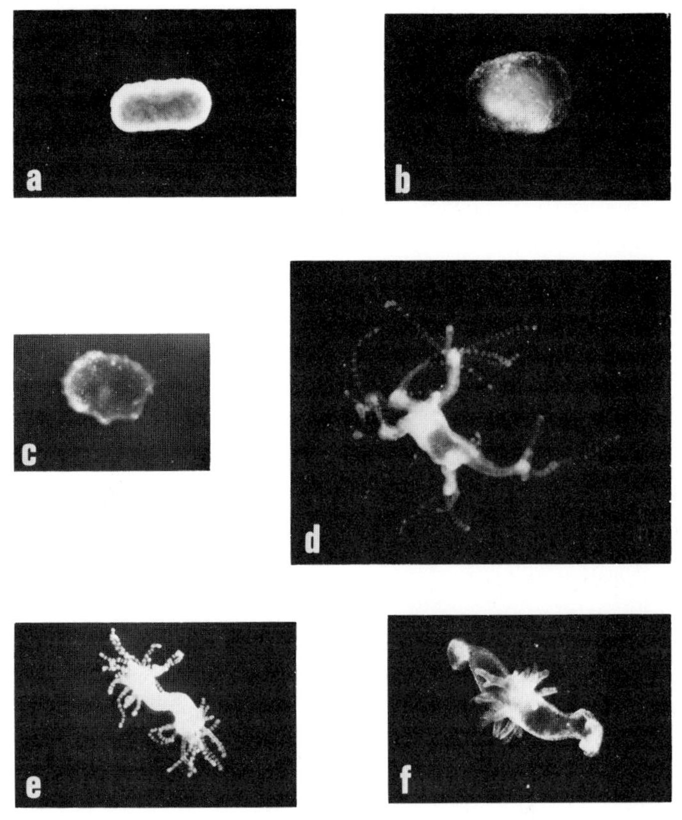

FIG. 4. Regeneration of hydra from aggregated cells (according to Gierer *et al.*, 1972; photographs by G. Hansmann). (a) Cell aggregates immediately after centrifugation. (b) After 20 hours cells have sorted out to form a (bilayered) hollow sphere. (c) After 2 days tentacle buds are visible. (d) After 3 days a multiheaded "monster" is formed (upon feeding and growth, it later separates into normal individual animals). A sequential arrangement of aggregates with cells derived from areas of the body column closer to (C), and more distant from (D), the head leads to heads preferentially at the ends if the sequence is CDC (e) and in the middle if the sequence is DCD (f).

If hydra is disintegrated into cells in fresh water, the cells lyse by osmotic shock. However, in certain media with higher salt concentrations cells are viable for some time (Trenkner *et al.*, 1973). In these media, whole animals eventually disintegrate into cells. A fresh cell preparation can be obtained by incubating hydra in the high-salt medium for a short time and then dissociating animals into cells by shearing. In the first few hours the cells tend to aggregate by themselves. Alternatively, one may produce an aggregate of defined size by centrifugation (Fig. 4a). Upon prolonged incubation of the aggregate in high salt, the clumps would again disintegrate into cells. However, if the medium is shifted gradually to the low-salt conditions of hydra media, the aggregates, after forming a smooth surface, sort out and form a two-layered hollow sphere within less than 24 hours (Fig. 4b). Staining of endodermal cells with Evans blue shows that they form the inner cell layer, whereas the original ectodermal cells again form the outside layer, with a mesoglea in between. Most of the nematoblasts and part of the interstitial cells are ejected or degraded in this process, while part of the interstitial cells and many nerve cells are found in the regenerate. Later, tentacle buds appear (Fig. 4c), and hypostomes grow out. Usually, a multiheaded animal is formed (Fig. 4d). It feeds and grows on *Artemia* and eventually gives rise to individual, normal animals.

An essential control in this type of experiment is to demonstrate that the regenerate is derived essentially from previously isolated cells. The cells aggregate in solution all the time, and it has not been possible to obtain cell preparations completely devoid of small clumps containing a few cells each, but preparations can be made with most epithelial cells and virtually all other cell types occurring as single cells. One may deduce from such data on cell distribution, in conjunction with measurements on cell numbers in regenerates, that most of the cells which eventually form the regenerate had been single before aggregation, and that single cells of all types, including epithelial cells, have contributed to forming the regenerate. Time-lapse films demonstrate directly that single epithelial as well as i-cells participate in forming aggregates.

If cell preparations are made from head areas, very large numbers of tentacles are formed. Foot cells form mainly feet. However, cells prepared from sections cut from the gastric column produce complete animals with head and foot. Therefore, in the double-layered hollow sphere of the regenerate, heads and feet are produced from cells that have not been parts of such structures before isolation.

Several implications of the regeneration of cell aggregates of hydra may be mentioned. The formation of the double-layered hollow sphere by cell sorting demonstrates a very high power of self-organization of the cells. The inside-out (radial) dimension of the structure of hydra appears to be determined by direct contact-mediated cell interaction. After formation of the double layer, there are processes capable of activating some areas which have never been heads before to form such new structures, and there must therefore be mechanisms to decide where to form them in the lateral dimensions.

The cellular aggregates provide an assay system for various features of development: One may study the pathway of differentiation of cells added to an aggregate. An example is David and Murphy's (1977) result on the multipotential character of interstitial cells mentioned above (Section II, C, 3), showing that an aggregate depleted of interstitial cells can be repopulated with new nerves and nematocytes by adding one stem cell. Further, one may construct artificial spatial arrangements of cells of various types, origins, or pretreatments to study the decision mechanism as to where, in a near-uniform tissue, a new head will form. An example will be given in the next section.

I. Regeneration, Tissue Polarity, and Prepattern Formation

Despite the large amount of subtle experiments on regeneration and transplantation in hydra, the basic fact to be understood, and the essential challenge for any theoretical concept, is still a simple and very old observation: Sections of the gastric column regenerate an animal with predictable positions of head and foot. The head develops at the terminal closest to the original head. It follows that the same group of cells can form a foot, or head, or nothing, depending on which other parts of the gastric column are present in the regenerate (Fig. 5). There must be a mechanism to decide where to form a head, and the decision cannot be based on the initial value of the concentration of any substances within the cells that form the head, nor can it be based merely on the fact that there is a cut. Rather, there must be some physical asymmetry in the hydra tissue which determines the orientation of the pattern to be formed, though not the pattern itself. This physical property is often called the polarity of the tissue.

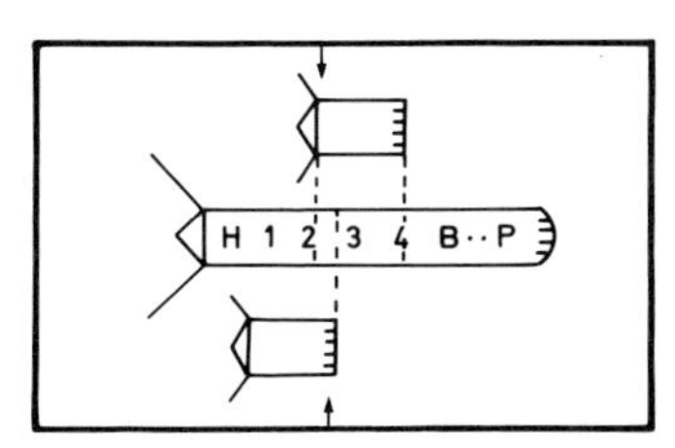

Fig. 5. Basic features of tissue polarity. A section from any part of the gastric column of hydra regenerates an animal with head and foot. Heads are formed in the area closest to the original head. This implies that the same group of cells of the gastric column (arrow) can form a head, or foot, or nothing, depending on the other parts of the cut tissue. Reprinted with permission of the publisher American Mathematical Society from "Lectures on Mathematics in the Life Sciences, Volume 7, Some Mathematical Questions in Biology. VI" Copyright © 1974 Volume 7, pp. 163–183

Two general types of concepts on polarity may be distinguished. One is to assume that the tissue contains asymmetric cells aligned parallel to each other, so that in any section the distal ("arrowhead") terminal is different from the proximal one. This, in turn, could give rise to activation of head formation at the "arrowhead" terminal. In an alternative general scheme, one assumes that there is a graded distribution of some cell type or substance in the gastric column, and that there are mechanisms deciding, within a cut section, which part is relatively highest in concentration, leading to head formation in the portion which was closest to the original head.

These alternatives can be studied using cellular aggregates (Gierer *et al.*, 1972). Separate cell preparations were made from areas closer to (C), and more distant from (D), the head. Aggregates were formed from each preparation and grafted immediately in various serial orders. It was found that the arrangement CDC produces head structures predominantly in the outer parts (Fig. 4e), DCD predominantly in the center (Fig. 4f). If the position of head formation were determined by orientation of asymmetric cells, no difference in the results between CDC and DCD grafts would be expected since the cells have been completely disoriented upon disaggregation. The conclusion holds, even if cells align parallel to each other after the aggregates have been formed because CDC and DCD should give equal results independent of any details of such mechanisms as long as the pattern is determined by orientation only. On the other hand, if substance gradients determine polarity, and if the substances remain enclosed in the cells upon disaggregation, the graft CDC has two maxima near the ends and DCD one in the middle. The observed position of head formation agrees with the notion that heads form at the maximal points. The effect, though clear-cut, is a statistical one because there are several complications involved in such experiments: Grafting produces discontinuities that do not occur naturally in animals, and the effect is expected to show up only for limited size ranges of aggregates. Moreover, the result does not exclude entirely that cell orientation mechanisms are somehow involved secondarily in pattern formation; but if they are, cells are expected to orient only in response to the gradient that defines polarity in the first place.

The concept that substance gradients rather than cell orientation determine tissue polarity receives support from another, very simple experiment on whole hydra. If the gastric column is cut into more than 10 thin slices and each slice is turned 180° to be grafted in the original serial order in reverse orientation, where will the new head form? Gradient models predict the terminal closest to the original head; cell orientation models the opposite end. The result of this experiment, which was carried out by Trenkner in our laboratory, again supports the gradient concept.

If polarity is due to substance gradients, this implies that head formation cannot depend merely on the local value of the concentration of this substance, because the same cells can also form a foot, depending on their position within the section (Fig. 5). Thus, the polarity-defining gradient cannot itself be a prepattern for head formation. Rather there must be cell communication over a wider area to decide, after cutting a section, which part is relatively highest in the polarity-defining substance, to activate this part of the area thereafter. Such localized activation is synonymous with the formation of a spatial distribution of some physical parameters varying in space, probably (though not necessarily) of the concentration of one or several morphogenetic substances. Their distribution, then, is a prepattern proper in the sense that local values (e.g., activator concentration) determine local events (e.g., head formation). Prepattern formation is fast, occurring long before head formation is visible: In a regenerate, head determination often takes only a few hours, as shown by transplantation experiments (Webster and Wolpert, 1966; MacWilliams, 1977). Changes in the polarity-defining gradient take longer, confirming its conceptional distinction from the prepattern: If a head is grafted to the opposite end of the gastric column of hydra, it takes days to revert tissue polarity. At earlier times, sections of the gastric column will develop heads closest to the original rather than to the transplanted head (Wilby and Webster, 1970).

The cellular origin of substance gradients defining polarity is not yet clear. One or several substances may be involved as constituents either of epithelial cells, the per cell content being graded along the gastric column or of nerve cells which themselves form a graded distribution, of both, or—less likely—of some other cell types. Improved techniques of cell type separation could help to solve this problem.

In summary, polarity appears to be due to a cellular property (probably a substance concentration) which is graded in hydra, fairly stable, and even maintained in disaggregated cells. In a regenerate, a prepattern is rapidly formed that activates part of the total area to form a new head. The polarity-defining gradient determines the orientation of the prepattern within the tissue. However, it cannot possibly be the prepattern itself. This rather is newly formed in a rapid process involving cell communication across the regenerating tissue.

III. Physical Aspects of Biological Pattern Formation

A. Prepatterns: Logical, Physical, and Biological Aspects

1. Prepatterns Exist; Shapes May Be Simple, but Values Are Exact

As exemplified for hydra, biological pattern formation involves various mechanisms and their combination, such as cell proliferation and differentiation, and contact-mediated cell interactions. While such mechanisms, by themselves, can produce spatial order, there are many cases (such as head formation in hydra), where a spatial distribution of physical properties, probably a concentration pattern of one or several substances, precedes and controls the location and formation of visible structures within cells and tissues. We will call any such distribution a prepattern, independent of its shape and mode of action. Prepatterns can, but need not, be isomorphic to visible patterns. The formation of prepatterns and the response they elicit in the cells present problems essential to an understanding of morphogenesis.

Prepatterns must be formed highly exactly to explain the reproducibility of the arising visible patterns, though their shape need not be complex. The simplest shape would be a monotonic (not necessarily linear) gradient, rendering a one-to-one correlation between concentration and position. The underlying principle was already applied by the Romans, who introduced the enumerated milestone into their road system. The numerical value gives unambiguous "positional information" for any place on a given road, e.g., in terms of distance to Rome. On the same principle, prepatterns consisting of monotonic gradients of morphogenetic substances have been proposed (e.g., Child, 1941; Wolpert, 1971) in the sense that cells respond specifically to the concentration of a graded morphogen and thus to position within the tissue. Such morphogens are expected to interact with enzymes, receptor proteins, or other compounds, which in turn participate in the regulation of gene activation and other cellular processes. Combinations of known features of enzyme kinetics could lead to complex interpretations of simple gradients; a response may occur, for instance, above a certain threshold of morphogen concentrations, or in certain concentration ranges. Simple monotonic gradients could thus give rise to any complex pattern in space. However, this does not mean that all prepatterns are simple monotonic gradients. For instance, where there is a periodic structure, it is not unlikely that the prepattern is periodic. Further it is possible that several substance gradients rather than one determine the pattern and that complex patterns are due to subpatterns produced within subsections of prepatterns rather than to complex interpretations of simple gradients.

2. *The Logical Issue: Patterns from Prepatterns, but Prepatterns from What?*

A concept of "prepatterns" popular in the 18th century was proposed by Bonnet (1762), who assumed that eggs contain miniature versions of the organism they produce, development requiring only growth. This concept implied that there are microversions for the generations thereafter. Logically it does not seem satisfactory to explain prepatterns by pre-prepatterns indefinitely. The conclusive point against this "puppet in the puppet" theory is a physical one, as exemplified by a simple thought experiment on regenerating hydra. Assume we cut 1/10 of the gastric column, let it regenerate a complete hydra, feed and grow, again cut 1/10 of the column, etc. After eight such rounds of regeneration and growth, the resulting animal is derived from less than 10^{-8} cm of the original one, that is, less than an atom's diameter. This slice could not possibly contain a pattern. Since the same events are expected to occur in each of the eight steps, the prepattern must have been *newly* generated in each regeneration.

Another much less trivial aspect of this thought experiment pertains to asymmetry: in regeneration of hydra sections, the direction of the new head points into the direction of the old one, and this can go on much beyond eight generations. Asymmetry and orientation are directed by the polarity of the tissue, that is by some preexisting physical asymmetries. Although there are other systems in development where the orientation of a pattern is not predictable and arises by true "symmetry breaking" due to random fluctuations, the most common case is like hydra. Asymmetric flies produce asymmetric eggs, and asymmetric eggs develop into asymmetric flies. This can go on indefinitely without physical or logical inconsistencies.

3. *Physical Theories of Pattern Formation: Concentrations Change as Functions of Concentrations*

The purpose of a theory of pattern formation is the understanding in terms of physics, that is, the interaction of molecules and molecular compounds (e.g., aggregates, subcellular organelles, and cells), and their movements according to physical laws. The chemistry of the pattern-forming system is not yet known, but this is not the only relevant aspect. Even if we knew all molecules involved in every structural detail, we would not be able to predict the concentration patterns generated without involved kinetic concepts and calculations.

Generally, molecular interactions and movements result in "kinetic" laws based on physics. For a very wide scope of physical interactions and movements, including the reactions and transport processes in fluid media and membranes, the physical laws are such that the concentration of any compound changes in time as function of the concentrations of the various compounds; spatial concentration patterns change in time as function of spatial concentration patterns. For a physical understanding of pattern formation we may, therefore, ask whether patterns with properties observed in biology can be generated by physical kinetics with concentrations changing as functions of concentrations, and which structural and molecular features of reactions are relevant for producing such patterns.

The most impressive phenomenon in development and regeneration is the formation of structure from relatively uniform distributions, of the organisms from the oocyte, of organs from initially near-homogeneous tissues. However, structure formation is no specifically biological phenomenon; on the contrary, the laws of physics are such that it is the rule rather than the exception: there are stars and galaxies, waves and clouds; there are crystals, mountains, and dunes. A rather general reason is that in physics, often, inhomogeneities are self-enhancing (e.g., a local density of matter slightly above average, in space attracts more matter by gravitation, giving rise to even more attraction: a star is formed). Small volumes of liquids are an exception to this rule. Usually soluble substances become distributed nearly evenly because of diffusion. Since there is diffusion in cells and tissues, the question arises as to how diffusible substances can nevertheless form spatial patterns.

This problem was solved some 25 years ago by Turing (1952), by considering self-enhancing features of reactions in liquids. He found that if there are at least two substances, acting on their own and each other's production by auto- and cross-catalysis, then, under certain conditions, spatial patterns are formed in spite of, and in a sense because of, diffusion. Although he mainly considered linear reactions, he already realized that nonlinear kinetics are more suitable for biological problems. Turing found, for instance, standing-wave solutions that he applied to the spacing of tentacles in hydra. Other workers have investigated and elucidated certain types and mathematical properties of such catalytic reactions (Guitro and Scriven, 1966; Prigogine, 1972; Segel and Jackson, 1972; Edelstein, 1972).

4. *What a Physical Theory of Prepatterns Should Explain*

While general nonlinear reaction kinetics are too varied and too complex to be helpful in explaining biological development, one may search for simple types of nonlinear reactions which may give rise to certain types of biological patterns with properties actually observed in embryology and regeneration. A type characteristic for hydra and many other biological systems can be described by a set of nontrivial features that have been outlined in detail in Section II and are summarized here in abstract form.

a. Structure develops from near-uniformity, the final structure being nearly independent of details of initial conditions for wide ranges of parameters.

b. The orientation of an asymmetric pattern can be determined by slight initial asymmetries called polarity, as a property either of the developing tissue or of its environment. Gradients which determine polarity specify the orientation but not the shape of the pattern to be formed.

c. Activation extends into, but is also confined to, part of the total area.

d. In many cases, there is size regulation. The activated area can adapt, within certain limits, to total size.

e. Activation can produce, under certain circumstances a secondary structure.

f. Inhibition either prevents secondary structures from forming, or spaces them at distances from each other. Periodic patterns can be explained on this principle.

B. Pattern Formation Involving Lateral Inhibition

1. *Principle of Lateral Inhibition*

Is there a general *type* of catalytic reactions which can lead to the general *type* of biological pattern formation described?

It was found that short-range activation, long-range inhibition, and certain simple rules as to the kinetics of activation and inhibition give rise to just this type (Gierer and Meinhardt, 1972).

Short-range activation in the form of induction of a structure by transplantation, and long-range inhibition of structures by similar structures in the vicinity have often been observed in embryology and regeneration, including head formation and budding in hydra (see Section II). The central point in the lateral inhibition theory is that the *same* inhibitory effect that prevents or spaces like structures *also* accounts for the basic problem of how a stable reproducible pattern is produced starting from near-uniformity. The term "lateral inhibition" employed in the context of pattern formation is derived from the field of brain function and pattern recognition (Hartline *et al.*, 1956; Kuffler, 1952; Kirschfeld and Reichardt, 1964; Wilson and Cowan, 1973). Mechanisms are very different, but formal analogies between pattern formation and recognition exist. For instance, in pattern recognition, neural interactions with long-range inhibition in conjunction with short-range activation can lead to the conversion of smooth into striking patterns by "edge enhancement."

2. *Outline of the Theory: Kinetic Criteria to Generate Molecular Models*

An activator [concentration $a\ (x,t)$] and an inhibitory effect [concentration $h\ (x,t)$] are assumed to interact catalytically with their own and each other's production and/or destruction, and to be spread in space by diffusion or other mechanisms in such a way that a has a short and h a comparatively long range. Concentrations change as function of concentrations:

$$\partial a/\partial t = f\,(a,\ h) \tag{1a}$$

$$\partial h/\partial t = g\,(a,\ h) \tag{1b}$$

If the second reaction is relatively fast, g is always close to 0 and the inhibitory concentration h can be approximated as a function of the activator concentration $\bar{a}$ averaged over the wide area of inhibition. Therefore,

$$\partial a/\partial t \approx f\,[a,\ h\,(\bar{a})] \tag{2}$$

$\partial a/\partial t$ is a function of activator distribution in space, with some terms (a) where the local values (averaged only over the small diffusion range of activator) matter, and other (inhibitory) terms determined by the average of activator $\bar{a}$ over the wider range of inhibition. On this basis it is possible to establish criteria of stability: Patterns are formed starting from near-uniformity if $\partial a/\partial t = 0$ has a near-uniform solution $a = \bar{a}$ which is stable for the average $\bar{a}$ to prevent an overall explosion of activator concentration, but labile for local deviations of a from $\bar{a}$ to "fire" a pattern. Then a local activator concentration above average, giving one part of an area a slight initial advantage over the other, is self-enhancing, but inhibition spreads into a wider range to cause deactivation elsewhere. Activation, while increasing, will thus be successively confined to a smaller and smaller part of the total area (see Fig. 7a). The pattern becomes stable when this confinement reaches a limit. If it is limited by activator diffusion, the activated area is near-independent of total size; if the limiting mechanism is saturation of activator production in the activated area, there is size regulation: The activated area "senses" the total area into which inhibition can spread, adapting to total size within certain limits.

Tissue polarity is considered an asymmetric property due to a (possibly very shallow) graded distribution $\rho(x)$ of a compound that somehow interferes with the pattern-forming system. Such a "source" may be, for instance, an enzyme involved in activator production, or a particular cell type within the tissue that produces activators (and/or inhibitors). Changes of source distributions resulting, for instance, from cell differentiation are expected to be relatively slow so that they need not be considered, in most cases, during the short period of "firing" of a pattern. There is no difficulty, however, to include slow changes of source distribution and its feedback on activator and inhibitor distribution into the equations of type (1) (see Meinhardt and Gierer, 1974).

The relatively highest values of source concentration $\rho(x)$ in a section determine where activator concentration is slightly above average initially, and thus where pattern formation is initiated. In this way, the orientation of a source gradient (that is, the sign of grad ρ) determines the orientation of activator and inhibitor gradients and thus of the pattern produced. However, the shape of the pattern formed is governed essentially by the kinetic features of the pattern-forming system such as catalysis, degradation, and diffusion rates of activators and inhibitors, and is not sensitive to origin and details of source distributions for wide ranges of conditions. No source gradient is required at all if the pattern is symmetrical, and/or initiated by random fluctuations.

Secondary peaks of activators can be induced in areas at a distance from primary activated areas out of reach of the inhibitor. Within sufficiently large areas a periodic pattern with several peaks can arise.

This rather informal description of the principle has been substantiated by introducing power terms into the reaction kinetics, and deriving criteria for the powers that do, and that do not, produce patterns. These criteria are nontrivial. If activator degradation is linear, activation must be "overlinear"; bimolecular reaction or reactions with a bimolecular term suffice. Inhibition kinetics can be of various types. The criteria can be considered as "recipes" to construct particular models that generate patterns (Gierer and Meinhardt, 1972, 1974).

3. *Some Equations for Pattern Formation*

Readers not interested in equations are asked to continue to the next subsection (B,4), p. 41.

A simple example of a pattern forming system is given by the following equations for activator $a(x, t)$ and inhibitor $h(x, t)$:

$$\partial a/\partial t = c\ [a^2/h - a + d_a(\partial^2 a/\partial x^2)] \tag{3a}$$

$$\partial h/\partial t = c'\ [a^2 - h + d_h(\partial^2 h/\partial x^2)] \tag{3b}$$

d_a is the ratio of diffusion and decay rate D_a/c for activator. According to physicochemical laws this ratio is proportional to the mean square of the range r_a^2 of activator, averaging distances between production and decay. d_h is proportional to the mean square of the range of inhibitor r_h^2. Lateral inhibition implies that range of inhibition considerably exceeds range of activation $(r_h > r_a)$. Pattern formation further requires d_a to be sufficiently small so that total area exceeds the range of activator r_a. The inhibitory reaction (3b) has to be relatively fast $(c' > c)$. Then, h assumes a distribution determined by a spatial average of a^2 over the wide range r_h of inhibition. In the limiting case of very large r_h, h equilibrates to a near-uniform distribution $\overline{a^2}$. If the averaging effect of the relatively small d_a is neglected, one obtains

$$\partial a/\partial t \approx \text{const.}[(a^2/\overline{a^2}) - a] \tag{4a};$$

a has a uniform solution $a = \bar{a} = 1$; this is stable for the mean value $\bar{a}$ but not for local deviations. A small local initial activation $1 + \Delta a$ will give rise to further increase

$$\partial a/\partial t \approx \text{const.}\ [(1 + \Delta a)^2 - (1 + \Delta a)] \approx \text{const.}\ \Delta a > 0 \quad \text{if}\ \ \Delta a > 0 \tag{4b}$$

so that a pattern is "fired" starting from near-uniform distributions. Incorporation of more parameters into the system and addition of further comparatively small terms, such as a basic activator production (ρ_0) is possible in a straightforward manner as long as the general criteria are met. For the sake of generality, source distributions $\rho(x)$ (such as shallow gradients or random distributions) may be introduced. For instance, the following equations, closely related to Eq. (4), generate patterns for wide ranges of parameters:

$$\partial a/\partial t = \rho_0\rho + c\rho(a^2/h) - \mu a + D_a(\partial^2 a/\partial x^2) \tag{5a}$$

$$\partial h/\partial t = c'\rho a^2 - \upsilon h + D_h(\partial^2 h/\partial x^2) \tag{5b}$$

The inhibitory term $1/h$ may be interpreted as approximately for $K_h/(1 + K_h \cdot h)$ assuming that the Michaelis constant for inhibition $K_h \gg 1/h$.

If activator production saturates

$$\frac{\partial a}{\partial t} = \rho_0 \rho + \frac{c\rho a^2}{h(1 + \kappa a^2)} - \mu a + D_a \frac{\partial^2 a}{\partial x^2} \tag{5a'}$$

size regulation can result.

4. *Some Examples of Molecular Models*

Any such kinetics can be given different molecular interpretations and only biochemistry could distinguish between them. The following examples are to illustrate the principle, not to suggest that these models are more likely than others.

Figure 6a–c gives an example of a molecular model based on Eq. (5) which would give rise to patterns of the lateral inhibition type. This special model involves release of activators and inhibitors from separate particulate structures, mediated by an allosteric receptor protein. The receptor is assumed to be activated by two activator molecules, and activator release is taken to be inhibited by the inhibitors.

Another model consistent with the general criteria is described in Fig. 6d,e, several features varying at a time: Pattern formation occurs within a single cell rather than within a tissue; inhibition is due to depletion of a substance required for activation rather than to an inhibitor; the depleted substance is simply a precursor converted to an activator by an allosteric enzyme. The autocatalytic effect is assumed to be on the enzyme and thus on synthesis rather than release. Again, any slight asymmetry in initial conditions, such as a shallow external gradient of activator or inhibitor, can "fire" a pattern. In the model for intracellular patterns this causes a focus of activator concentration on a small part of the cell directed toward the external gradient. Such a focus could in turn lead to chemotactic movement in the direction of a gradient or to the induction of a polar, anisotropic development of the cell oriented within an external field. It can be shown that it would take only a fraction of a minute to fire such an intracellular pattern. If the inhibitory effect does not equilibrate rapidly, a spatial activator pattern would be produced that pulses periodically in time (Meinhardt and Gierer, 1974) as observed in cellular slime molds (Shaffer, 1958).

5. *Properties of the Pattern-Forming Systems Demonstrated by Computer Simulation*

The properties of such pattern-forming systems have been demonstrated by computer calculations (Gierer and Meinhardt, 1972, 1974; Meinhardt and Gierer, 1974). Examples are given for models based on Eq. (5). For wide ranges of parameters this equation leads to the firing

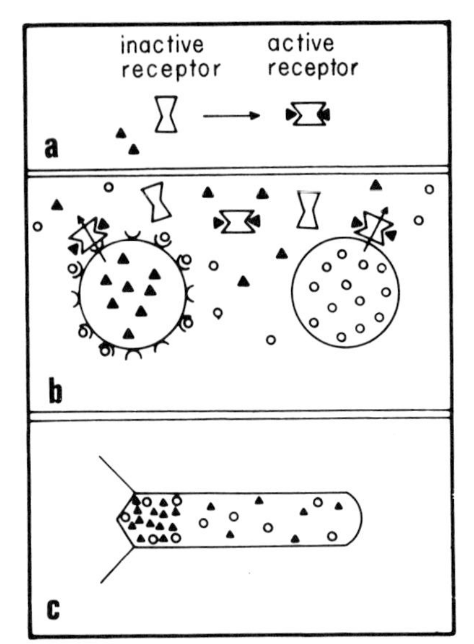

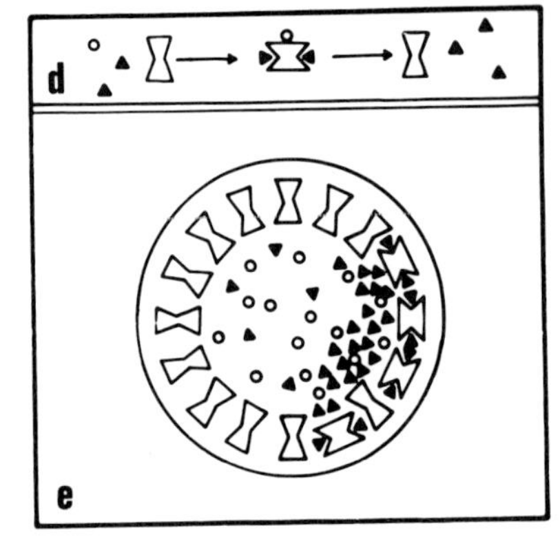

FIG. 6. Examples for molecular models of pattern formation by lateral inhibition (from Gierer and Meinhardt, 1974). (a–c) A release model for intercellular pattern formation, e.g., in hydra. (a) Two molecules of activator are assumed to cause an allosteric transition of a receptor protein toward the active state. (b) Activator ▲ and inhibitor ○ are contained in different particulate structures. Release is catalyzed by the activated receptor. Release of activator is assumed to be inhibited by the inhibitor acting on membrane sites. Upon release, inhibitor is assumed to have a larger average range due to diffusion and decay as compared to the activator. (c) The model leads to activation of part of the total area. It occurs near one end of the system if there is a very shallow gradient (not shown) of cells containing the particulate structures, or some other initial asymmetry that specifies tissue polarity. (d,e) A model for an intracellular pattern. (d) Two activator molecules are assumed to cause an allosteric transition of an enzyme toward the active state. The enzyme converts a precursor (○) into an activator (▲). The activator has a short range owing to decay and slow diffusion. Lateral inhibition is due to depletion of the precursors within a larger area. (e) Uniform distribution of the allosteric enzyme on the cell membrane and uniform initial conditions, except for a slight external gradient of activator, leads to a focus of activation at the membrane of the cell pointing into the direction of the external gradient. Reprinted with permission of the publisher American Mathematical Society from "Lectures on Mathematics in the Life Sciences, Volume 7, Some Mathematical Questions in Biology. VI." Copyright © 1974 Volume 7, pp. 163–183.

of patterns with all properties a–f mentioned above (Section III, A, 4) to characterize the lateral inhibition type. Structure is formed from near-uniformity (Fig. 7a). Asymmetry and orientation, but not the general shape, are specified by initial conditions determined, e.g., by a shallow source gradient that defines polarity. Strikingly different source distributions which have in common only the orientation of the

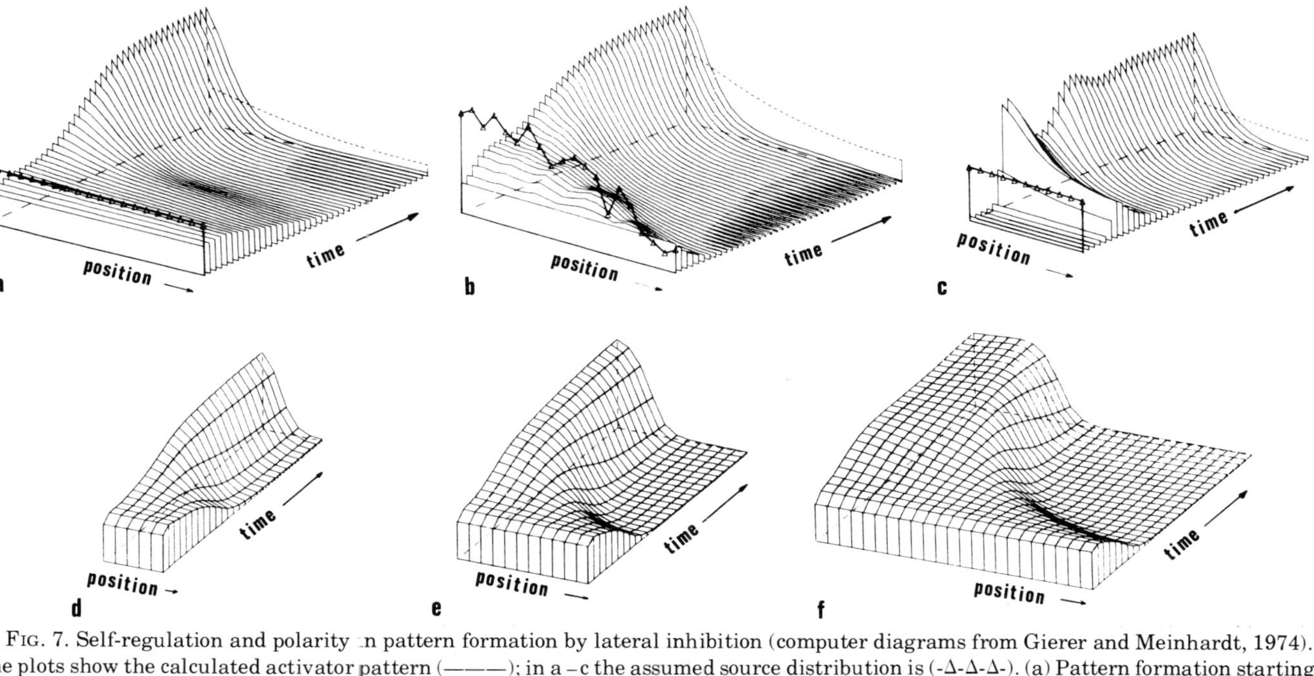

FIG. 7. Self-regulation and polarity in pattern formation by lateral inhibition (computer diagrams from Gierer and Meinhardt, 1974). The plots show the calculated activator pattern (———); in a – c the assumed source distribution is (-Δ-Δ-Δ-). (a) Pattern formation starting from even initial distributions of activator. A shallow source gradient determines the orientation of the pattern. Note how, in the course of time, activation (left) leads to deactivation in the right part until a stable pattern is formed. (b) The pattern (a) is not significantly affected by a different shape and statistical fluctuations, of the source distribution for a wide range of parameters as long as the mean slope orients in the same direction. Patterns formed according to Eq. (5) are closely similar even if absolute values of source concentrations are very different. (c) Subsections cut from the final distribution (a) "regenerate" a pattern, the orientation being retained. (d–f) Size regulation is obtained by a version based on Eqs. 5a′, 5b, limiting maximal activator concentrations: Activated area adapts nearly proportional to total size. Reprinted with permission of the publisher American Mathematical Society from "Lectures on Mathematics in the Life Sciences, Volume 7, Some Mathematical Questions in Biology. VI." Copyright © 1974 Volume 7, pp. 163–183

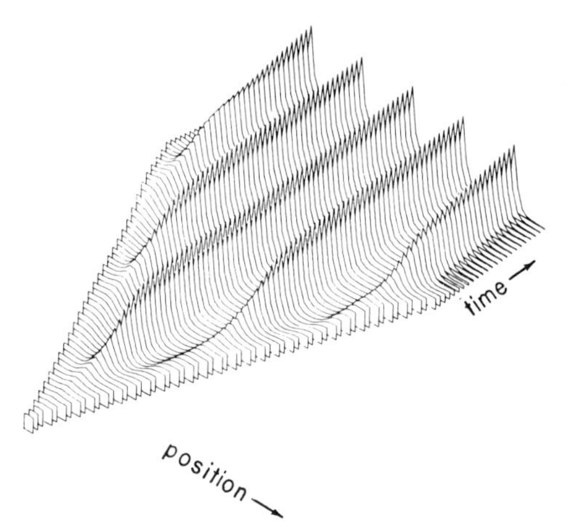

FIG. 8. Periodic patterns. If total area exceeds the range of inhibitor, periodic patterns can be formed. For instance, upon marginal growth, peaks are added consecutively to form a periodic pattern. From Gierer and Meinhardt (1974). Reprinted with permission of the publisher American Mathematical Society from "Lectures on Mathematics in the Life Sciences, Volume 7, Some Mathematical Questions in Biology. VI." Copyright © 1974 Volume 7, pp. 163–183.

mean slope lead to patterns very similar in shape and, with versions of the theory like Eq. (5), even absolute values (Fig. 7a,b). Sections cut from any part of the area "regenerate" a pattern, the original orientation being retained (Fig. 7c). There are versions, Eqs. (5a′) and (5b), showing size regulation (Fig. 7d–e).

Secondary peaks are formed if total size exceeds the range of inhibition, and periodic structures can be produced successively by internal or marginal growth (Fig. 8). This formation of periodic structures is related to a mechanism proposed independently by Wilcox, Mitchison, and Smith (1973) for the spacing of differentiated cells in the algae *Anabaena*.

In two dimensions, one version of the lateral inhibition theory (with ranges of activators small compared to the total size of the field) leads to near equal distribution of peaks of activity on a plane (bristle type, Fig. 9a), or a cylinder (Fig. 9b–d), the latter resembling certain leaf arrangements in plants. Another version, with a range of activator comparable to total field size, leads to a slope in one dimension within a two-dimensional field (Fig. 9f). Evidently, a second gradient-forming system can then specify "positional information" in a second dimension (Fig. 9g), explaining how two axes in two dimensions can arise independently in the morphogenesis of asymmetric organisms.

Although the theory is also applicable to three-dimensional problems, prepatterns in many biological systems specify "positional information" only in one or two dimensions within cell layers. Often the third "inside-out" dimension is determined by the time sequence of differentiation and/or by direct contact-mediated cell interactions. The latter applies to cells forming the double layer of hydra tissue. Intercellular prepatterns determine only the two "lateral" dimensions of the epithelium, namely the anterior–posterior (head–foot) dimension, and the angular dimension spacing tentacles and buds on the body column. In cortical and retinal structures of the vertebrate nervous system, the "inside-out" arrangement of cell layers is probably determined by the time sequence of proliferation and differentiation of neuroepithelial cells (Sidman *et al.,* 1959; LaVail and Cowan, 1971) in conjunction with direct cell interaction (Sheffield and Moscona, 1969). Again, the two axes within the cell layers are determined by prepatterns oriented by tissue polarity (Hunt and Jacobson, 1972), probably involving lateral inhibition (Meinhardt and Gierer, 1974).

6. *Pattern Interactions and Combinations*

In the course of development of an organism, prepatterns may affect growth, proliferation, differentiation, interaction, communication, migration and death of cells, and the formation of new margins. This in turn will alter or extinguish a prepattern, and can lead to new prepatterns in subsections. There is no difficulty in introducing such effects (e.g., changes of source concentrations or diffusion rates) into the formalism of the theory. The phenomenon of induction of a pattern in a tissue by a pattern or prepattern in an adjacent tissue can also be incorporated into the formalism.

A few nontrivial types of pattern combinations and dynamics will be treated explicitly in this subsection. If there are two pattern-forming systems in one dimension, and each of the two inhibitors involved has a slight cross-inhibiting effect on the other system, then two complementary peaks of activity will tend to develop near opposite margins as long as the total area is within the range of the inhibitors. This may account for polar patterns with two distinct structures near the margins, like a head and a foot in hydra (Fig. 10a). In other cases such a mechanism might produce an enzymic source for a substance on one end and a sink on the other, giving rise to a linear gradient in between as proposed by Crick (1970).

If, in a pattern-forming tissue, there is uniform growth or a continuous reduction of diffusion constants in the course of time (e.g., by closing of intercellular junctions), pattern formation will lead to a consecutive firing of intermediary peaks. This "digital" type of subpattern

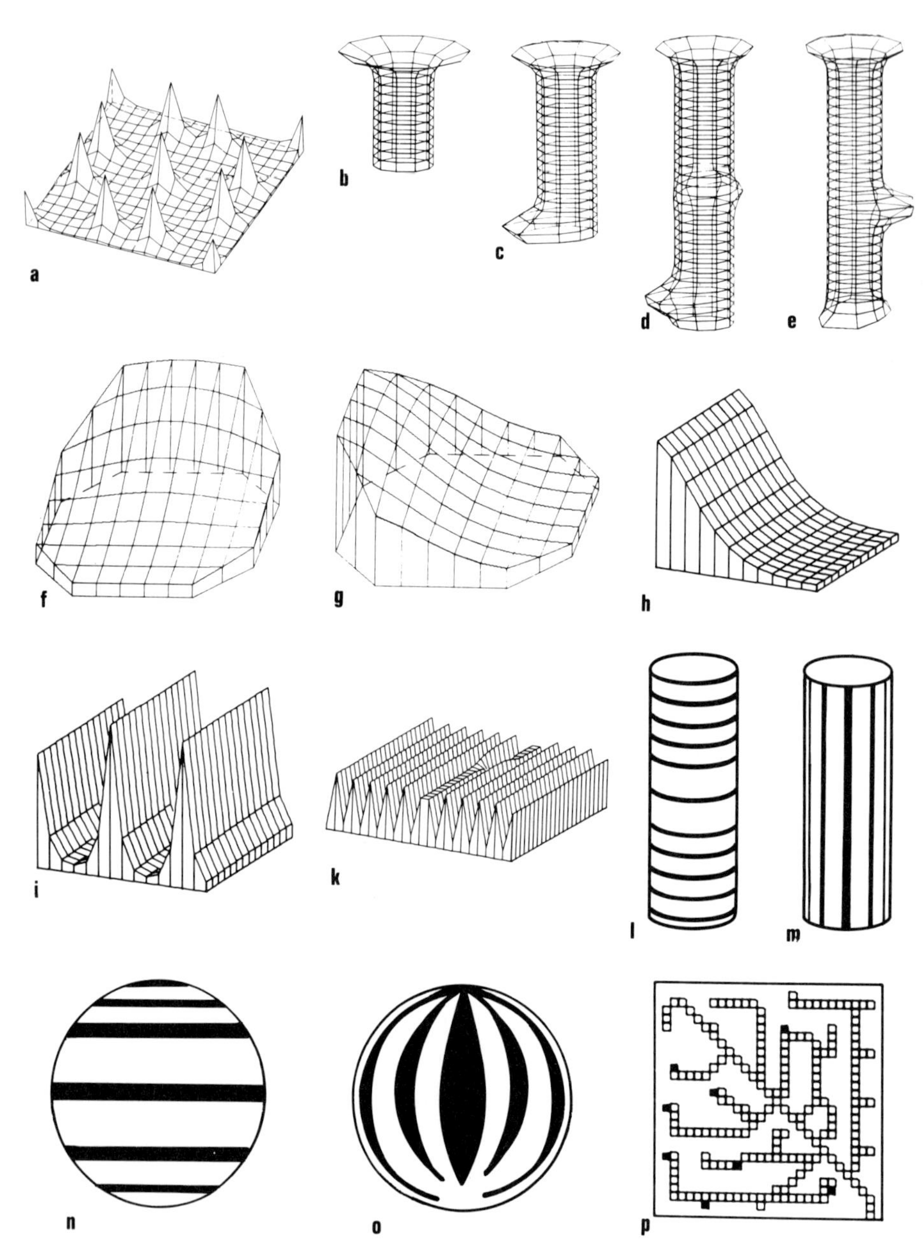

FIG. 9. Pattern formation in two dimensions. Basic types. (a) If range of activation is sufficiently small, a bristle type pattern is formed with near equal spacing of peaks of activation on a plane. (b–d) On the same principle, a growing cylinder can produce peaks of activity alternatively on opposite sides of the cylinder accounting for bud spacing in

formation can lead, for instance, to five peaks; but even large numbers of peaks can be formed without being too sensitive to variations in parameters. Size regulation would be possible, but only for factors considerably below two. Terminal growth could add further peaks of activity, so that any number of peaks could be produced. It is not inconceivable that such mechanisms are involved in somite formation.

Many tissues are anisotropic, with anisotropic cells aligned in the direction of an axis. (This may itself be the result of a gradient that has produced and oriented *intra*cellular patterns). The anisotropic nature of the tissue may, in turn, affect the formation and orientation of intercellular patterns formed across the tissue. Because of an anisotropic alignment of intercellular junctions, or for other reasons, tissue anisotropy can lead to anisotropic diffusion rates of various substances. Now, if diffusion rates are such that there is lateral inhibition in one dimension, whereas in the other the range of activator is comparable to or in excess of that of inhibitor, intercellular patterns are formed only in one (the first) of the two dimensions. As a result, gradients and other patterns formed are oriented nearly parallel or perpendicular to the axis of tissue anisotropy (Fig. 9h). Periodic patterns may be formed in one dimension within a two-dimensional field. For example, stripes and segmentation can be produced on planes, cylinders, and spheres (Fig. 9i–o).

---

hydra, and leaf arrangements in many plants. (e) There are versions that can produce two opposite peaks simultaneously at one level; in this case the next bud forms nearly at right angles. (f) If total area is comparable to activator range, a shallow initiating gradient can cause a slope-type pattern specifying positional information in one of the two dimensions. (g) Evidently a second pattern-forming system in a different orientation can specify a second axis independently (Fig. a–g from Meinhardt and Gierer, 1974; reproduced with permission).

Many tissues are anisotropic, with cells oriented along an axis. The result may be that diffusion rates are also anisotropic, e.g., by an anisotropic alignment of intercellular junctions. This may orient prepatterns formed by lateral inhibition in directions parallel or perpendicular to this axis, rather than in the direction of an initiating gradient. Panel h shows a slope-type pattern computed on the basis of Eq. (5) extended to two dimensions. It is assumed that the ratio of activator range to inhibitor range is 0.2 : 1 in the dimension left to right, but 0.7 : 1 in the dimension front to rear. Although the shallow gradient that initiated this pattern was oriented diagonally, the gradient of the pattern produced slopes in the dimension where lateral inhibition is effective, left to right. On the same principles, based on tissue anisotropy, periodic patterns, like stripes and segments, can be produced in one dimension within a two-dimensional field on planes (i, k), cylinders (l, m), and spheres (n, o). Direct computer plots are shown in panels i and k for stripes on a plane. Stripes drawn in panels l–o indicate areas of activation obtained by computer simulation. (p) Meinhardt (1976) has shown that pattern formation in conjunction with cell differentiation can lead to lines and nets in a two-dimensional field accounting, for instance, for vesicular nets in leaves.

Net structures can also be obtained on the basis of lateral inhibition. Meinhardt (1976) has found that certain interactions of cell differentiation and pattern formation by lateral inhibition produce lines, branches, and even connections accounting for various net types observed, for example, in leaves of plants (Fig. 9p).

These considerations are to show the wide range of different patterns that can be produced on a basis of lateral inhibition. It is emphasized that the theory is consistent with very different molecular mechanisms: Inhibition may be due to inhibitors or to the depletion of substances required for activation; production of activators and inhibitors to synthesis or release; spreading to diffusion or convection; and removal to degradation or leakage. Autocatalytic and cooperative features of activation may result from allosteric shifts of proteins or other mechanisms. It could be due to reaction kinetics in the cytoplasm, but might also involve the genes, phase transitions in the cytoplasm, alterations in membrane properties and intercellular interactions. Molecular features required are common in molecular biology, but only biochemistry could reach a decision on any particular mechanism in each case.

C. Application of the Lateral Inhibition Theory to Hydra

The lateral inhibition theory has been used to treat a variety of biological systems and properties of their development (Meinhardt and Gierer, 1974). In this chapter, I wish to discuss features of hydra on the basis of the theory (Gierer and Meinhardt, 1972; Meinhardt and Gierer, 1974).

Activating and inhibiting effects, as they occur in the theory, are essential features of previously proposed models on hydra morphogenesis (e.g., Burnett, 1966; Wolpert, 1971), especially with respect to budding and the formation of secondary heads. These models have contributed much to our understanding of the system, but they employ variable thresholds, assumptions on margins and other features in the form of verbal statements that are not easily interpretable in molecular and physical terms. The lateral inhibition theory accounts for basic features of hydra, including the formation of structures from near-uniform sections in regeneration, on the basis of consistent physical mechanisms with concentrations changing only as functions of concentrations.

a. The Key Experiment. The crucial test for any concept is the basic fact described in Fig. 5. Any section of the gastric column regenerates a complete animal; the head regenerates at the terminal closest to the original head. In the lateral inhibition theory, this is a straightforward consequence of a polarity-defining, shallow source gradient which directs the orientation but not the general shape of the head-activating prepattern. The effect is easily simulated by computer. It is obtained with closed boundaries as well as with certain (not all) types of leakage across the margins.

b. Steady State. Prepatterns, which are formed relatively fast, direct morphogenesis, cell differentiation, and synthetic processes and thus may slowly change the concentration of the sources. The relatively slow change may in turn feed back on the prepattern of activators and inhibitors, but this does not introduce arbitrariness and inconsistency into the theory. Equations for the change of ρ can be introduced into the set of equations of type (5) in a straightforward manner. One obtains a steady state of growth, proliferation, and differentiation, maintaining a spatial pattern indefinitely as observed in mature growing and budding hydra.

The theoretical distinction between slowly changing source concentrations (ρ) and more rapidly formed prepatterns (a) is supported experimentally by involved kinetic graft experiments (MacWilliams, 1977) demonstrating different rates of alteration and different susceptibility to inhibitors for the two effects.

c. Transplantation Experiments. A series of experiments by Wolpert *et al*. (1971) shows that heads can be induced by transplants, the probability of head formation being inversely related to the distance of the transplant from the head in the animal from which the transplant was derived, and directly to the distance to the head of the host into which the transplant is inserted (Fig. 3). These results can be simulated by computer on the basis of the lateral inhibition theory, using a simple equation like Eq. (5). To account for more kinetic details, such as the dependence of the *rate* of prepattern formation and regeneration on position in the gastric column, would require more parameters, but the principle is expected not to be affected.

d. Foot Formation. Foot formation appears to involve a specific prepattern-forming system differing from the head-forming system (MacWilliams and Kafatos, 1968, 1974), but some cross-reaction between head and foot formation seems to occur, tending to push them to opposite ends of a regenerate. As discussed in the preceding subsection (III, B, 6), a slight mutual cross-inhibition exerted by the inhibitors of the head- and foot-forming system can account for such complementary terminal structures (Fig. 10a). Cross-inhibition also explains the observation (Hicklin *et al.,* 1969) that a head may form internally and feet at the ends if, in a regenerate, terminal head formation is inhibited by chemical agents (Fig. 10b).

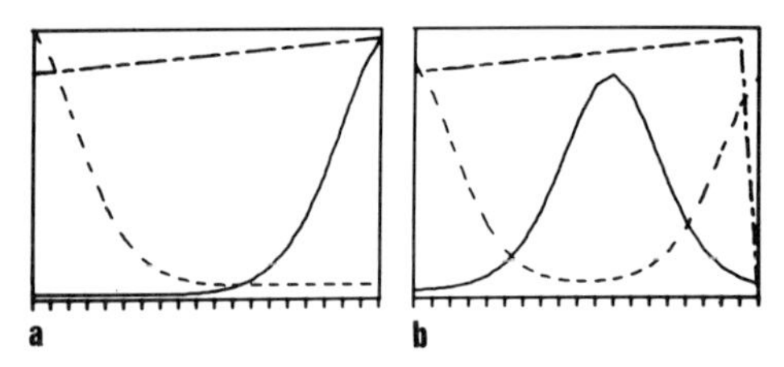

FIG. 10. Cross-inhibition produces polar patterns with complementary marginal structures. (a) Two pattern-forming systems with a slight cross-inhibition lead to complementary peaks of activation (——, ---) on opposite ends if total area is within the reach of inhibitors. A shallow source gradient (—— – ——–) for one of the systems suffices to orient the pattern. Cross-inhibition accounts for polar structures with distinct terminals, such as head and foot in hydra. (b) Altering the boundary conditions by inhibiting one of the sources at the right end (or both ends) leads to a pattern of different symmetry with activation of one type in the middle and of the other type at the ends. This pattern simulates the response of a hydra regenerate to certain chemical agents by producing a head in the middle and two feet at the ends (Hicklin *et al.*, 1969). The following equations based on Eq. (5) were used in the computer calculation, a and a' denoting the two activators, and $i = 1 \ldots 20$ the element within the area, with boundaries assumed to be impermeable:
$r_i = 1 + 0.01 \cdot i$ (except $r_{20} = 0$ in panel b; patterns very similar to panel b are formed if, in addition, $r_1 = 0$)

$$\Delta a_i = 0.0002 \cdot r_i + 0.004 \cdot r_i \cdot a_i^2/(h_i + 0.1\, h_i') - 0.004 a_i + 0.01 \cdot (a_{i+1} + a_{i-1} - 2a_i)$$
$$\Delta h_i = 0.006 \cdot r_i \cdot a_i^2 - 0.006 \cdot h_i + 0.3(h_{i+1} + h_{i-1} - 2h_i)$$
$$\Delta a_i' = 0.0002 + 0.004 \cdot a_i'^2/(h_i' + 0.1 \cdot h_i) - 0.004 \cdot a_i' + 0.01 \cdot (a_{i+1}' + a_{i-1}' - 2a_i')$$
$$\Delta h_i' = 0.006 \cdot a_i'^2 - 0.006 \cdot h_i' + 0.3(h_{i+1}' + h_{i-1}' - 2h_i')$$

e. Budding. The lateral inhibition mechanisms produce the observed spacing of buds on a growing cylinder of the gastric column: mostly they occur alternatively on opposite sides (Figs. 1a and 9b–d), similar to leaves in many plants. If occasionally two buds develop simultaneously at the same level, they appear opposite to each other, and the next one appears at right angles (Fig. 9e). It is not known whether budding involves the same pattern-forming system as head formation, or a different one. If the systems are the same, there must be an additional determinant to distinguish heads from buds. If the systems are different, there is, again, some cross-reaction, since heads and buds mutually inhibit each other to a considerable extent (e.g., Shostak, 1974).

The ring of regularly spaced tentacles could be explained if head activation would be a precondition to fire a secondary pattern resulting in peaks of activity on a ring.

Chemical identification of activators and inhibitors participating directly in prepattern formation presents a difficult experimental problem, and it has not been solved so far. The substance that has been shown to activate head and bud formation (Schaller, 1973; Schaller and

Gierer, 1973) and a substance that inhibits such processes (Berking, 1977) could, but need not, be involved in the auto- and cross-catalytic processes of prepattern formation. They may have other functions as well, such as the regulation of the concentration of nerve cells or interstitial cells in the tissue, with indirect effects on morphogenesis.

D. Recursive and Other Types of Pattern Formation

Aside from the lateral inhibition type, there are other types of biological pattern formation. Asymmetric structures could be formed if polarized cells align parallel to each other within an aggregate. Various types of pattern-forming mechanisms within such oriented arrays have been proposed (Lawrence, 1966; McMahon, 1973). Another type of pattern formation is recursive in the sense that relatively proximal parts of a structure regenerate relatively more distal parts, but not the other way round. The regeneration of limbs, imaginal disks in insects, and insect legs seem to be of this type. Whereas a removed distal structure is regenerated, isolated distal structures produce another distal structure by symmetric duplication, if anything. Regeneration results eventually from growth, and it has been suggested that the structures to be formed are laid sequentially in proximodistal order in the course of growth (Summerbell *et al.,* 1973). Often, excised internal parts are regenerated intercalarily. In this case, however, the tissue at the relatively more distal edge of the junction can contribute to the regeneration of relatively more proximal parts (Bohn, 1971). This shows that the fate of cells participating in regeneration is not determined by an internal clock counting proliferation, but is rather strongly influenced by communication with the preexisting cells nearby. Further, it has been observed that in regenerating insect legs patterns are laid down by morpholactic processes (Bullière, 1972). Near a cut, the hypodermal cell sheet loses its specificity with regard to position, and forms rudiments of all structures to be regenerated without detectable cell division. This does not exclude that various segments are laid down sequentially in time, but cell division and growth occurs only thereafter. The morpholactic process resembles pattern formation in hydra, but there are additional features to be explained: Only missing–not all–structures are newly produced. Possibly boundary conditions somehow cause only the missing part of the pattern to be laid down; or, after formation of a prepattern mechanisms sensing discontinuities at the boundary to preexisting structures select only the missing parts for expression and growth. A complication is that intersegmental and intrasegmental discontinuities show distinguishable effects and have to be considered separately.

Further studies are required to understand such recursive pattern formation and regeneration, and to decide to what extent findings made on individual organisms can be generalized. Tentatively, it appears that cell communication and probably the principle of lateral inhibition are involved. A main feature seems to be mechanisms sensing discontinuities in the spatial sequence to initiate and regulate regeneration and growth. Whereas it is possible that different substances produced in different sections participate in this regulation, a simple hypothesis can be based on the gradient theory postulating a graded distribution of production capacities for a particular morphogenetic substance. Then removal or excision of parts of the tissue produces a new terminal or a discontinuity in the gradient; this in turn may locally elicit a regeneration signal. It can be shown that catalytic effects are capable of such gradient discontinuity sensing. An example of a model (Fig. 12) is given in the Appendix.

E. Effects of Prepatterns

Among the effects of prepatterns, those on cell differentiation and tissue evagination are of particular interest for the understanding of morphogenesis.

If the per cell probability of determination or differentiation in a given direction is influenced by the concentration of a morphogen, a continuous prepattern is expected to lead to a continuous distribution of the concentration of differentiated cells in the tissue, e.g., to a gradient of nerve cells in hydra.

For many developing systems, a striking feature is the existence of sections with distinct boundaries. Such compartments exist even in the absence of overt discontinuities (Garcia-Bellido *et al.,* 1973). It is conceivable that boundaries are initiated by a periodic prepattern (see Fig. 8). An alternative mechanism that is very likely to occur in biology is a discontinuous cell response to a continuous morphogen gradient dividing an area into distinct sections.

To discuss this effect requires some model considerations on cell differentiation per se. The various states of determination and differentiation of a cell are expected to differ in the set of genes or gene products regulated to be active. Each state appears to be relatively stable. A likely explanation of this stability is to assume that producing structures, such as genes, are regulated by their products in such a way that the feedback produces multiple stable states, each one corresponding to a state of determination or differentiation. Possibly the regulation is combinatorial, a given state being defined by a set of regulatory proteins, each one stabilizing its own synthesis by positive feedback once it is turned on (Gierer, 1967, 1973; Kauffman, 1973). If a step of determination consists in turning just one of these circuits off or on, this would explain the fact that in determination, from any given state, there are but a few (perhaps only two) directions.

Systems with multiple stable states often respond by discontinuous transitions to continuously varying inducers. It is instructive to discuss the formal points for a multiple stable mechanical system of everyday life, the umbrella. It has two stable states 1 and 2 (Fig. 11). For small deviations y from state 1, there will be a returning force f (and a returning velocity y) proportional to the deviation. For larger deviations, however, an overproportional effect will overcome the returning force giving rise to a transition toward state 2. If there is wind of a strength w above a threshold w_0, there is a shift from state 1 to state 2 which remains after the wind is gone. A simple approximation requires a nonlinear relation between force and effect, such as:

$$f = \text{const.}\, \dot{y} = -y + y^2/(1 + Ky^2) + w \tag{6}$$

For $w = 0$ there are two stable states, $y = 0$ and $y = y_0$. There is a threshold w_0 so that for $w > w_0$ transition from the lower to the higher state occurs.

If cell differentiation is due to transitions between multiple stable states, there are simple models formally analogous to that given for the umbrella. For example, if a gene product activates its own gene, and if the feedback is somewhat overproportional, e.g., because allosteric receptor proteins are involved in gene activation, whereas degradation is linear, Eq. (6) can again be taken as an approximation; now y describes the concentration of the gene product. The cell would be bistable, one state producing little, the other much of this product. If a morphogen

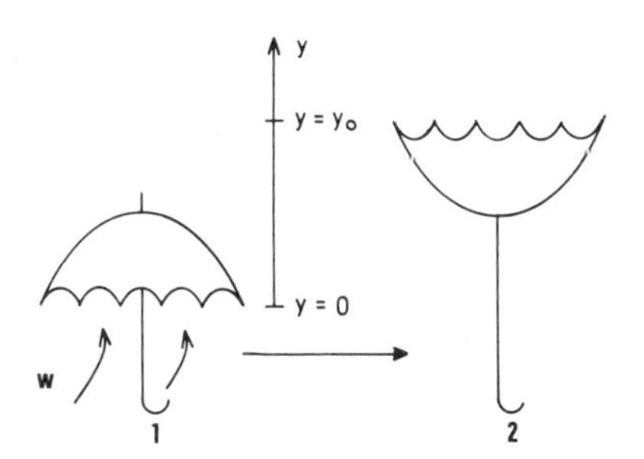

FIG. 11. Bistable system as model for cell differentiation. A bistable mechanical system responds to a continuous variable (wind of strength w) by a discontinuous transition from state 1 to state 2. Mathematically analogous models of cell differentiation (considered as shift between multistable states) may explain discontinuous cell response to a continuous morphogen gradient (see text), leading to differentiation in a defined section of the total area with distinct boundaries.

(in analogy to wind w) stimulates gene activation, cells would differentiate to the state of high production in those parts of a morphogen gradient where the morphogen concentration is above a threshold value w_0, thus separating a tissue into distinct sections. More complex gene regulation could lead to more complex segmentation of an area. Very interesting mathematical theorems on discontinuous response to continuous stimuli, especially in multidimensional fields, have been discovered by Thom (1972). Generally, if one considers cell determination as due to shifts between multiple stable states, then discontinuous segmentation and compartmentalization in response to continuous prepatterns of morphogens can be explained in a rather straightforward manner.

Another main effect of prepatterns is to determine the location at which tissues evaginate or invaginate to build a new structure, e.g., by budding. Many mechanisms can be conceived to contribute to the evagination of cell layers. Localized enhancement of cell proliferation, and effects on tissue anisotropy such as orientation of planes of division may result in forces that cause evagination. However, proliferation and growth do not, in any case, seem to be prerequisites of tissue evagination. As exemplified by hydra regeneration, prepatterns can affect existing, nondividing epithelial cells of a tissue changing interactive properties and shapes in such a way that curvatures change locally and a new structure, e.g., a head, is produced. Concepts on the physics of such cell interactions will be discussed in a separate paper.

F. Conclusions; Relations of Chemical, Physical, and Mathematical Aspects of Morphogenesis

In this essay, I have discussed features of hydra that show in a simple form elementary processes involved in morphogenesis: the time course and spatial pattern of cell differentiation and its self-regulating features; responses of regenerates to very low concentrations of organic substances which influence morphogenesis; cell interaction producing structures, such as a double-layered hollow sphere of hydra regenerates; and processes of prepattern formation deciding whether and where to form new heads, buds, and feet.

Of the main theoretical issues of morphogenesis: How do cells differentiate? How does a tissue evaginate? How do prepatterns arise that direct and space such processes? I have mainly discussed the latter aspect. Prepatterns in hydra exhibit a set of features typical of many other (though certainly not all) biological systems. This lateral inhibition type can be accounted for by short-range activation, long-range inhibition, and certain kinetic conditions that lead—starting from near-uniform initial conditions—to the firing of stable self-regulating patterns that show a set of properties of many biological patterns. Probably only few such pattern-forming systems occur in the development of an organism, but each one is fired repeatedly at different places and times of development. The catalytic processes may involve allosteric transitions of proteins and could be quite simple. However, very different mechanisms (including, for instance, cooperative transitions in membranes) would also be consistent with the lateral inhibition concept if its kinetic criteria are met. Whereas two catalytic substances, one activating and one inhibiting, suffice to generate patterns, it is not excluded that an entire set of substances is involved in the firing of a single prepattern, activation and inhibition describing system properties rather than individual substance concentrations. Such very interesting aspects related to complexity or simplicity could be resolved not by any refinement of mathematical analysis but only by progress in the biochemistry of pattern formation of which we know so little. Only biochemical evidence could support any specific molecular model. On the other hand, one cannot expect to understand pattern formation merely by studying the structures of the molecules involved. If patterns are formed by catalytic mechanisms, the relation between chemical structures of molecules, and the concentration patterns they generate, is a most indirect one. It is mediated by physical kinetics which is therefore an essential feature in explaining patterns. Some classical concepts of developmental biology, such as "gradients" and "polarity" can be given specific formal meanings by physical kinetics; but, generally, the kinetics involved in generating patterns cannot be adequately and consistently described, or substituted for, by models using intuitive verbal concepts. For a comprehensive understanding of pattern formation it is necessary to combine empirical evidence on molecular and cellular properties with mathematical physics.

The mathematics need not be complicated and out of reach of the experimental biologist. A main point in the lateral inhibition theory is that linear relations do not suffice but quite simple nonlinear ones based on fairly simple molecular mechanisms give, at least qualitatively, an entire set of features observed in biology. Of course quantitative refinement would require the introduction of more parameters, but the essential step toward understanding is the introduction of the simple nonlinearities. This principle of "modest nonlinearity" may be somewhat more widely applicable to biology and structure formation in general. Linear interactions do not easily lead to order in space and time. However, rather simple nonlinearities suffice in theories accounting for prepatterns (as described in this article), for cell differentiation as shift between multiple stable states, for the cell cycle interpreted as limit cycle oscillation (Tyson and Kauffman, 1975), and, as will be discussed in a separate paper, for nontrivial biological structures formed by contact-mediated cell interaction.

APPENDIX

Recursive Type of Pattern Formation in Regeneration: A Catalytic Model for Gradient Discontinuity Sensing

A model involving "lateral activation" will be chosen as an example. Assume that the graded source $\rho(x)$ produces an inhibitor $[h(x, t)]$ locally and, in addition, a diffusible activator $a(x, t)$. The ratio a/h is then above average at a terminal, and near excisions that produce discontinuous steps of the ρ gradient. There catalytic mechanisms could elicit a regeneration signal by producing a substance $g(x, t)$. An

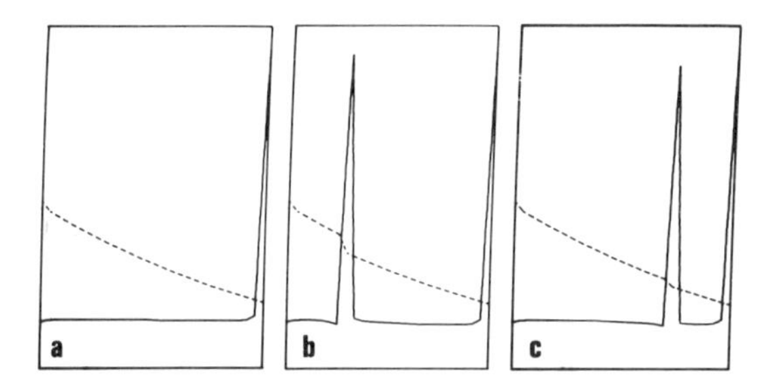

FIG. 12. Gradient discontinuity sensing to initiate regeneration of removed parts of a tissue. A graded source $\rho(x)$ (---) is assumed to produce substances interacting catalytically according to Eq. (7). High concentrations of g are assumed to initiate regeneration if distal or internal parts are excised (see Bohn, 1970). In computer simulations based on Eq. (7) a peak of substance g is fired at lower terminals produced by removal of distal parts, and at discontinuities produced wherever a piece is excised. The most distal section of the complete structure is expected to be insensitive to the g signal. (a) Continuous gradient. A peak of g is produced at the lower terminal. Panels (b) and (c) show the firing of an internal g signal if 12% of total length is excised in the left part (b), and 6% in the right part (c) of the gradient. Parameters have been chosen so that no signal is fired if 3% or less is excised. A step distribution for ρ, with small steps, would thus be nearly equivalent to a continuous distribution. There are other, closely related schemes of gradient discontinuity sensing involving diffusible inhibitors instead of diffusible activators, and upward instead of downard ρ gradients

example is given by the following type of auto- and cross-catalysis:

$$\partial a/\partial t = c_a\rho - v_a a + D_a(\partial^2 a/\partial x^2) \quad (7a)$$

$$\partial h/\partial t = c_h\rho - \nu_h h \quad (7b)$$

$$\partial g/\partial t = g_0 + c_g[g^2/(1 + \chi g^2)]a/h - \nu_g g \quad (7c)$$

The choice of parameters required corresponds to the assumption that they have been set, either by evolution or by regulatory processes within newly produced cells, to a level just below the values that initiate a g signal in the absence of cell communication ($D_a = 0$).

Computer simulations show that g signals are fired at the lower terminal and at discontinuities of the ρ gradient (Fig. 12), accounting for the initiation of regeneration of distal and intermediary sections as described in Bohn's (1970) experiments on insect legs. It is emphasized, however, that this model describes but one of many possible catalytic mechanisms for gradient discontinuity sensing, and that the gradient theory is but one among other possibilities to model for the "recursive" type of pattern formation.

ACKNOWLEDGMENTS

I am much indebted to my colleagues Dr. Hans Meinhardt, Lynn Graf, and Dr. Stefan Berking for helpful discussions and the critical reading of the manuscript.

REFERENCES

Aisupiet, M. P. (1935). *Biol. Zentralbl.* **4**, 802.

Berking, S. (1977). *Wilhelm Roux' Arch. Entwicklungsmech. Org.* **181**, 215–225.

Bertalanfry, L. V., and Rella, M. (1942). *Wilhelm Roux' Arch. Entwicklungsmech. Org.* **141**, 99–110.

Bode, H., Berking, S., David, C. N., Gierer, A., Schaller, H., and Trenkner, E. (1973). *Wilhelm Roux' Arch. Entwicklungsmech. Org.* **171**, 269–285.

Bode, H., Flick, K., and Smith, G. S. (1976). *J. Cell Sci.* **20**, 29–46.

Bohn, H. (1970). *Wilhelm Roux' Arch. Entwicklungsmech. Org.* **165**, 303–341.

Bohn, H. (1971). *Wilhelm Roux' Arch. Entwicklungsmech. Org.* **167**, 209–221.

Bonnet, C. (1762). "Considérations sur les corps organisés."

Browne, E. N. (1909). *J. Exp. Zool.* **7**, 1–23.

Bryant, P. (1974). *Curr. Top. Dev. Biol.* **8**, 41–80.

Bulliere, D. (1972). *Am. Embryol. Morphog.* **5**, 61–74.

Burnett, A. L. (1966). *Am. Nat.* **100**, 165–189.

Burnett, A. L. (1968). *In* "The Stability of the Differentiated State" (H. Ursprung, ed.), pp. 109–127. Springer-Verlag, Berlin and New York.

Campbell, R. D. (1967). *J. Morphol.* **121**, 19–28.

Campbell, R. D., and David, C. N. (1974). *J. Cell Sci.* **16**, 349–358.

Child, C. M. (1941). "Patterns and Problems of Development." Univ. of Chicago Press, Chicago, Illinois.

Clarkson, S. G. (1969). *J. Embryol. Exp. Morphol.* **21**, 33–70.
Clarkson, S. G., and Wolpert, L. (1967). *Nature (London)* **214**, 780–783.
Crick, F. (1970). *Nature (London)* **225**, 420–422.
David, C. N., and Campbell, R. (1972). *J. Cell Sci.* **11**, 557–568.
David, C. N., and Challoner, D. (1974). *Am. Zool.* **14**, 537–542.
David, C. N., and Gierer, A. (1974). *J. Cell Sci.* **16**, 359–375.
David, C. N., and Murphy, S. (1977), to be published.
DeLong, G. R. (1970). *Dev. Biol.* **22**, 563–583.
Diehl, F. A., and Burnett, A. L. (1965). *J. Exp. Zool.* **158**, 299–317.
Edelstein, B. B. (1972). *J. Theor. Biol.* **37**, 221–243.
Garcia-Bellido, A., Ripoll, P., and Morata, G. (1973). *Nature (London), New Biol.* **245**, 251–253.
Gierer, A. (1967). *Naturwissenschaften* **54**, 389–396.
Gierer, A. (1973). *Cold Spring Harbor Symp. Quant. Biol.* **38**, 951–961.
Gierer, A., and Meinhardt, H. (1972). *Kybernetik* **12**, 30–39.
Gierer, A., and Meinhardt, H. (1974). *Am. Math. Soc.* **7**, 163–183.
Gierer, A., Berking, S., Bode, H., David, C. N., Flick, K., Hansmann, G., Schaller, H., and Trenkner, E. (1972). *Nature (London), New Biol.* **239**, 98–101.
Gmitro, J. I., and Scriven, L. E. (1966). *Symp. Int. Soc. Cell Biol.* **5**, 221.
Ham, R. G., Fitzgerald, D. C., and Eakin, R. E. (1956). *J. Exp. Zool.* **133**, 559–572.
Hartline, H. K., Wagner, H. G., and Ratliff, F. (1956). *J. Gen. Physiol.* **39**, 651–673.
Herlands, R. L., and Bode, H. R. (1974a). *Wilhelm Roux' Arch. Entwicklungsmech. Org.* **176**, 67–88.
Herlands, R. L., and Bode, H. R. (1974b). *Nature (London)* **248**, 389–390.
Hicklin, J., Hornbruch, A., and Wolpert, L. (1969). *Nature (London)* **221**, 1268.
Hunt, R. K., and Jacobson, M. (1972). *Proc. Natl. Acad. Sci. U.S.A.* **69**, 780–783.
Kauffman, S. (1973). *Science* **181**, 310–318.
Kirschfeld, L., and Reichardt, W. (1964). *Kybernetik* **2**, 43–61.
Kuffler, S. W. (1952). *Cold Spring Harbor Symp. Quant. Biol.* **17**, 281–292.
LaVail, J. H., and Cowan, W. M. (1971). *Brain Res.* **28**, 421–441.
Lawrence, P. A. (1966). *J. Exp. Biol.* **44**, 607–620.
Lehn, H. (1951). *Z. Naturforsch. Teil B* **6**, 388–391.
Lentz, T. L. (1965). *Science* **150**, 633–635.
Lentz, T. L. (1966). "The Cell Biology of Hydra." North-Holland Publ., Amsterdam.
Lesh, G. E., and Burnett, A. L. (1964). *Nature (London)* **204**, 492–493.
Loomis, W. F., and Lenhoff, H. M. (1956). *J. Exp. Zool.* **132**, 555–573.
McMahon, D. (1973). *Proc. Natl. Acad. Sci. U.S.A.* **70**, 2396–2400.
MacWilliams, H. K. (1977), to be published.
MacWilliams, H. K., and Kafatos, F. C. (1968). *Science* **159**, 1246–1247.
MacWilliams, H. K., and Kafatos, F. C. (1974). *Am. Zool.* **14**, 633–645.
Meinhardt, H. (1976). *Differentiation* **6**, 117–123.
Meinhardt, H., and Gierer, A. (1974). *J. Cell Sci.* **15**, 321–346.
Noda, K. (1971). *Zool. Magazine* **80**, 99.
Park, H. D., Ortmeyer, A. B., and Blankenbaker, D. P. (1970). *Nature (London)* **227**, 617–619.
Prigogine, I. (1972). *Nova Acta Leopold.* **206**, 139–150.
Rand, H. W., Bovard, J. F., and Minnich, D. E. (1926). *Proc. Natl. Acad. Sci. U.S.A.* **12**, 565–570.
Rich, F., and Tardent, P. (1969). *Rev. Suisse Zool.* **76**, 779–789.

Rösel von Rosenhof, A. (1755). "Historie der Polypen und anderer kleiner Wasserinsekten." Nürnberg.
Saunders, J. W. (1948). *J. Exp. Zool.* **108**, 363–403.
Schaller, C. H. (1973). *J. Embryol. Exp. Morphol.* **29**, 27–38.
Schaller, C. H., and Gierer, A. (1973). *J. Embryol. Exp. Morphol.* **29**, 39–52.
Segel, L. A., and Jackson, J. L. (1972). *J. Theor. Biol.* **37**, 545–559.
Shaffer, B. M. (1958). *Q. J. Microsc. Sci.* **99**, 103–122.
Sheffield, J. B., and Moscona, A. A. (1969). *Exp. Cell Res.* **57**, 462–466.
Shostak, S. (1974). *Am. Zool.* **14**, 619–632.
Sidman, R. L., Miale, I. L., and Feder, N. (1959). *Exp. Neurol.* **1**, 322–333.
Slautterback, D. B., and Fawcett, D. W. (1959). *J. Biophys. Biochem. Cytol.* **5**, 441–452.
Summerbell, D., Lewis, J. H., and Wolpert, L. (1973). *Nature (London)* **244**, 492–496.
Tardent, P., Rich, R., and Schneider, V. (1971). *Dev. Biol.* **24**, 596–608.
Thom, R. (1972). "Stabilité structurelle et morphogénèse." Reading, Massachusetts.
Trembley, A. (1744). "Mémoires pour servir à l'histoire d'un genre de polypes d'eau douce à bras en forme de cornes." Leyden.
Trenkner, E., Flick, K., Hansmann, G., Bode, H., and Bode, P. (1973). *J. Exp. Zool.* **185**, 317–325.
Turing, A. (1952). *Philos. Trans. R. Soc. London, Ser. B* **237**, 32–72.
Tyson, S., and Kauffman, S. (1975). *J. Math. Biol.* **1**, 289–310.
Vögeli, G. (1972). *Rev. Suisse Zool.* **79**, 649–674.
Webster, G., and Wolpert, L. (1966). *J. Embryol. Exp. Morphol.* **16**, 91–104.
Weiss, P., and Moscona, A. (1958). *J. Embryol. Exp. Morphol.* **6**, 238–246.
Wilby, O. K., and Webster, G. (1970). *J. Embryol. Exp. Morphol.* **24**, 595–613.
Wilcox, M., Mitchison, G. J., and Smith, R. J. (1973). *J. Cell Sci.* **12**, 707–723.
Wilson, H. R., and Cowan, D. J. (1973). *Kybernetik* **13**, 55–80.
Wilson, H. V. (1907). *J. Exp. Zool.* **5**, 245–258.
Wolpert, L. (1971). *Curr. Top. Dev. Biol.* **6**, 183–224.
Wolpert, L., Hicklin, J., and Hornbruch, A. (1971). *Symp. Soc. Exp. Biol.* **25**, 391–415.
Wolpert, L., Clarke, M. R. B., and Hornbruch, A. (1972). *Nature (London), New Biol.* **239**, 101–105.
Yao, T. (1945). *J. Exp. Biol.* **21**, 147–155.
Zumstein, A. (1973). *Wilhelm Roux' Arch. Entwicklungsmech. Org.* **173**, 294–318.

CHAPTER 3

MOLECULAR ASPECTS OF MYOGENESIS*

John Paul Merlie, Margaret E. Buckingham, and Robert G. Whalen

SERVICE DE BIOCHIMIE,
DÉPARTEMENT DE BIOLOGIE MOLÉCULAIRE,
INSTITUT PASTEUR, PARIS, FRANCE

I. Introduction

A useful definition of differentiation has been proposed by Jacob and Monod (1963) in which they consider that: "two cells are differentiated with respect to each other if, while they harbor the same genome, the pattern of proteins which they synthesize is different." In large part, the study of differentiation has become the study of differential gene expression. Such studies have by necessity dealt with the terminal steps of pathways giving rise to highly specialized tissues, such as lens, red blood cells, silk gland, chick oviduct, or skeletal muscle. It has been in these kinds of systems that current methodology for the detection and quantitation of specific gene products has been developed.

* This text was assembled from separate parts written by the individual authors. We apologize for the resulting inconsistency of style. The order of authorship was chosen at random.

For the present, molecular studies of cell differentiation are limited to these terminal events. Earlier transitions from one cell type to another have not yet been defined in molecular terms. For example, it is not known how the pattern of proteins synthesized by the muscle cell precursor differs from that of its stem cell in the mesoderm. It is, however possible to define protein synthesis patterns in the terminal compartments and in some cases in the penultimate compartments. And it is, therefore, reasonable to ask how the transitions from one cell type to another are controlled.

Embryonic muscle cell cultures offer many unique advantages in the study of genetic expression during terminal differentiation [see Yaffé (1966) and Hauschka (1972) for reviews of the cellular aspects of myogenesis *in vitro*]: (1) Two basic cell populations are distinguishable: one that expresses the specialized muscle phenotype, and the precursor to this population, which expresses no apparent muscle function. (2) These two populations are separable in time, precursors being abundant early in culture and muscle cells arising afterward, with a relatively synchronous transition between the two. (3) Passage from precursor to muscle cell is followed or accompanied by a dramatic morphological event, that of cell fusion and fiber formation (see Scheme 1). (4) Gene expression in the developing cells can perhaps be modulated by a host of external factors including innervation (Guth, 1968).

A special problem in defining the muscle phenotype from that of its precursor is the fact that many muscle like proteins exist in most if not all cell types, including, in all likelihood, the muscle cell precursor—

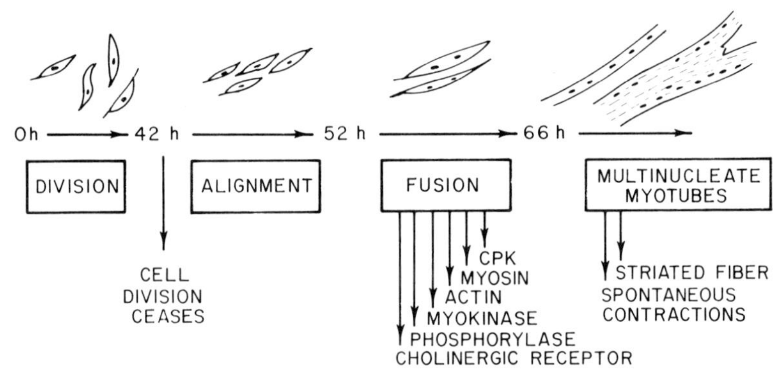

SCHEME 1. This graphic description of *in vitro* myogenesis is meant to give a general idea of the sequence of events accompanying differentiation of embryonic calf skeletal myoblasts. The morphological events indicated by boxes serve as useful markers for the design of biochemical experiments involving components or processes indicated by the vertical arrows. CPK, creatine phosphokinase.

the myoblast. It is becoming clearer that these musclelike proteins are ubiquitous, distinct isozymic forms of their muscle counterparts, and are probably involved in cell architecture and motility (Pollard and Weihing, 1974). This is not the case for such a specialized protein as the acetylcholine receptor, whose presence in muscle cells can be regarded as unique.

In the following review, we have attempted to critically discuss the relevant literature in only those areas of myogenesis that deal with the quantitative and qualitative changes in protein synthesis accompanying the terminal steps of muscle cell differentiation and the molecular mechanisms controlling these changes.

II. Protein Synthesis and Muscle Differentiation

A. Quantitative Aspects of Contractile Protein Synthesis

Aside from the morphological criterion of cell fusion, one of the attractive features of cultured muscle cells is the facility they offer for measuring the synthesis and accumulation of proteins normally associated with muscle tissue. Although myosin, actin, and tropomyosin have all been identified in many nonmuscle cells (see Pollard and Weihing, 1974), the quantitative (as well as perhaps the qualitative) features of their presence in muscle tissue are nevertheless distinctive. The heavy subunit of myosin (molecular weight 200,000) has been widely employed as a measure of myogenesis because its large size and unique solubility properties facilitate its analysis. The actual quantitative rise in the rate of myosin synthesis during myogenesis is of some interest. In chicken embryo muscle cell cultures, Paterson and Strohman (1972) have measured a 35-fold overall increase in rate of synthesis during the period from beginning to end of cell fusion (a period of about 32 hours). When normalized to the number of fused nuclei per dish, the maximal measured increase was only 8-fold. The actual rates of incorporation measured by Paterson and Strohman (1972) are probably valid, since they have verified that under their labeling conditions the [^{3}H]leucine was not degraded to other amino acids and that the leucine pool sizes remained similar in fused and unfused cells. These precautions are unfortunately not always taken.

The problem of how to normalize the data illustrates one problem in ascertaining what is the true situation. Many authors, somewhat ambiguously, have normalized rates of myosin synthesis to amount of total protein, to protein in actomyosin precipitates, per culture dish, or as percent of total protein synthesis. Ideally, it is the rate of synthesis per myosin gene that is of interest, although normalizing to the amount of DNA or total nuclei is more experimentally feasible. With these considerations in mind, Emerson and Beckner (1975) have carefully measured the rate of heavy-chain synthesis in cultures of Japanese quail breast muscle. In fused cultures, 10% of total [^{3}H]leucine incorporated was recovered in myosin heavy chain whereas in unfused cultures only about 0.2% was identified as heavy chain. When expressed as molecules synthesized per minute per nucleus, the increase was over 60-fold, attaining values of more than 20,000 molecules per nucleus per minute in cultures containing 85% fused cells. Calculations of the rate of heavy-chain synthesis per nuclei per minute for chick embryo muscle (Paterson and Strohman, 1972) give values more than 5-fold lower. Interestingly enough, and in contrast to the results of Paterson and Strohman cited above, the rate of myosin synthesis normalized to only those nuclei in multinucleate fibers was relatively constant throughout the fusion period. Furthermore, the observed level of myosin synthesis in young cultures (containing 1% fused cells) could be almost entirely accounted for by the myosin synthesis coming from the contaminating myotubes.

Thus two important points emerge from Emerson and Beckner's study of quail breast myoblasts. First, the constant rate of heavy-chain synthesis per fiber nucleus implies that synthesis reaches its maximal level very soon after (or indeed perhaps before, see Emerson and Beckner, 1975, Fig. 4) the nuclei enter multinucleate fibers. This is in contrast to the lag between fusion and myosin synthesis normally reported for chick embryo myoblasts (Paterson and Strohman, 1972), rat primary cultures (Yaffé and Dym, 1973), rat established myoblast lines (Loomis *et al.*, 1973), or veal myoblasts (Buckingham *et al.*, 1974a). Second, the quantitative increase in the rate of myosin synthesis per unit of DNA is much larger for the quail system than values reported for other commonly used systems. Whether this is related to differences among systems or culture conditions remains to be established. Further careful measurements are needed, possibly employing an antibody, to quantitate specific heavy-chain synthesis.

The second major muscle protein, actin, is less amenable to quantitation in cultured muscle cells. Although possessing several unique biological properties, its average size (MW 42,000) and lack of very specific solubility characteristics have made quantitative measurements less frequent. Furthermore, nonmuscle cells clearly contain large amounts of actin. In particular, nonmuscle cells maintained in cell culture, being strongly attached to a surface and growing in two dimensions, may contain more actin for structural purposes than they normally would *in situ*.

Very general measurements of actin synthesis in chick muscle cultures were reported by Paterson *et al.* (1974). Their values showed about a 9-fold difference between cultures at 26 hours (fusion <5%) and those at 72 hours (fusion = 70%). However, since these values were per culture dish, the significance of these rates of synthesis is not clear. In correlation with these values, Paterson *et al.* found that the percentage of translatable actin mRNA increases by about the same increment, but these indirect measurements may be subject to other criticisms.* Concerning the other well-known components of muscle tissue, such as tropomyosin, troponin, and the light-chain subunits of myosin, virtually nothing is known concerning the rate or coordination of synthesis in cultured muscle cells. Data for these proteins are needed in order to understand the higher-level problem of assembly of muscle proteins and to ascertain whether the organization (or reorganization) of these proteins into the contractile apparatus represents an element of control in myogenic differentiation. Holtzer *et al.* (1973) have presented a photograph of a well-developed cultured myotube which in most respects resembles the sarcomeric patterns seen in muscle tissue. Although this degree of assembly might be attained in prolonged culture, most authors have simply demonstrated thick (myosin) and thin (actin and tropomyosin) filaments existing in cultured myotube cytoplasm (Fischman, 1970; Etlinger and Fischman, 1973; Holtzer *et al.,* 1973) or in fusion-blocked myoblasts (Emerson and Beckner, 1975; Paterson and Strohman, 1972). The temporal process of filament assembly and formation of M and Z bands merits further study in developing cultured myotubes. In particular, how do these structures differ from similar arrangements in nonmuscle cells, structures supposedly accounting for motility rather than concentration (Pollard and Weihing, 1974)?

B. Qualitative Aspects of Contractile Protein Synethesis

In addition to the quantitative and coordinate features of muscle protein synthesis, it is of interest to determine which of several possible "isozymic" forms may be present in cultured myotubes and how this pattern changes under certain influences. Concerning the myosin heavy chain, evidence has been obtained for an embryonic myosin differing in primary structure and secondary modification from the adult type. Huszar (1972) has shown that young (21 day) rabbit skeletal myosin contains a peptide (presumably arising from fetal myosin)

* The basis for these *in vitro* translation experiments is that the cell-free system will utilize the messenger RNA even if it is not translated *in vivo,* and that the response accurately reflects mRNA levels.

homologous to a methylhistidine-containing adult peptide. This peptide, which is unmethylated, has two conservative amino acid substitutions out of the 13 sequenced. This result, together with the sequence of the corresponding cardiac myosin peptide, is evidence for the existence of at least three myosin genes: fetal, and adult skeletal and cardiac. Supportive evidence has been obtained by comparison of the tryptic fragmentation patterns of rabbit embryo and adult fast, slow, and cardiac myosins (Sreter *et al.*, 1975). Embryonic myosin was digested by trypsin in a manner similar to slow muscle myosin but distinct from fast muscle myosin. Furthermore, the light meromyosin (LMM) paracrystals from embryonic myosin gave an electron microscopic staining pattern distinct from those of the three adult types. These data, taken together, again suggest that embryonic muscle, at least in rabbit, expresses a gene different from the myosin gene expressed in the adult.

The question of possible muscle myosin isozymes and the comparisons with nonmuscle tissue myosin have recently been clarified by the work of Burridge and Bray (1975), who have purified myosin from a number of muscle and nonmuscle tissues of chicken. In particular, they have found differences in the fragments of myosin from various tissues produced by chemical and enzymic degradation. Their work has led to the conclusion that five primary types of myosin heavy chain exist: three muscle types, from skeletal, smooth and cardiac muscle, and two nonmuscle types, exemplified by myosin from brain and blood platelets.

The expectation is that cultures of unfused myoblasts contain nonmuscle myosin and that the myosin synthesized in quantity after fusion is one of the muscle types, although given the multiplicity of types it is difficult to predict which form or combination of forms might be present (Burridge and Bray, 1975). Chi *et al.* (1975b) have shown that fluorescent antibodies against chicken skeletal light meromyosin are bound to fused myotubes but not to replicating myoblasts, fibroblasts, or chondroblasts. They argue that, since replicating myoblasts contain myosin, there must be immunologic differences between this myosin and the muscle type. However, since the limits of sensitivity of the immunologic technique are unspecified and unfused myoblasts certainly contain less myosin than myotubes (Chi *et al.*, 1975a), these indirect arguments leave the situation unresolved for the moment. In a more direct fashion, Chi *et al.* (1975a,b) have shown that the myosin light chains of nonmuscle and prefusion myoblasts differ from those of fused myotube myosin. The light chains from prefusion myoblasts and nonmuscle cells are, however, similar, in partial agreement with the observations of Burridge and Bray (1975). The resolution of this situation is necessary in order to correlate the presence of various myosin isozymes with the study of the myosin heavy- and light-chain messenger RNAs (see Section IV, C). The questions of interest relate to determining whether a distinct myosin isozyme exists in prefusion myoblasts, how the isozyme changes upon formation of myotubes, and how the control of messenger RNA or protein synthesis is involved in the conversion. In addition, it is not clear whether myotubes in culture contain the fetal or adult forms of myosin (Huszar, 1972). Likewise, since cultured myotubes are noninnervated (but do, however, contract spontaneously), does their fiber type resemble slow or fast muscle tissue and, more interesting still, how will this phenotype change upon innervation?

Although the question of isozymic form is perhaps most important for the case of myosin heavy and light chains, given the physiologic correlations of myosin ATPase activity with contraction speed and thus muscle fiber type, the possibility of other muscle protein isozymic forms is not to be ignored. Peptide mapping studies of muscle and nonmuscle tropomyosin have shown that primary structure differences exist in the tropomyosins isolated from various tissues (Fine and Blitz, 1975). However, the situation in muscle cell cultures is as yet unclear. In addition, a number of studies have compared nonmuscle actin with muscle actin by peptide mapping (see Pollard and Weihing, 1974). When iodination or labeling with [^{35}S]methionine has been used to prepare radioactive nonmuscle actin, only a subset of all peptides could be examined, and thus, when overall similarity was found, it was not possible to say definitively whether the nonmuscle actin in question was in fact identical (Pollard and Weihing, 1974). By labeling with lysine and arginine, Gruenstein and Rich (1975) have prepared actin in which all but the carboxyl-terminal tryptic peptides were radioactive. They have thus been able to clearly demonstrate differences of primary structure between chick brain and muscle actin. Subsequently, Elzinga *et al.* (1976) provided definitive evidence of multiple genes for actin by sequencing one of the cyanogen bromide peptides from human platelet and cardiac actin. The platelet actin had one amino acid difference out of nine when compared to the corresponding cardiac peptide, whose sequence was identical to the peptide from rabbit skeletal muscle.

The existence of multiple genes for actin suggests that prefusion myoblasts may contain non-muscle actin and that a conversion to a muscle form would occur as myoblsts fuse to yield myotubes. Indeed, we have found this to be the case in cultures of calf embryo muscle cells (Whalen *et al.,* 1976a). When actin was isolated from cultures of myoblasts before and after fusion and subjected to isoelectric focusing in the presence of urea, three bands were detected (indicated by the arrows in Fig. 1). One band was substantially diminished in prefusion cultures (B) but became predominant in fused cultures (C). This form corresponds to the actin isolated from fetal calf muscle tissue (A) and has been called α-actin (Whalen *et al.*, 1976a). The two forms that were predominant in prefusion cultures, called β- and γ-actin, were also found in kidney cell cultures (D) and would appear to correspond to

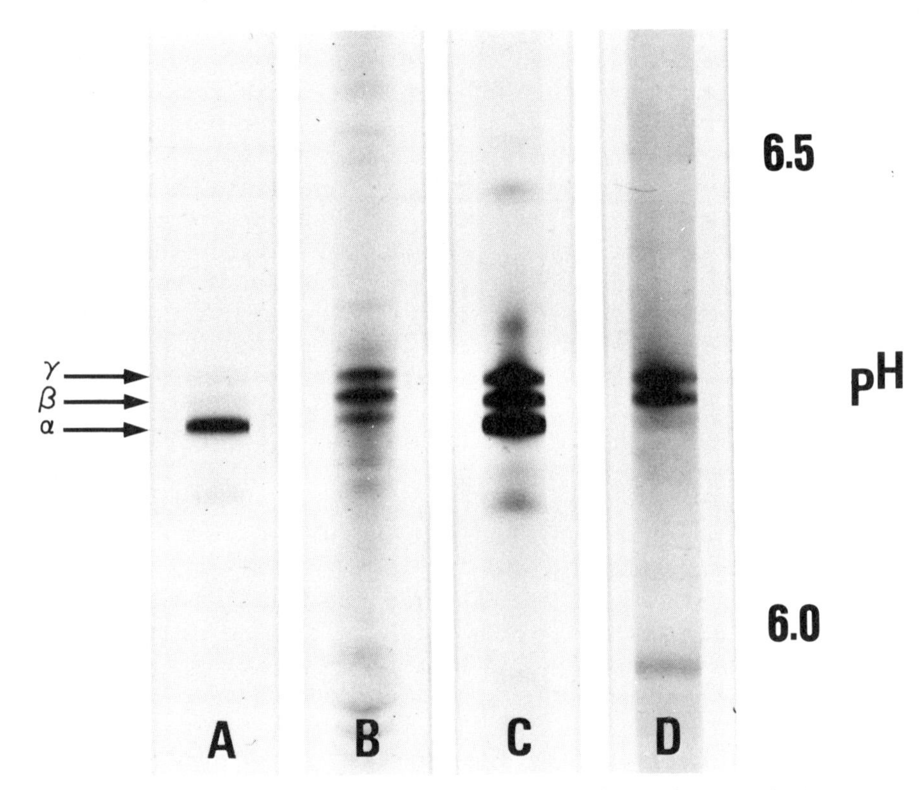

FIG. 1. The separation of multiple actin species by isoelectric focusing. Actin was prepared from several sources by extraction of an acetone powder and subsequent polymerization in 0.1 M KCl and 0.001 M $MgCl_2$ (Whalen *et al.*, 1976a). The resulting F-actin was analyzed by isoelectric focusing in the presence of urea and the nonionic detergent NP-40, as described by O'Farrell (1975). The isoelectric focusing gels were then stained with Coomassie blue and destained. The gels represent the analysis of actin prepared from: fetal muscle tissue (A), prefusion muscle cell cultures (B), fused muscle cell cultures (C), and confluent kidney cell cultures (D). The analysis of mixtures of muscle tissue actin (A) with prefusion muscle cell actin (B) or kidney cell actin (D) has shown that it is indeed the muscle tissue form that is diminished or lacking in these samples (Whalen *et al.*, 1976a).

nonmuscle-type actin. It is not yet clear why two distinct forms of nonmuscle actin are found, but it is nevertheless evident that the actin found in muscle tissue is only one of several possible isozymic forms. Taken together, the available evidence suggests that multiple genes for actin do exist and that differential gene activity may account for the production of muscle actin in fused muscle cell cultures.

C. Further Studies of Protein Synthesis

Most efforts to study protein synthesis in cultured muscle cells have been directed toward measuring the rates of synthesis of the major contractile proteins, chiefly myosin (see Section II, A). A second large body of work consists of measuring activities of enzymes associated specifically with muscle tissue, either because of their high activity in muscle or their specific muscle isozymes. Enzyme levels in general are controlled by the accumulation of enzyme protein, and therefore increased levels can in principle be produced by changes in rates of degradation, rather than by large changes in synthesis. One further reservation in relating enzyme levels to protein synthesis is the possibility of enzyme activation either by modification of the enzyme or the appearance of a cofactor, thus provoking an alteration in enzyme levels not involving alterations of synthesis or degradation rates.

For the most part, measurements have been made of acetylcholinesterase (Wilson *et al.*, 1973), adenylate cyclase (Zalin and Montague, 1974), creatine phosphokinase (Turner *et al.*,1974), glycogen phosphorylase (Loomis *et al.*, 1973), and myokinase (Shainberg *et al.*, 1971).* Creatine phosphokinase, an enzyme with an obvious role in muscle energy metabolism, has been the most extensively studied of these enzymes, in part owing to its ease of measurement and because of its specific muscle isozyme. These various studies have been carried out basically (1) to determine when, under culture conditions, the full expression of the muscle phenotype takes place (e.g., Turner *et al.*, 1974), (2) to characterize established cell lines of muscle cells (e.g., Shainberg *et al.*, 1971), (3) to characterize muscle cell mutants (e.g., Loomis *et al.*, 1973), and (4) in connection with problems concerning the requirement of cell fusion or RNA synthesis on the induction of the various activities (e.g., Yaffé and Dym, 1973).

Studies of *de novo* synthesis of these enzymes will probably require the use of immunological techniques to precipitate labeled protein. Ultimately the question is to ascertain if an increase in the rate of

* See Schudt *et al.* (1975) for a study of a large number of glycolytic enzymes, not all, of course, specifically associated with muscle.

synthesis of enzyme protein is part of the differentiation process, the expectation being that differential gene activity leading to increased messenger RNA levels will be responsible. The fact that only measurements of overall activity are possible for many muscle specific enzymes (in addition to studies of isozyme transitions for aldolase and creatine phosphokinase: Turner *et al.*, 1974; Gearhart and Mintz, 1975) illustrates the inability to obtain data on rates of synthesis for all but the most major proteins (two recent exceptions are studies of acetylcholine receptor synthesis (Merlie *et al.*, 1975) and acetylcholinesterase resynthesis after treatment with difluorophosphate (Wilson and Walker, 1974).

One possible approach to this problem is to look at overall polypeptide synthesis during development in culture. Such studies are useful if only to indicate how limited or extensive are the qualitative or quantitative changes. We have undertaken such studies in this context as well as to correlate these patterns with the products of cell free translation (see Section IV, D). Analyses of the proteins synthesized in pre- and postfusion calf embryo muscle cells by sodium dodecyl sulfate (SDS) gel electrophoresis revealed a limited number of differences at the two stages, but more striking was the very similar rate of synthesis of many of the major species, including actin, separated by this technique (Whalen *et al.*, 1976a). Although the resolution of such electrophoretic procedures is adequate for many purposes, clearly a reliable analysis of minor polypeptide species requires higher-resolution techniques. Accordingly, a two-dimensional analysis, involving isoelectric focusing and SDS gel electrophoresis (O'Farrell, 1975), was applied to this system (Whalen *et al.*, 1976a). The separation achieved by this technique (Fig. 2) allows an evaluation of the rates of synthesis of species of widely different abundancy classes. Once again, the overall conclusion is that although a restricted number of polypeptide species can be seen to appear only after fusion, a large majority seems to be present at all stages. It should be noted, however, that some species undergo quantitative changes in rates of synthesis relative to others (Whalen *et al.*, 1976a, 1977).

The implications of these results probably relate to the following considerations. First, living muscle cells will contain many metabolic processes in common with cells of other tissues, giving rise to common stores of the so-called "housekeeping" enzymes. Likewise, many cellular structures in muscle will be maintained by proteins similar to those in nonmuscle tissue. Aside from the obvious cases of ribosomes and certain membrane proteins, the finding of myosin, actin, and tropomyosin in nonmuscle tissue (although perhaps in different

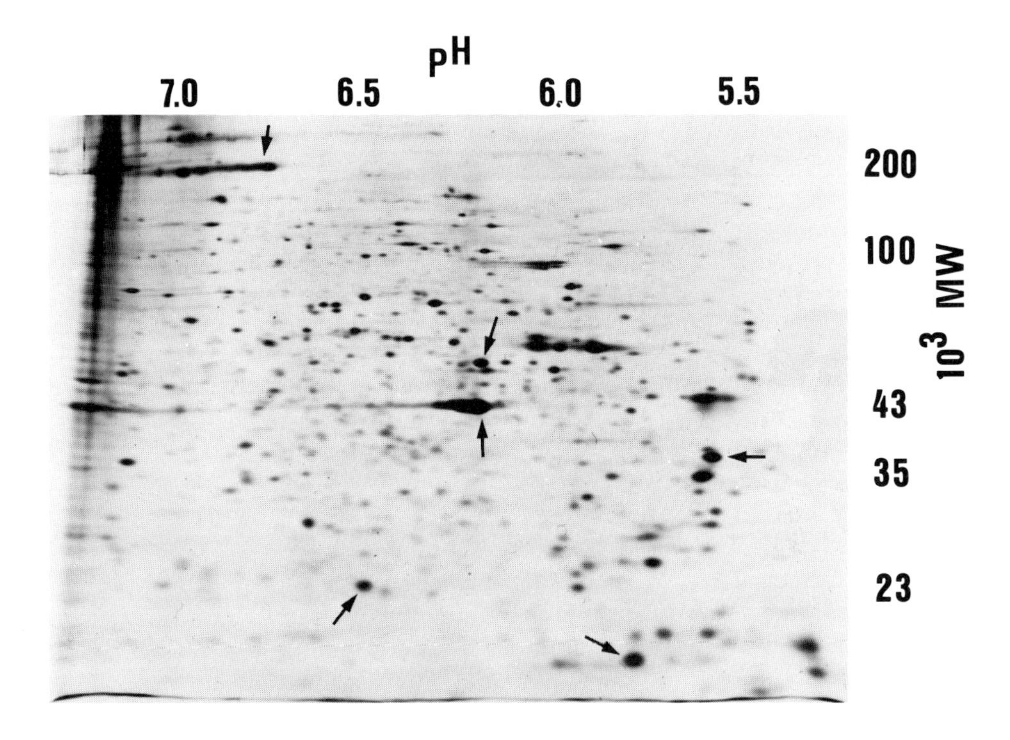

FIG. 2. Autoradiogram of the two-dimensional analysis of proteins from fused muscle cell cultures. Cultures of fused calf muscle cells were labeled for 2 hours with media containing [^{35}S]methionine. The cytoplasmic extracts were prepared as previously described (Whalen *et al.*, 1976a) and subjected to the two-dimensional separation described by O'Farrell (1975). The first dimension involves isoelectric focusing in urea and the nonionic detergent NP-40, and the approximate pH values are noted at the top of gels. Migration in the second dimension is carried out in the presence of sodium dodecyl sulfate to separate according to molecular weight; the approximate values of molecular weight in thousands are indicated at the side of the gel. This autoradiogram has been exposed for 390 hours. Myosin is located at pH 6.7–7.0, MW 200,000, and does not appear to form distinct spots under the conditions of focusing employed. The multiple actin spots (see text and Fig. 1) are located at pH 6.25, MW 43,000. The two major tropomyosin components are located at approximately pH 5.6, MW 35,000. Several of the proteins that are found only after fusion or are synthesized more rapidly after fusion are indicated with arrows. Included in these proteins are myosin, the muscle form of actin, and the higher molecular weight component of tropomyosin. The great majority (>90%) of protein species are however present in the labeling of prefusion muscle cell cultures.

isozymic forms) is an example of this phenomenon. Second, it is clear from the two-dimensional analysis that even though the number of species involved is small, those proteins whose rates of synthesis do increase are of widely different abundancy classes. Third, it is worth noting that as myotubes are formed, polypeptides appear rather than disappear. In other words, the number of species synthesized is increased, not decreased, as though the differentiated cell were adding to its metabolic and structural repertoire as opposed to limiting it. It is possible that this situation is true for the period just preceding and just following cell fusion and that mature myotubes in fact restrict the number of proteins synthesized. Alternatively, the levels of some species may be increased through increased stability of certain proteins.

In conclusion, although cultured muscle cells in principle offer numerous possibilities for the study of protein synthesis in a dynamic differentiating system, the potential remains incompletely exploited. It seems likely though that this situation will be resolved, as more highly refined techniques are applied to measure the quantitative and qualitative aspects of the several excellent markers of the muscle system.

III. Differentiation of the Myotube Plasma Membrane

Two characteristic features of the muscle plasma membrane are its chemical and electrical excitability. These two processes deal with the reception and transduction of the nerve impulse to initiate the muscle impulse, which is then transmitted along the fiber (Katz, 1966). Muscle cells in tissue culture also exhibit these properties, thus permitting studies of the molecular and developmental aspects of chemical and electrical excitability during muscle differentiation. Chemical excitability* will be discussed here in terms of a specific protein component of this process the acetylcholine receptor (ACh-R) (Katz, 1966; Hall, 1972). We have attempted to view neuromuscular interaction and synapse formation as playing important roles in the regulation of gene expression during myogenesis.

A. Regulation of Acetylcholine Receptor *in Vivo*

Functional ACh-R molecules can be detected by their sensitivity to iontophoretically applied ACh, as measured by a change in membrane potential and by their specific binding of radioactively labeled α-neurotoxins (Changeux, 1975).

Normal adult muscle fibers possess ACh sensitivity only at the motor end plate, which represents but a small fraction of the total fiber surface (Del Castillo and Katz, 1955). Embryonic muscle fibers have this ACh sensitivity distributed over their entire surface. Upon inner-

* See Ritchie and Fambrough (1975) and Kidokoro (1975a,b), for discussion of the electrical properties of cultured muscle cells, which we will not discuss.

vation and maturation, sensitivity becomes localized at the motor end plate and extra synaptic sensitivity disappears (Diamond and Miledi, 1962).

If an adult muscle is denervated, a situation in some ways similar to that in embryonic muscle arises where the ACh sensitivity and toxin binding capacity spreads over the entire fiber into extrasynaptic areas (Axelson and Thesleff, 1959; Miledi and Potter, 1971). The total receptor content of such a denervated muscle may increase as much as 20-fold in a period of a few days (Berg *et al.*, 1972; Miledi and Potter, 1971). Extrasynaptic receptor densities (10^3 toxin binding sites per $1\mu m^2$ of surface area) never quite achieve that of the synaptic membrane ($>10^4/\mu m^2$) (Fambrough and Hartzell, 1972; Porter *et al.*, 1973). If allowed to reinnervate, the nerve will seek out the original end-plate region (Gutmann and Young, 1944), and upon synapse formation the extrasynaptic sensitivity to ACh disappears as in embryonic life (Miledi, 1960). The role of the nerve in this process is suggested by experiments which show that the extrasynaptic ACh sensitivity of denervated muscle can be abolished by direct electrical stimulation of the muscle fiber (Drachman and Witzke, 1972). Furthermore, the rate at which reduction of extrasynaptic sensitivity is effected has been shown to depend on the frequency of stimulation (Lømo and Westgaard, 1975).

What are the molecular mechanisms by which ACh sensitivity and synapse formation are controlled? Some recent experiments with denervated rat diaphragm in organ culture have indicated that the regulation of the rate of turnover of ACh-R (synthesis and/or decay) is an important aspect of this problem. Studies on the loss of radioactive α-bungarotoxin from synaptic and extrasynaptic sites of organ-cultured denervated rat diaphragm have revealed dramatic differences in the stability of these two receptor types (Berg and Hall, 1975).

Circumstantial evidence suggests that the specific loss of radioactive label reflects true degradation of the receptor proteins (Berg and Hall, 1974, 1975; Devreotes and Fambrough, 1975). Assuming this, synaptic receptor would appear to have a half-life ($t_{1/2}$) of several days (a minimum due to dissociation of the receptor–toxin complex) and the extrasynaptic receptor a $t_{1/2}$ of 8–11 hours (Berg and Hall, 1974). Similar experiments done in intact animals have given essentially the same result and conclusions (Berg and Hall, 1975; Chang and Huang, 1975) ($t_{1/2}$ synaptic: 5–8 days; $t_{1/2}$ extrasynaptic: 19 hours). Further support for the difference in turnover of synaptic and extrasynaptic receptor has been provided by the finding that only in extrasynaptic areas could *de novo* synthesis of receptor be shown to occur when denervated diaphragms were incubated in organ culture (Brockes and Hall, 1975c).

There have been several reports that synaptic and extrasynaptic receptors may differ functionally in their affinities for certain cholinergic ligands (Beranek and Vyskocil, 1967; Almon *et al.*, 1974; Brockes and Hall, 1975a). One report describes a physicochemical difference in these two receptor types, detected as a difference in isoelectric point by focusing in a pH gradient in polyacrylamide gels (Brockes and Hall, 1975b). These differences could prove of interest in understanding the processes of stabilization and localization of synaptic receptor.

In summary, we would suggest that innervation entails at least two distinct and separate events relative to receptor metabolism:

1. A reduction of the steady-state level of extrasynaptic receptor density to levels many times lower than in synaptic areas; this could be achieved by regulation either at the level of synthesis or degradation of receptor polypeptides.

2. A stabilization of synaptic receptor such that turnover is negligible and packing density is maximal (Changeux, 1975). This could be achieved either by some modification of the receptor itself or of its immediate membrane environment, such as, for example, the organization of membrane-associated structural proteins. Actinlike proteins and tubulin have been proposed as possible structural determinants for the control of surface localization of lymphocyte receptors (Edelman *et al.*, 1973). Experimental findings clearly indicate that functional transmission and muscle activity are necessary factors for the normal regulation of the low steady-state level of receptor in extrasynaptic areas. These may also prove to be requirements for localization–stabilization of synaptic receptor.*

B. Acetylcholine Receptor of Cultured Muscle Cells

There exists a large body of literature concerning the appearance of ACh-R in differentiating cultured muscle cells. However, very little has been published concerning the molecular aspects of the synthesis, assembly, and degradation of this protein. Even though these studies might be hampered by the fact that they must deal with relatively minor cell components, the availability of highly specific and sensitive immunological and biochemical methods for detection, affinity labeling, and purification should permit a profitable approach to these problems (Changeux, 1975).

Sensitivity to ACh, conferred by the presence of functional nicotinic-type ACh-R, is one of the most specific and well-characterized

* Guth (1968) and Harris (1974) are recommended for review of the roles of tropic factors and neuromuscular transmission in these processes.

traits of cultured muscle cells. It is a distinctly developmental trait in that it is detected on multinucleate myotubes and to a relatively lesser degree on mononucleate cells (presumably those postmitotic cells just prior to fusion), and not at all in fibroblast cultures or cultured embryonic heart cells (Fambrough and Rash, 1971).

The characterization of the ACh-R in cultured muscle cells has been facilited by very sensitive methods for detecting activity. The first of these is the electrophysiological response to iontophoretically applied ACh. Using this technique it was determined that applied ACh evokes an end plate-like potential when applied to multinucleate myotubes grown in culture (Fambrough and Rash, 1971; Rash and Fambrough, 1973; Fischbach, 1970; Harris *et al.*, 1971).

A second technique which has proved to be very useful for ACh-R detection is that of the binding of radioactive α-neurotoxins prepared from the venom of one of several species of snakes (Changeux *et al.*, 1970). Using this technique it was possible to demonstrate that the inactivation of functional ACh-R measured by iontophoretic application of ACh followed the binding of radioactive toxin (Steinbach *et al.*, 1973; Hartzell and Fambrough, 1973). Thus the two techniques seem to measure the same molecular entity in cultured muscle.

1. Pharmacological and Biochemical Properties

The chemical and pharmacological properties of the ACh-R from cultured muscle cells closely resemble those of the well-characterized receptors from the electric organs of electric fish (Changeux *et al.*, 1976) and from adult denervated muscle (Brockes *et al.*, 1976). Pharmacologically the receptor *in situ* is of the classical nicotinic skeletal muscle type (Table I) (Patrick *et al.*, 1972; Catterall, 1975; Nurse and O'Lague, 1975; Vogel *et al.*, 1972; Merlie *et al.*, 1975).

Patrick *et al.* (1972) have described an "ACh-receptor" in mononucleate L_6 myoblasts which manifested itself by the production of a hyperpolarization (rather than depolarization) in response to applied ACh. This response was insensitive to α-neurotoxin and may thus represent a different or modified form of ACh-R. It must be emphasized that extensive and precise ligand binding studies to receptor from cultured muscle cells have not been reported. These studies could yield important information since there is both *in vivo* (Beranek and Vyskocil, 1967) and *in vitro* (Almon *et al.*, 1974; Brockes and Hall, 1975a,b) evidence that synaptic and extrasynaptic receptors from adult denervated muscle may be distinguished by slight differences in their affinities for certain ligands. It may thus be possible to determine whether synaptic-type receptor is present in cultured muscle cells or

TABLE I

INHIBITION OF TOXIN BINDING BY CHOLINERGIC LIGANDS[a,b]

Ligand	Concentration (μM)	^{3}H-Labeled toxin bound (pmole)	% Rate of control
Control	—	0.242	100
Hexamethonium	33	—	99
Atropine	3.3	0.248	102
	33	0.188	78
Carbamylcholine	0.33	0.123	51
	3.3	0.056	23
	33	0.025	10
Decamethonium	0.33	0.071	30
	3.3	0.025	10
	33	0.008	3
Gallamine	0.33	0.180	75
	3.3	0.090	38
	33	0.008	3
d-Tubocurarine	0.033	0.068	28
	0.33	0.006	3

[a] From Merlie *et al.* (1975).

[b] The effect of several concentrations of the listed compounds was tested on the rate of toxin binding to sonicated myotubes. The binding assays were done by the Millipore method in a total volume of 0.6 ml containing 0.41 pmole of toxin binding sites at a toxin concentration of 1.6 nM. The initial rate in the control assay was linear until 2.5 hours. Duplicate assays for each concentration assayed at 1.75 hours agreed within 10%.

whether the appearance of a receptor with distinct pharmacological properties is dependent upon the innervation of these cells (see below).

The biochemical characteristics of ACh-R from muscle cells in culture are quite similar to those of receptors from other sources (electric organ, denervated muscle). In general all toxin-binding activity is membrane bound and found in a heavy particulate fraction. All toxin-binding material may be solubilized in 1% Triton X-100-containing buffers. In its extracted form the receptor gives a single 9 S peak of toxin-binding material on sucrose gradient centrifugation (Fig. 3) and a single band on nondenaturing polyacrylamide gel electrophoresis (Merlie *et al.*, 1975; J. P. Merlie, unpublished results; Devreotes and Fambrough, 1975). We have occasionally noticed a low molecular weight toxin-binding component sedimenting between the 9 S peak and the peak of free toxin. Toxin binding to this component is also

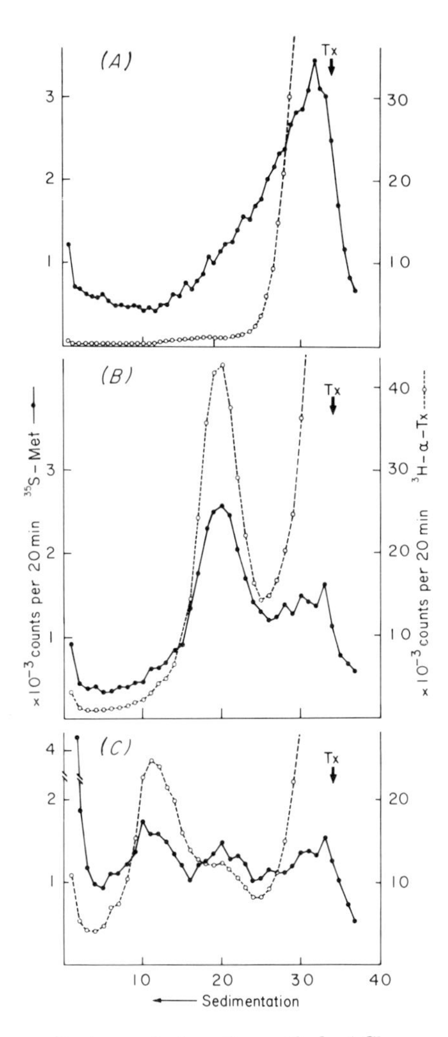

FIG. 3. Sucrose gradient analysis of purified ACh-receptor (ACh-R) from [^{35}S]methionine-labeled muscle cell culture. Purified material eluted from the DE-52 column (see Table II) was incubated with [^{3}H]α-neurotoxin and either normal rabbit serum (B) or with serum from a rabbit immunized with purified *Electrophorus electrophorus* ACh-R (C); (A) was ^{35}S-labeled material from the same cell extract submitted to a mock purification on an affinity column of bovine serum albumin in place of α-neurotoxin. This material also was incubated with [^{3}H]α-neurotoxin before gradient analysis. Gradient A shows that no 9 S toxin-binding material is purified nonspecifically by chromatography on protein Sepharose beads. Gradient B shows that a large portion of the [^{35}S]methionine-labeled material purified on toxin Sepharose beads cosediments with the 9 S toxin-binding material. Gradient C shows that the [^{35}S]-methionine-labeled material cross-reacts with anti-ACh-R serum, as does the toxin-binding activity. Tx indicates the peak of free toxin (Merlie *et al.*, 1975).

abolished by cholinergic compounds. It is possible that this material is a proteolytic product of the more rapidly sedimenting form. Proteolysis may be a particularly important problem in dealing with receptor from muscle tissue (Dolly and Barnard, 1975).

As mentioned previously, Brockes and Hall (1975b) have reported differences in the isoelectric pH of synaptic and extrasynaptic receptor–toxin complexes. This property could prove to be useful in determining whether the appearance of synaptic receptor in tissue culture requires neuronal input.

2. *Synthesis and Degradation*

The appearance of toxin-binding activity as well as ACh sensitivity has been examined in developing muscle cells in culture and has been shown to roughly follow cell fusion and increases in other muscle-specific markers (Fig. 4) (Patrick *et al.*, 1972; Fambrough and Rash, 1971; Hartzell and Fambrough, 1973; Sytkowski *et al.*, 1973; Merlie *et al.*, 1975; Paterson and Prives, 1973). Hartzell and Fambrough (1973) have shown that the rate of appearance of toxin-binding sites corre-

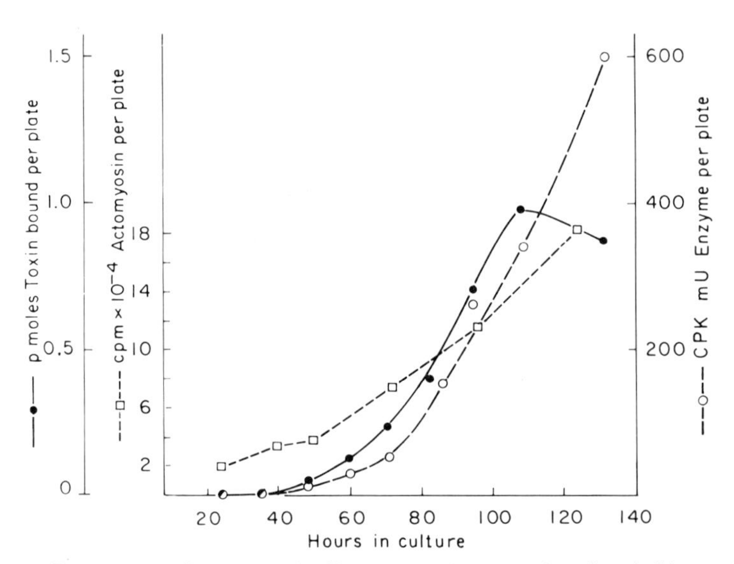

FIG. 4. Time course of increase of ACh-receptor sites, creatine phosphokinase (CPK) activity, and rate of synthesis of actomyosin. There was approximately a 4-fold increase in total protein per plate from 24 to 120 hours (Merlie *et al.*, 1975).

sponds to the site density increase seen by autoradiography, leading to the idea that newly synthesized receptor is inserted into the surface membrane.

In fact, a good deal of information about the synthesis and degradation of ACh-R has been obtained by the use of radioactive toxin. Before detailing some of these experiments, it should be stated that, in each case where the assumption that toxin binding is a valid probe of receptor polypeptide metabolism is made, one must evaluate the conclusions in the light of this assumption.

The rate of appearance of toxin-binding sites detected by labeling with radioactive toxin in the culture medium was shown to be sensitive to the temperature of incubation (optimum 35°C) and to inhibition by energy poisons and inhibitors of protein synthesis such as cycloheximide and puromycin (Devreotes and Fambrough, 1975). This is suggestive evidence for the fact that protein synthesis is involved in the appearance of toxin-binding sites at the cell surface, but because of the experimental design it is not possible to conclude whether the primary effect of each of these agents is at the level of *de novo* synthesis, an assembly process, or a process of translocation of receptor from internal sites of synthesis to the cell surface.

The above-mentioned experiments with inhibitors of protein synthesis have shown that the appearance of sites that could be labeled by toxin present in the medium (and thus defined as surface or external) continued for 2–3 hours after addition of the inhibitor. Furthermore, it was shown that a class of toxin-binding sites existed that could be labeled only after cell lysis. The quantity and kinetics of disappearance after inhibition of protein synthesis of this latter class of sites were similar to those of the cycloheximide puromycin-insensitive sites which become available to toxin in the medium during the 2–3 hours after inhibition of protein synthesis (Devreotes and Fambrough, 1975). These results have led the authors to suggest that the sites that are unavailable to toxin in the culture medium constitute a pool of receptor precursors that may exist preassembled in some internal membrane structure (see also Fambrough *et al.,* 1974). Clearly, these hypotheses are of interest in that they relate to general mechanisms of plasma membrane synthesis as well as the more specific problem of ACh-R synthesis. However, they must be tested by direct studies of precursor–product relationships as well as membrane fractionation and characterization.

Devreotes and Fambrough (1975) have reported measurements of the degradation of receptor–toxin complexes. These studies have been done by prelabeling cells with radioactive toxin, washing out the unbound toxin, and observing the fate of the bound material. The assumption is made that toxin is degraded or lost from the bound complex because of, or during, the process of receptor degradation. The arguments for the validity of this assumption have been presented (Berg and Hall, 1975; Devreotes and Fambrough, 1975). Devreotes and Fambrough (1975) find an average half-life for receptor–toxin complex of 22 hours with a range of 16–28 hours. The value for the half-life does not vary significantly with the age or maturation of the cultures. It was also found that degradation could be inhibited by extremes of pH in the culture medium, by low temperature, and by energy poisons. Increased rates of degradation were found when cells were incubated in medium with reduced protein content.

In an attempt to address these problems more directly, methods for the study of receptor synthesis and degradation have been developed (Merlie *et al.*, 1975). These methods depend upon the pulse-labeling of cells with high specific activity [^{35}S]methionine and subsequent purifi-

TABLE II

PURIFICATION OF ^{35}S-LABELED ACh RECEPTOR[a,b]

	^{125}I-Labeled toxin binding (pmoles)	^{125}I-Labeled toxin binding (% recovery)	^{35}S cpm	^{35}S/pmol[c]
1. Total	6.3	100	1.45×10^9	2.3×10^8
2. Membrane	5.1	81	3.42×10^8	6.7×10^7
3. TNT extract	3.3	52	1.90×10^8	5.8×10^7
4. Toxin column	2.5	40	1.38×10^4	—
5. DE-52	0.86	14	1.08×10^4	1.26×10^4

[a] From Merlie *et al.* (1975).

[b] ACh receptor (ACh-R) was purified from [^{35}S]methionine-labeled cells. In the first step, nuclei-free membranes were prepared by differential centrifugation in sucrose. ACh-R was extracted into Triton-containing buffer and adsorbed to an affinity support of α-neurotoxin coupled to Sepharose beads. Receptor was subsequently released by incubation with decamethonium, 0.1 *M*. Decamethonium was removed, and the column eluate was concentrated by chromatography on DE-52 ion exchange cellulose. The final material is about 20,000-fold purified relative to the specific activity of the starting material.

[c] ^{35}S/pmole is a ratio of ^{35}S cpm/pmole toxin-binding activity and is in fact an inverse specific activity (Merlie *et al.*, 1975).

cation of the receptor by affinity chromatography on columns of α-neurotoxin. A summary of a typical purification is given in Table II. The identity of the purified material was established by: (1) specific adsorption and elution from toxin columns; (2) cosedimentation with toxin binding activity in sucrose gradients; (3) its cross-reaction with antisera raised against purified ACh-R from *E. electricus* (Merlie *et al.*, 1975) (Table II and Fig. 3).

At present only a rather limited amount of information has been obtained from this type of experiment. The finding that [^{35}S]methionine is incorporated into receptor polypeptides provides proof of *de novo* synthesis (Merlie *et al.*, 1975). This has recently been confirmed by Devreotes and Fambrough (1976), who demonstrated the density shift of receptor appearing during incubation of cells with amino acids containing stable heavy isotopes.

Useful information concerning receptor subunit structure has also been obtained from [^{35}S]methionine labeling experiments. High-resolution two-dimensional electrophoresis (O'Farrell, 1975) of the material purified by affinity chromatography demonstrates the degree of purity of the preparation (Fig. 5A). The spot marked by the arrow coelectrophoreses with purified actin from cultured muscle cells (Merlie *et al.*, 1977). Furthermore, antiserum made against purified actin does not cross-react with ACh-R. It is concluded from these findings that ACh-R from cultured muscle cells is composed of a single molecular weight species of about MW 40,000–42,000. The minor species with different isoelectric pH but identical molecular weight are assumed to arise from the major species by some secondary modification, but this conclusion awaits further characterization of the separate species.

A further important point that results from labeling experiments is that the incorporation of [^{35}S]methionine into receptor polypeptides can be quantitated. It was found that receptor synthesis represents from 0.005% to 0.05% of the total [^{35}S]methionine incorporated into protein during a 4-hour pulse (Merlie *et al.*, 1977).

More recent experiments demonstrate that receptor half-lives determined by radioactive toxin binding are in good agreement with those determined by pulse-chase experiments with [^{35}S]methionine labeling of receptor polypeptides (Fig. 6) (Merlie *et al.*, 1976). It has been found that the half-life of receptor does not vary with the age of the culture and that the rate of synthesis increases more than 15-fold from 48 to 144 hours in culture (J. P. Merlie, unpublished). It can be concluded therefore that the increase in the rate of accumulation of toxin-binding sites (Fig. 4) is due to an increased rate of synthesis.

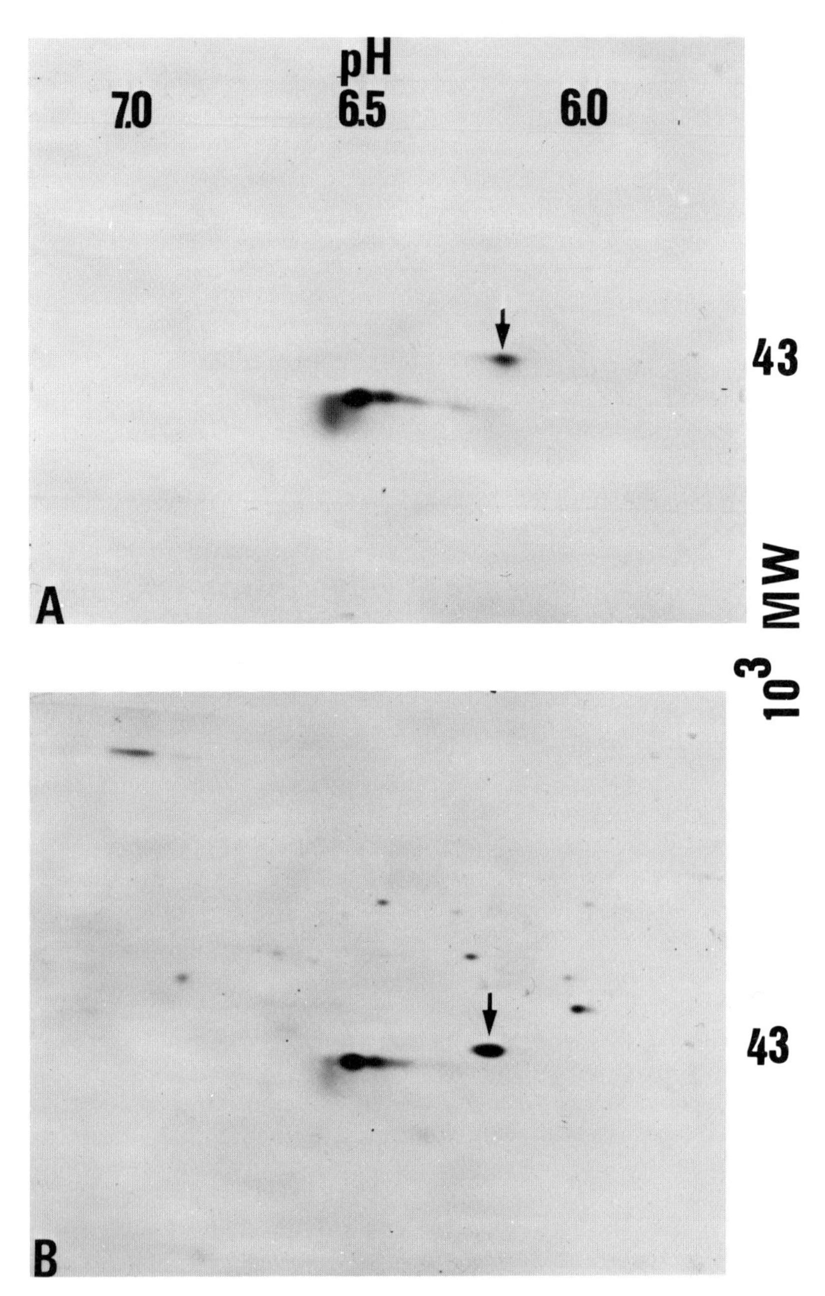

FIG. 5. Autoradiogram of [^{35}S]methionine-labeled, purified ACh-receptor submitted to two-dimensional electrophoresis (see legend to Fig. 2). (A) Purified sample. (B) Purified sample mixed with small quantity of total cytoplasmic extract. Only the relevant portions of the autoradiograms are shown: the spot at pH 6.25, MW 43,000, coelectrophoreses with actin.

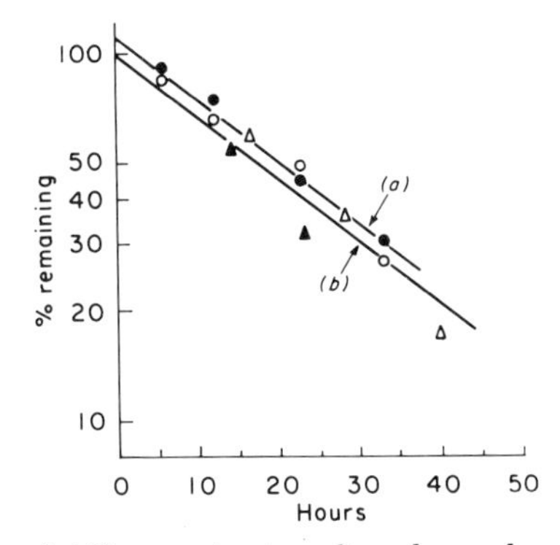

FIG. 6. Degradation of ACh-receptor in cultured muscle cells measured by loss of bound[^{125}I]α-bungarotoxin (a) or by pulse chase experiments with [^{35}S]methionine (b). Curve a: Cells were exposed for a brief period to medium containing [^{125}I]α-bungaratoxin and washed; the original medium was returned to the plates. At the given times 4 plates were washed with PBS and scraped in 2 ml of buffer containing 1% Triton $\times 100$, and an aliquot was counted in the gamma counter (●, ○ indicate two separate experiments). Curve b: Cells were pulsed for 4 hours with [^{35}S]methionine and washed with complete medium; the original medium was returned to the plates with added nonradioactive methionine at 0.1 m*M*. At the given times Triton extracts were prepared, submitted to the purification scheme summarized in Table II, and analyzed on sucrose gradients. Correction was made for the yield in each case. For both methods radioactivity remaining in ACh-receptor was normalized to the zero time sample. The $t_{1/2}$ determined by these two methods is the same and is equal to 16 hours.

One of the principal interests in developing those aspects of ACh-R that relate to myogenesis is its involvement in synapse formation and neuromuscular interaction. We will therefore review briefly some of the literature concerning synapse or contact formation in tissue culture.

C. SYNAPSE FORMATION IN CULTURE

Several systems have been used successfully for the formation of functional neuromuscular contacts in tissue culture. One of the earliest to be described was that of embryonic muscle cells cultivated at low density and dissociated spinal cord cells (Shimada *et al.*, 1969; Fischbach, 1970). Morphologically this system gives only rather primitive contacts. No postsynaptic membrane specialization was observed (Shimada *et al.*, 1969). Fischbach has characterized the contacts by physiological methods and has found that in general they resemble immature or embryonic-type neuromuscular junctions. It was not possible to demonstrate any localization of ACh-E or ACh-R induced as a result of functional contact formation. "Extrasynaptic" ACh sensitivity was not significantly decreased on those fibers having demonstrable contacts, and although neurites did terminate over areas of increased ACh sensitivity, such areas could be demonstrated on myotubes grown in the absence of neuronal cells (Fischbach, 1972). These areas of increased ACh-R density in cultured primary embryonic muscle cells have been observed by others (Sytkowski *et al.,* 1973; Hartzell and Fambrough, 1973), and it has been suggested that they may function as determinants of recognition of presumptive sites for synapse formation by the exploring axon.

Although primitive synapse formation was shown not to be sufficient to reduce the ACh sensitivity of the innervated fiber, it was possible to demonstrate that direct chronic electrical stimulation reduced the average sensitivity per fiber by greater than 10-fold. In this case, however, sensitivity was also lost from the hot spot areas (Cohen and Fischbach, 1973). The inability of primitive contact formation to reduce extrasynaptic ACh sensitivity in this model system may be due to the lack of the proper frequency of stimulation (see Cohen and Fischbach, 1973; Lømo and Westgaard, 1975).

An alternative explanation for the failure of dissociated spinal cord cells to elicit a "tropic" response in cultured dissociated muscle cells is that the system may be incomplete and may require a higher structural complexity than that attained under cell culture conditions. Crain and Peterson (1974) have reviewed a system used in their laboratory which used organ cultures of muscle and spinal cord tissue. In this case, a dependence upon cord tissue for maintenance of the muscle has been demonstrated. Newly formed synapses with well developed pre- and postsynaptic membrane have been observed. This system seems to best reflect the *in vivo* behavior of neuromuscular junctions. The structural integrity of tissue explants may account for this finding.

Another approach to the use of dissociated cells in tissue culture for the study of neuromuscular synapse formation has been that of clonal lines of rat myoblasts and of mouse neuroblastoma, a continuous line of (autonomic) nerve cells (Harris *et al.,* 1971). Although functional transmission at contact sites has never been demonstrated in this system, rather interesting tropic phenomena have been described. These authors have shown that noninnervated L_6 myotubes grown in the absence of neuroblastoma did not exhibit areas of increased ACh sensitivity, as do primary cultures. Cultures to which neuroblastoma cells had been added had myotubes that seemed to be contacted by nerve cell processes, and these areas underwent a sequential loss of ACh sensitivity followed by the development of an increased sensitivity. Areas away from the contact point were lower in final ACh sensitivity (Harris *et al.,*

1971). By blocking the muscle ACh-R site with α-neurotoxin and the synthesis of ACh in the neuroblastoma by pretreatment with pyridinium, Steinbach *et al.* (1973) were able to show that the localization of ACh sensitivity induced by the presence of nerve termini was independent of ACh release or reception. The obvious differences between this and the system of cultured primary muscle, particularly with respect to the role of the nerve in inducing localized areas of ACh sensitivity, have not been resolved. However, Kidokoro and Heinemann (1974) have recently demonstrated functional synapse formation between L_6 myotubes and rat spinal cord explants. The electrophysiological properties of these contacts resemble those reported for primary chick cultures of dissociated spinal cord cells (Fischbach, 1972). This finding demonstrates the capacity of L_6 to form functional contacts and suggests that the failure to observe contact formation between L_6 and neuroblastoma cells may have been due to a defect in the neuroblastoma clone used. In fact, Nelson *et al.* (1976) have described functional high-frequency synapse formation between primary tissue cultures of mouse myotubes and a hybrid clone derived from neuroblastoma and glioma cell lines.

Other successful nerve muscle combinations include primary cell cultures of chick embryo muscle innervated by fibers from explanted chick ciliary ganglia (Hoosima *et al.*, 1975; Betz, 1976) and cell cultures of newborn rat skeletal muscle and dissociated cells from the superior cervical ganglion (Nurse and O'Lague, 1975). The latter system seems to result in high-frequency synapse formation and, like all the above-described systems, is cholinergic and nicotinic in nature. The effect of innervation on the distribution of ACh sensitivity of the myotube has not been extensively studied, but the authors report that in one culture maintained for more than 3 weeks sensitivities were localized to 2–3 spots per fiber, which were greater than 30- to 40-fold more sensitive than neighboring membrane.

Clearly, *in vitro* synapse formation is an experimentally approachable problem. The variety of systems available should permit the kinds of biochemical experiments necessary to elucidate the control mechanisms operating in the interaction of nerve and muscle cells.

IV. Control of the Expression of the Differentiated Phenotype

A fundamental aim in studying the terminal differentiation of muscle cells is to define the type of molecular control mechanism that leads to expression of the muscle phenotype. As already discussed, differentiation is accompanied by the accumulation of muscle proteins, both of muscle enzymes, such as creatine phosphokinase (e.g., see Shainberg *et al.,* 1971), and of proteins of the contractile apparatus, such as myosin (e.g., see Coleman and Coleman, 1968). This accumulation has been shown, in the case of myosin, for example, to be associated with a marked increase in its rate of synthesis (e.g., Emerson and Beckner, 1975) as well as its high stability. That *de novo* protein synthesis is involved is indicated by labeling experiments and by the effects of inhibitors of protein synthesis, such as cycloheximide, which block the increase in muscle proteins (Yaffé, 1969).

Control of changes in the synthesis of muscle proteins can be envisaged, classically, as acting either at the transcription level on messenger RNA (mRNA) production, or posttranscriptionally on nuclear or cytoplasmic processing of mRNA or on mRNA translation and stability.

A. Experiments with Actinomycin D

The first experiments that attempted to resolve this question used actinomycin D to inhibit transcription. Yaffé and Dym (1973) reported that in primary cultures of fetal rat muscle the addition of actinomycin D, at a sufficiently high concentration (2 μg/ml) to inhibit mRNA as well as ribosomal RNA (rRNA) synthesis for a 6-hour period immediately before or at the onset of fusion, did not inhibit either fusion itself or the immediate increase in creatine phosphokinase activity or myosin synthesis. Indeed the initial rise in myosin synthesis occurred earlier in the treated cultures. Subsequent increase in the rate of synthesis was inhibited in the presence of the drug. In the case of creatine phosphokinase, it can be shown that the initial increase seen in control and actinomycin D-treated cultures is due in both cases to expression of the M isozyme (Yaffé *et al.,* 1975). Molinaro *et al.* (1974) have also examined the effect of exposure for 8-hour periods to low doses (0.05 μg/ml) of actinomycin D on the differentiation of chick muscle cells. Fiber formation is not affected by the drug. Similarly, the later phase of myosin synthesis is unaffected (93–100 hours), but the initial increase in myosin synthesis (53 hours) is inhibited to 27% of the control level on addition of the drug 8 hours previously. A precise comparison between the experiments is difficult since the timing of differentiation is different in the two systems, and it is possible that mRNA synthesis is not inhibited at the low doses of actinomycin D used by Molinaro *et al.* The general conclusion drawn is that transcription is not necessarily required immediately prior to and during the expression of the muscle phenotype, at least where fusion, creatine phosphokinase, and myosin are concerned (Yaffé and Dym, 1973). In chick cultures, where the time scale is more contracted, some transcription is apparently necessary within the 8-hour period before fusion in order that differentiation take place.

A limitation of such experiments with actinomycin D is that, because of the toxic effects of the drug, it is not possible to add it to the cultures for a longer period than 6–8 hours at any time. A difficulty in the interpretation of this type of experiment arises from the fact that the effect of actinomycin D, particularly at high doses, is not limited to transcription. Apart from effects on cell morphology and viability, the drug has been shown to be capable of acting specifically at the level of translation, affecting initiation and thus distorting conclusions about RNA synthesis (e.g., Singer and Penman, 1972; Murphy and Attardi, 1973). In particular, relevant to these results is the phenomenon of superinduction whereby administration of actinomycin D leads to an increase in the synthesis of proteins, already present in the cell. Explained by Tomkins *et al.* (1969) in terms of negative control by a repressor molecule, such as an unstable RNA species, or more simply by Schimke (1974) as a result of increased availability of translational components that are limiting when normal levels of mRNA are present, superinduction may explain the somewhat premature burst of myosin synthesis reported by Yaffé and Dym (1973). Since the control on the effect of actinomycin D on myosin synthesis in dividing cell populations has not been reported, it remains possible that the stimulation seen at the time of fusion when the drug is added just prior to this event, is a result of overproduction of the basal level of myosin, rather than the initiation of a program of differentiation. Less ambiguous is the example of creatine phosphokinase (Yaffé *et al.,* 1975) since the increase in enzyme is due to the muscle-specific isozyme, whereas the brain form is the principal component prior to differentiation. The experiments suggest that the mRNA for the M isozyme is already present, before M-type creatine phosphokinase is synthesized in quantity. Here again, however, since the isozymes are detected by their enzymic activity, this interpretation should be treated with caution, and the presence of inactive forms of the M type of creatine phosphokinase prior to differentiation cannot be ruled out, although experiments with cycloheximide (Yaffé, 1969) suggest that this is not the case.

B. The Identification of Myosin Messenger RNA

Experiments using inhibitors of protein synthesis can only provide rather circumstantial evidence about control mechanisms. In order to obtain direct information, it is necessary to look at specific mRNA species. In this respect, muscle has the apparent advantage that the large subunit of myosin (MW 200,000) is bigger than the majority of polypeptides. Interest has centered on its mRNA, and attempts to isolate it from other messengers have been based mainly on the criterion of size.

As early as 1968 a fraction of RNA sedimenting at 26 S, isolated from myosin-synthesizing polysomes of embryonic chick muscle, was shown to direct the synthesis of the large subunit of myosin *in vitro* (Heywood and Nwagwu, 1968, 1969). Identification of the radioactive product from a homologous cell-free system was based on electrophoretic mobility, antibody precipitation and DEAE-cellulose chromatography, where it behaved identically to the myosin added as carrier. Subsequently the same laboratory demonstrated myosin synthesis in a partially fractionated *in vitro* system (muscle initiation factors + chick erythroblast ribosomes) on addition of muscle 26 S RNA. A peptide map of the product (Rourke and Heywood, 1972) was published, although the complexity of the protein makes absolute identification on this basis difficult. In further experiments, ribosomal RNA (rRNA) was largely removed from heavy polysomes by chromatography on Sepharose 4B. The resultant RNA migrated on gel electrophoresis at 32 S relative to rRNA (Morris *et al.*, 1973). Similarly, Mondal *et al.* (1974) have prepared RNA from the heavy polysomes of chick embryonic muscle, using filtration through Millipore filters, followed by chromatography on cellulose to eliminate ribosomal RNA, and obtained a homogeneous band of RNA migrating slower than 28 S rRNA in formamide acrylamide gels. On addition to a homologous *in vitro* system, this RNA directed the synthesis of a protein, which, when subjected to peptide analysis after cleavage with cyanogen bromide, could be shown to contain peptides identical to those of the myosin heavy chain (Sarkar *et al.*, 1973). The same authors (Mondal *et al.*, 1974) have also demonstrated the synthesis of myosin directed by similar RNA preparations in a rabbit reticulocyte lysate, thus avoiding the problem of endogenous myosin RNA, which is a potential complication in the interpretation of results obtained in homologous *in vitro* systems. The full peptide characterization of the myosin product synthesized in a heterologous system has not been performed. From cultured chick embryonic muscle cells, an RNA (18–26 S) has been isolated in ribonucleoprotein particles (30–40 S) obtained after puromycin treatment of polysomes prepared from well-fused cultures (Przybyla and Strohman, 1974). In a reticulocyte lysate this fraction of RNA directed the synthesis of myosin heavy chains, as identified by SDS–acrylamide gel electrophoresis. Recently the groups of Sarkar and Heywood have purified the myosin mRNA from its free ribonucleoprotein particle, following the initial observations of Buckingham *et al.* (1974a) of the very large size of this particle (see Section IV, C).

Taken together, these results indicate that the mRNA for the large subunit of myosin migrates at about 26 S on sucrose gradients, 30–32 S on acrylamide gels, and suggest that 26 S RNA is the predominant mRNA species of large size. Sarkar *et al.* (1973), for example, estimate from gel analyses that less than 3% of molecules not migrating in this band are present in preparations from heavy polysomes. Identification of the peptides synthesized *in vitro,* however, suggested that about 40% of the labeled protein copurifies as myosin. The remainder may be due to incomplete chains or to the synthesis of products other than myosin. We would, thus, conclude that the mRNA for the large subunit of myosin does sediment at 26 S (30–32 S on acrylamide gels), but that the degree of homogeneity of this material is not yet established. At present, the purification of other mRNA molecules coding for muscle proteins has not been achieved, since they are less amenable to purification on the basis of size.

In order to examine mRNA metabolism during muscle cell differentiation, two approaches are possible: either to look directly at the synthesis and steady-state levels of mRNA in the cultures, or to extract the RNA from the cells, add it to an *in vitro* protein-synthesizing system, and make deductions from the resultant peptide products (see, e.g., Paterson *et al.,* 1974; Yaffé *et al.,* 1975). Both approaches will be discussed in the following sections.

C. Experiments on Messenger RNA from Muscle Cells in Culture

1. Synthesis and Degradation of Messenger RNA

A study of RNA synthesis during myogenesis has been carried out by Buckingham *et al.* (1974a) on primary cultures from fetal calf muscle. RNA extracted from cells after pulse labeling with [^{3}H]uridine for 2 hours was analyzed on sucrose gradients, and mRNA was identified on the basis of its binding to poly(U) filters. It was observed (Fig. 7) that muscle cultures before and after differentiation contain a pronounced peak of poly(A) (+) RNA sedimenting at about 26 S. Analysis of other cell types (Buckingham *et al.,* 1974b) indicated that this peak is characteristic of lines which are capable of synthesizing myosin in quantity. This, together with a correlation between the presence of pulse-labeled 26 S in heavy polysomes and a high level of myosin synthesis in the cultures at differentiation, provided cir-

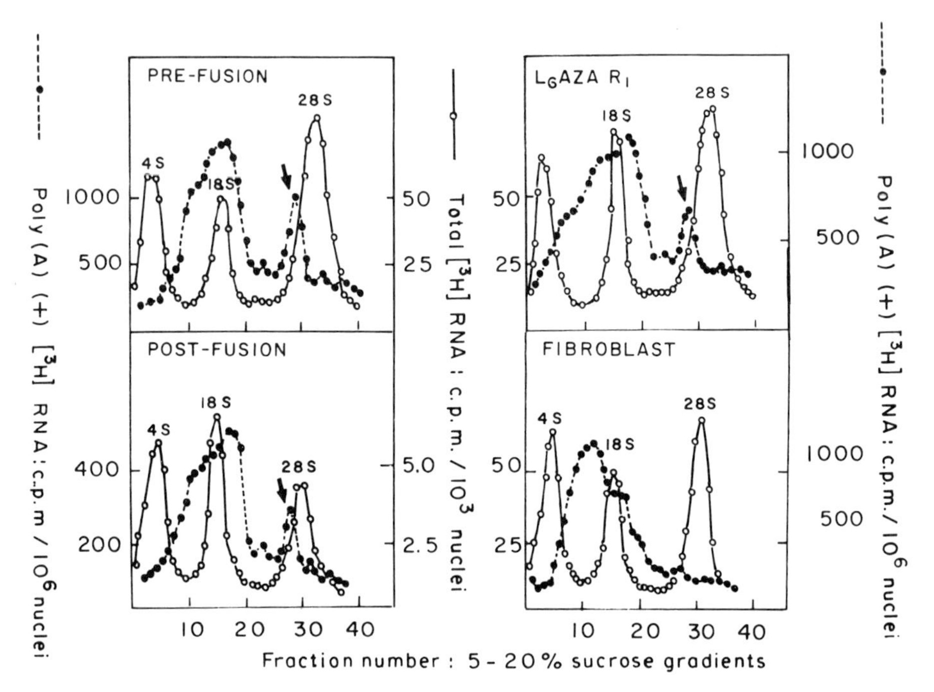

FIG. 7. RNA synthesis in pre- and postfusion primary cultures, in 3T6 fibroblasts and in normal (L_6azaR$_1$) muscle cell lines. The cultures were pulse-labeled for 2 hours with 200 μCi/2.5 ml of [^{3}H]uridine (20 Ci/mmole), and the RNA was extracted and analyzed on sucrose gradients. Part of each fraction was counted directly (○——○), and the remainder was hybridized to poly(U) filters (●----●). The position of 26 S RNA is indicated by an arrow. The fibroblast lines, which do not have the capacity to synthesize myosin in quantity, do not contain a pronounced peak of 26 S poly(A) (+) RNA.

cumstantial evidence for the identification of the material as myosin mRNA. In addition, the pulse-labeled 26 S RNA found in the cultures had similar migration characteristics to myosin mRNA on gradients and gels. Pulse-chase experiments (Buckingham *et al.,* 1974a) indicated that the peak of 26 S RNA present in dividing myoblasts had a half-life of about 10 hours, equivalent to that of a large class of mRNAs in these cells. In the period of cell alignment preceding fusion, the half-life of the RNA sedimenting in this position becomes very much longer, increasing by a factor of 5 to 6. The half-life of the bulk of cell messengers increases at this time by a factor of about two. Examination of the cytoplasmic localization of 26 S RNA indicated that prior to myotube formation, it was predominantly nonpolysomal (Buckingham *et al.*, 1974a, 1976). The stable 26 S radioactive material present immediately prior to differentiation could be chased into the heavy polysomes after fusion (Fig. 8). A number of other poly(A)-containing RNA species apparently also exist as stable, nonpolysomal RNAs before differentiation, subsequently appearing in the polysomes.

These results were taken to suggest that myosin mRNA is synthesized in dividing myoblasts, but turns over rapidly, without being translated. Just prior to fusion, it accumulates in the cytoplasm, and is later used for myosin synthesis. At present, the weakness in the argument lies in the identification of the pulse-labeled 26 S RNA. Attempts to demonstrate that the species present before and after fusion are

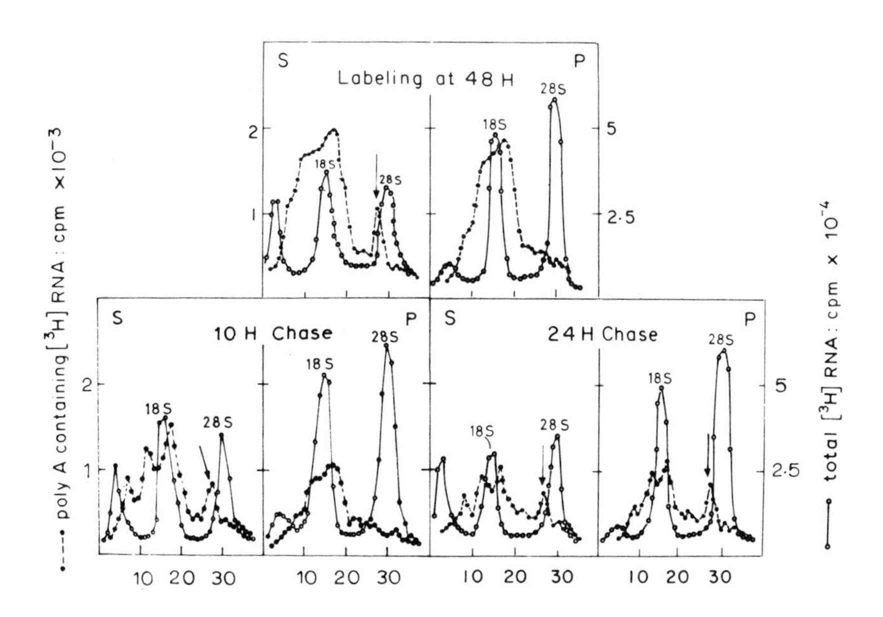

FIG. 8. Chase experiments on poly(A) (+) [^{3}H]RNA in the supernatant and polysomal fractions of cytoplasmic extracts from myoblasts immediately before fusion (48 hours), and after 10 hours and 24 hours of chase with cold uridine (see Buckingham *et al.*, 1974a, 1976). Cultures were labeled for 2 hours with [^{3}H]uridine (200 μCi/2.5 ml; 20 Ci/mmole), and the label was chased for the times indicated before the cytoplasmic extracts were separated on 10–40% sucrose gradients. The subunit-trisome region of each gradient (S) and the rest of the polysomes (P) were pooled, and RNA was extracted. This was separated on 5 to 20% sucrose gradients, and each fraction was analyzed for total (○——○) and poly(A) (+) (●----●) RNA. The position of 26 S RNA is indicated by an arrow.

identical, by complementary DNA (cDNA) hybridization experiments (Buckingham *et al.*, 1974a) have been unsatisfactory because of the high R_0t values obtained and hence evident heterogeneity of the mRNA used to make the cDNA.

Other evidence for the accumulation of mRNAs coding for muscle proteins immediately prior to differentiation comes from the actinomycin D experiments already mentioned (Section IV, A) (Yaffé and Dym, 1973; Molinaro *et al.*, 1974). In view of the results discussed above, differing reports of the effects of the drug on the initial increase in myosin synthesis may result from the timing of its addition before or during the phase of messenger accumulation, which varies in different culture systems. Recently, experiments on the capacity of RNA, extracted from rat cultures at different stages of development, to program the synthesis of myosin light chains *in vitro* (Yaffé *et al.*, 1975) have indicated that these messenger species accumulate in the period immediately preceding fusion. In contrast, similar experiments carried out on the *in vitro* synthesis of actin (Paterson *et al.*, 1974) led the authors to conclude that translatable actin mRNA was present before and after fusion in quantities proportional to the relative level of actin synthesis in the cultures (for discussion of *in vitro* experiments, see later sections).

2. *Steady State Levels of Messenger RNA*

Pulse labeling represents one approach to studying mRNA metabolism; another is to measure directly the steady-state level of mRNA in cultures at different stages of development.

These experiments depend on the use of cDNA, and although a cDNA made against total mRNA would be expected to give information about differences in abundancy classes (see, e.g., Campo and Bishop, 1974), more precise data on specific gene products depends on using cDNA made from homogeneous messengers. These types of experiments have not yet been possible in the muscle system owing to difficulty in obtaining a pure messenger RNA species. As discussed, efforts to purify mRNA for the large subunit of myosin have been based on the criterion of size. The purification of other muscle mRNAs will probably depend on using the technique of antibody precipitation of polysomes (Palacios *et al.*, 1972), although there is a possibility (R. G. Whalen and D. Caput, 1975, unpublished observations) that actin mRNA may be present in sufficient amounts compared to other RNAs to be purified from them by cDNA hybridization techniques.

In considering the use of specific cDNAs as probes for muscle mRNAs, the apparent universality of muscle-type proteins poses a problem. If indeed different isozymic forms exist for myosin, actin, etc. (see Section II, B) and some of these are characteristic of muscle while others are not, then some heterogeneity in the mRNA for myosin, for example, may be expected when it is isolated from primary cultures containing different cell types. The possibility of isolating a muscle-specific fraction then depends on this being the major species. At present, the situation for the proteins is not sufficiently clear; it is not known, for example, if the postulated "universal fibroblast type" myosin continues to be synthesized in differentiating muscle. Brain-type creatine phosphokinase apparently is synthesized, but as a very minor component (Eppenberger *et al.,* 1964). In this situation, the use of specific antibodies against muscle-type isozymes to precipitate the corresponding polysomes appears to be the best approach, although given the relatively small proportion of any one protein synthesized, it will undoubtedly be difficult.

3. The Presence of Poly(A) in Messenger RNA

The development of cDNA against mRNAs specific for muscle appears to be essential for future studies on the system. Some idea of the steady-state level of mRNA in the cells, however, can be obtained from estimating the content of poly(A)-containing RNA, by hybridization with radioactive poly(U) (see Rosbash and Ford, 1974). Using this technique, little difference was found in the overall quantity of message present before or after fusion (Goto *et al.,* 1977). The further interest of these experiments depends on being able to distinguish by this technique a class of RNA sedimenting at 26 S, corresponding to the material seen after pulse labeling. In fact, it was found (Goto *et al.,* 1977) that although a shoulder of RNA could be discerned in the 26 S region by [^{3}H]poly(U) hybridization, it was not sufficiently resolved from the rest of the RNA for questions about quantity and accumulation to be answerable.

An important piece of information, relevant to the interpretation of the pulse-labeling experiments already described, is the proportion of mRNAs in muscle cells that contain poly(A). The majority of eukaryotic messengers have been shown to be poly(A) (+) (for review, see Brawerman, 1974), the exception being the histone messengers, although a number of other reports, for example, on HeLa cells (Milcarek *et al.,* 1974), suggest that other messenger species may lack poly(A). A number of different experiments suggest that in muscle cells the majority of messengers contain poly(A). Kaufman and Gross (1974), using [^{3}H]poly(dT) hybridization, estimated that most mRNA in the polysomes of fused myotubes contains poly(A). *In vitro* experiments indicated that the proteins synthesized, with the exception of the histones, are very similar, whether directed by total cytoplasmic RNA or that selected on the basis of its poly(A) content (Whalen and Gros, 1977b) (see Section IV, D, 1). Pulse labeled mRNA present in ribonucleoprotein particles separated by density centrifugation on metrizamide gradients (Buckingham and Gros, 1975) has been shown to contain poly(A) (c.80%). In dividing myoblasts the proportion of poly(A) (−) molecules is rather higher ($\simeq$25%), probably owing to histone mRNA, a supposition supported by the translation experiments already mentioned. In these experiments, pulse-labeled 26 S RNA was shown to be poly(A) (+). This is in agreement with the findings of Sarkar *et al.* (1973) on 26 S RNA isolated from embryonic muscle tissue. Przybyla and Strohman (1974), however, have reported that in chick cultures myosin mRNA does not contain a sufficiently long sequence of poly(A) to bind to oligo(dT) under their conditions, although Bester *et al.* (1975) isolated myosin mRNA from chick muscle by this technique.

In principle, the length of the poly(A) sequence of different mRNAs may be one of the factors playing a role during differentiation, influencing, for example, messenger stability. This has been investigated by [^{3}H]poly(U) hybridization after digestion of the non-poly(A) part of RNA molecules and migration of the poly(A) sequence on polyacrylamide gels. Cytoplasmic RNA of different size classes, from calf myoblasts at different stages of development, was isolated and analyzed. A consistent correlation existed between the length of the poly(A) sequence and the size of the mRNA, messenger molecules ranging from 6 S to 30 S, having lengths of poly(A) of 40 to 170 nucleotides (Fig. 9). A similar observation has been made on mRNA extracted from chick embryo polysomes of different sizes (Mondal *et al.*, 1974). Mondal *et al.* (1974) have reported that myosin mRNA contains a tract of about 200 poly(A) residues at the 3′ end, a figure that corresponds to the length seen for large messengers in muscle cells. It should be noted in this context that the calculations of Kaufman and Gross (1974) for the poly(A) content of messengers in muscle polysomes are based on the assumption that the length of poly(A) per molecule is constant. The lengths of the poly(A) sequence of different size classes of messengers remained the same throughout differentiation, and no correlation could be found with changes in messenger stability, cytoplasmic distribution,

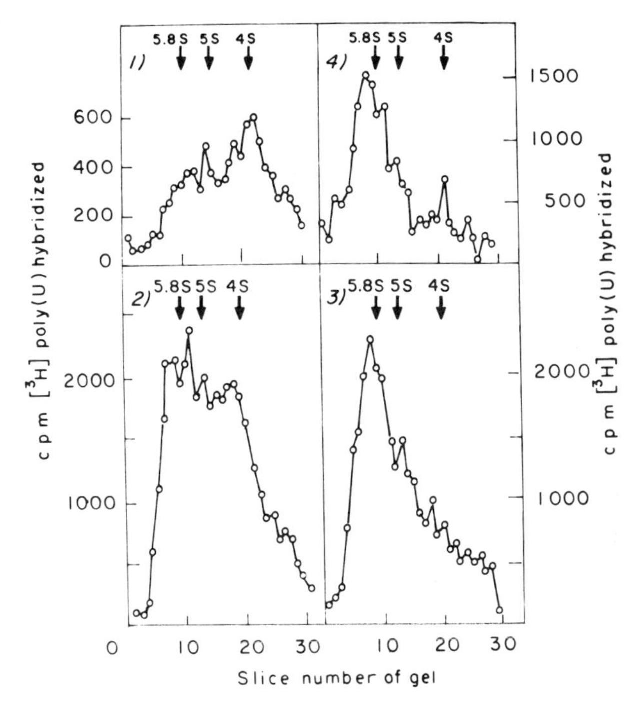

FIG. 9. The length of the poly(A) sequence in different size classes of mRNA. RNA was extracted from muscle cells, passed once through oligo(dT) cellulose, and separated on 80% formamide–sucrose gradients. Fractions of the gradient from 7 to 9 S *(1)*, 12 to 15 S *(2)*, 18 to 21 S *(3)*, and 24 to 28 S *(4)* were taken, digested with T_1 and A ribonucleases, the resulting poly(A) sequences separated on oligo(dT) cellulose, and then analyzed by gel electrophoresis. Their size distribution on the gel was demonstrated by hybridization with [^{3}H]poly(U) after elution from slices of the gel. The position of marker RNA molecules at 4 S, 5 S, and 5.8 S are indicated. Muscle cells before or after fusion gave an essentially similar size distribution.

etc. (Goto *et al.*, 1977). These results indicate that the poly(A) sequence itself is not a factor that changes during differentiation and is therefore unlikely to play a direct role in this process.

4. The Cytoplasmic Distribution of Messenger RNA

The pulse labeling experiments on mRNA metabolism (Buckingham *et al.*, 1974a, 1976) suggested that, prior to differentiation, most 26 S poly(A) (+) RNA ($\simeq$95%) was nonpolysomal and present in a particle sedimenting at about 70–100 S. It was distributed between polysomal (60%) and nonpolysomal (40%) compartments after fusion (Table III). This situation apparently pertained to other classes of mRNA too. Kaufman and Gross (1974) had also noted the presence of

TABLE III

CYTOPLASMIC DISTRIBUTION AND STABILITY OF PULSE-LABELED POLY(A) (+) RNA DURING MUSCLE CELL DIFFERENTIATION[a]

RNA	Stability, $t_{1/2}$ (hours)	Distribution (% cpm)	
		In RNP	In polysomes
From dividing myoblasts			
Most poly(A) (+) RNA	≤10	35–50	50–65
Most poly(A) (+) RNA after 12-hour chase		35–50	50–65
26 S RNA	≤10	90–95	5–10
26 S RNA after 12-hour chase		90–95	5–10
From myoblasts just prior to fusion			
Most poly(A) (+) RNA	20–25	45–55	45–55
Most poly(A) (+) RNA after 10-hour chase		40–50	50–60
Most poly(A) (+) RNA after 24-hour chase		40–50	50–60
26 S RNA	50–60	90–95	5–10
26 S RNA after 10-hour chase		90–95	5–10
26 S RNA after 24-hour chase		40–50	50–60
From myotubes			
Most poly(A) (+) RNA	20–25	40–50	50–60
Most poly(A) (+) RNA after 24-hour chase		40–50	50–60
26 S RNA	50–60	40–50	50–60
26 S RNA after 24-hour chase		40–50	50–60

[a] The results were obtained after centrifugation of cytoplasmic extracts on polysome gradients either immediately after a 2-hour labeling of the cells with [^{3}H]uridine (200 μCi/2.5 ml; 20 Ci/mmole) or after a further chase with cold uridine. RNA from polysomal and supernatant compartments was extracted and analyzed on sucrose gradients, poly(A) (+) RNA was detected by hybridization to poly(U) filters. Messenger half-lives were estimated from the results of chase experiments.

nonpolysomal poly(A) (+) RNA in cultured myotubes. Experiments on the *in vitro* translation of RNA from puromycin-dissociated polysomal particles indicated that myosin mRNA was present in undetectable amounts in polysomes before fusion (Przybyla and Strohman, 1974). In contrast to the results described, Young *et al.* (1975) have claimed, on the basis of polysome runoff experiments, that there is a difference of less than a factor of 2 between the quantity of myosin mRNA present in polysomes before and after fusion. These experiments should perhaps be treated with reservation, since the identification and quantitation of synthesis of the large subunit of myosin is not very satisfactory. Characterization of the nonpolysomal RNA indicates that, in embryonic chick muscle, RNA extracted from the 70–90 S region of polysome gradients will direct myosin synthesis *in vitro* (Heywood *et al.*, 1975a). Correspondingly, actin synthesis is directed by RNA extracted from 16–40 S particles present in postribosomal supernatants of the same tissue (Bag and Sarkar, 1975). Further characterization of such particles by their RNA and protein content, and buoyant density on cesium chloride or metrizamide gradients (Buckingham and Gros, 1975; Bag and Sarkar, 1975; Buckingham *et al.*, 1976) suggests that they correspond to free ribonucleoprotein particles (Spirin, 1969; for review, see Williamson, 1973).

The evidence available suggests that these particles are important in the accumulation of mRNA which apparently precedes differentiation. In a number of embryological systems they have such a role; for example, in the egg prior to fertilization, the histone messengers are stored as ribonucleoprotein particles (Gross *et al.*, 1973). Experiments on *in vitro* protein synthesis (Bag and Sarkar, 1975; Heywood *et al.*, 1975a; Yaffé *et al.*, 1975) indicate that the storage forms of mRNA from muscle are capable of translation, and that the primary sequence of the messenger is, thus, probably not modified. As discussed in the preceding section, the length of the poly(A) sequence is unaltered. It therefore seems likely that the other component of ribonucleoprotein particles, namely the protein, may be an important controlling factor in the stability and utilization of muscle mRNAs. If this is the case, the protein content of ribonucleoproteins containing unstable 26 S RNA, stable 26 S RNA, and 26 S RNA recycling with the polysomes, for example, should differ. At present, there is a lack of information in general concerning proteins associated with free ribonucleoproteins (see Williamson, 1973). Protein components have been identified that are associated with the poly(A) sequence (Kwan and Brawerman, 1972), and two major proteins have been described that are associated with ribonucleoproteins released from polysomes (see Blobel, 1973). In the case of free cytoplasmic ribonucleoprotein particles, the majority of proteins seem to be larger than ribosomal proteins (Buckingham and Gros, 1975; Bag and Sarkar, 1975), and Bag and Sarkar (1975) have reported that particles in the size range where actin mRNA is found contain a major polypeptide of MW 44,000, together with at least eight others. Resolution of the complex pattern of proteins associated with these particles will probably require two-dimensional analysis. Cytoplasmic contamination also remains a problem and rigorous controls are necessary.

Finally, the translational activity of free ribonucleoprotein particles compared with the corresponding mRNA is undefined at present. Recently, it has been suggested (Bester *et al.*, 1975; Heywood *et al.*, 1975b) that an additional RNA component, described as translational control RNA (tcRNA), may be present in ribonucleoprotein particles and regulate the translation of, for example, myosin mRNA. This proposal awaits further confirmation (for discussion, see Section IV, D, 4).

5. RNA Transcription

The experiments discussed in the preceding sections on RNA metabolism during myogenesis have been concerned uniquely with cytoplasmic RNA. Changes in the activity of RNA polymerases (Marchok and Wolff, 1968) and a brief account of nuclear RNA synthesis (Buckingham *et al.*, 1973) have been published. However, meaningful studies of nuclear RNA metabolism and of transcription from muscle cell chromatin await the development of cDNA probes. Similarly, reverse copies of specific or total preparations of muscle mRNA are important tools in studies on the proportion of unique sequences present and of their relative abundance. An investigation of the proportion of unique sequences transcribed from the chick genome during myogenesis has appeared recently (Colbert *et al.*, 1976). By hybridization experiments between ^{3}H-labeled nonrepetitive DNA and excess RNA extracted from whole cells, it was found that in dividing myoblasts about 8% of unique sequences are transcribed and that this figure rises to about 10% in myotubes (in myoblasts in which fusion is inhibited by BUdR, the figure falls to about 5%). These data would suggest that, while posttranscriptional control is probably an important factor in the terminal differentiation of myoblasts, changes in transcription clearly occur also.

D. *In Vitro* TRANSLATION EXPERIMENTS

The second approach to the study of mRNA metabolism during muscle cell differentiation depends on the use of cell-free protein-synthesizing systems, either to make direct deductions about the amount of functional mRNA present at any stage of differentiation or to examine the role of different translational components of the muscle system in order to identify possible controlling elements at this level.

1. In Vitro Translation of Extracts of Muscle Cell RNA

Such success as has been attained with the myosin heavy-chain mRNA is in very large part due to its size, which allows it to be separated from the bulk of cellular messengers. Actin mRNA, coding for a protein of much more ordinary size, is less amenable to purification. However, due to the relatively high concentration of this mRNA in several tissues, the cell-free synthesis of actin from total mRNA fractions has recently been reported by several groups (Paterson *et al.*, 1974; Gozes *et al.*, 1975; Bag and Sarkar, 1975; Whalen *et al.*, 1976b).

Characterization of the synthesized actin, by means of its unique biochemical properties as well as peptide mapping, has left little doubt of its successful and efficient synthesis, thus permitting detection of the actin mRNA by its cell-free translation. Indeed, Paterson *et al.* (1974) have measured translatable levels of actin mRNA in developing chick muscle cultures and found an apparent* correlation between the mRNA levels and *in vivo* actin synthesis, thus implying a possible transcriptional control in its expression. Also by means of cell-free translation, Bag and Sarkar (1975) have found actin mRNA in free ribonucleoprotein particles isolated in bulk from chick leg muscle. These examples serve to illustrate that possibilities exist for studying messenger RNA metabolism without the need to purify the individual species, given the current technology of cell-free protein synthesis.

This approach has been applied by Yaffé *et al.* (1975) to studies of the myosin light-chain components, detecting the mRNAs by cell-free synthesis in the wheat germ lysate. It has been suggested that the light-chain mRNAs appear before cell fusion prior to myosin heavy-chain synthesis, the implication being that the mRNAs are present before the onset of light-chain synthesis. These interesting preliminary observations will, however, require more definitive evidence of cell-free synthesis of the light chains as well as correlations with the *in vivo* patterns of light-chain synthesis.

In an attempt to examine possible changes during myogenesis in the overall spectrum of translatable mRNAs, we have translated RNAs isolated at various times during muscle development in culture. The choice of the cell-free system originally described by Schreier and Staehelin (1973a) was made in part because of its high efficiency of synthesis, but also because of the observation that total cytoplasmic RNA could be translated in this system. Thus, the high concentration of ribosomal RNA relative to mRNA does not inhibit synthesis, and this has enabled us to show that the great majority of calf muscle mRNAs contain long tracts of poly(A) (Buckingham *et al.*, 1975; Whalen and Gros, 1977b). Total cytoplasmic RNA was separated into poly(A) (+) and poly(A) (−) RNA by oligo(dT)-cellulose chromatography, and the various fractions were translated in the cell-free system. All translatable products (analyzed by SDS-gel electrophoresis) produced by the total RNA were produced by the poly(A) (+) RNA, with the exception of bands that comigrate with histones, known to be coded for by mRNAs lacking poly(A) (Greenberg and Perry, 1972). The histone bands repre-

* Apparent because actin synthesis was expressed as a percentage for *in vitro* synthesis, but in absolute terms (normalized per culture dish) for the *in vivo* measurements (see Section II, A).

sent the only examples of enrichment of translation products in the poly(A) (−) RNA, and thus we conclude that a very large fraction of calf muscle mRNAs do contain poly(A), a conclusion of importance since most studies of mRNA rely on poly(A) content for analysis (see discussion, Section IV, C, 3).

In addition, the translation of total cytoplasmic RNA was examined pre- and postfusion (Whalen *et al.,* 1976a,b). The analysis by SDS-gel electrophoresis demonstrated that very few differences could be noted in the products of mRNAs isolated at various times during myogenic development. This finding is less surprising in light of the results of *in vivo* patterns of protein synthesis (Section II, C) and serves to confirm the notion that the content of major mRNAs does not undergo large variations during the period studied. As these experiments used total cytoplasmic RNA, further work must be directed toward translation of RNA isolated from cellular compartments (RNP, polysome, membrane-bound polysomes, etc.) to ascertain how the different messengers are distributed during the various periods of myogenesis. However, these few examples illustrate the possibilities for studying mRNA metabolism via cell-free translation.

2. *Study of the Control of Protein Synthesis*

The ability to pass from studies on embryonic muscle to studies in tissue culture is a major advantage of the muscle system, and investigations into the control of protein synthesis are but one area to profit from this feature. Most of the work to date concerned with protein synthesis has been carried out on embryonic muscle, particularly chicken, but it is worth considering here, given the presumed applicability to the cultured cell system.

Some of the basic features of protein synthesis and the mechanisms for its control have, in fact, been worked out in the muscle system, in particular by Heywood, Rich, Sarkar, and their colleagues. Heywood *et al.* (1967) isolated various size classes of chicken embryo leg muscle polysomes and, by elongation of nascent chains *in vitro,* showed that only the heaviest polysome fraction (50–65 ribosomes) produced a product that comigrated with myosin on acrylamide gels. Later work (Heywood and Rich, 1968) extended this observation to include claims of the cell-free synthesis of actin and tropomyosin, each from polysomes of unique size. The *in vitro* synthesis by polysome elongation has since been carried out for myosin heavy and light chains (Sarkar and Cooke, 1970; Low *et al.,* 1971) and as a whole can be regarded as evidence that each of these muscle proteins can be synthesized from monocistronic RNAs. This finding is in accord with a general lack of evidence for polycistronic cellular mRNAs in higher cells (Brawerman, 1974). The important implication is that the synthesis of these various contractile proteins can be independently controlled, although a certain degree of coordination is expected.

Proposals for the mechanisms that control protein synthesis at the level of mRNA or the translational machinery have been made in three forms, derived from experiments on the muscle system: (1) specific factors exist that permit or stimulate initiation of protein synthesis on certain mRNAs, (2) "translational control RNAs" (tcRNA) exist which repress or block the translation of an mRNA, and (3) mRNAs exist as ribonucleoprotein (RNP) particles, the proteins of which control the stability and/or functionality of an mRNA. Each of these proposals and their experimental basis will be considered separately.

3. Protein Initiation Factors

The ability to isolate myosin mRNA fractions producing heavy chain in a cell-free system prompted investigations as to the requirement for homologous muscle tissue initiation factors. Heywood (1970a) reported that when salt-washed reticulocyte ribosomes were employed in the *in vitro* system, only muscle initiation factors (i.e., proteins removed from muscle ribosomes by KCl washing) were capable of directing myosin heavy-chain synthesis and that reticulocyte factors could not substitute for muscle factors when salt-washed muscle ribosomes were used. When assayed for globin synthesis, an analogous situation was found in which heterologous ribosomes would translate the globin messenger when supplied reticulocyte initiation factors, whereas muscle factors worked only poorly. In subsequent experiments, the ribosome salt wash was separated to give three crude fractions of initiation factors, and the specificity for myosin heavy-chain synthesis was found to reside in fraction IF-3 (Rourke and Heywood, 1972). This fraction was furthermore found to be the only one to bind messenger RNA to ribosomes (Heywood, 1970c; Heywood and Thompson, 1971), and this binding was tissue specific: muscle IF-3 bound muscle mRNA preferentially, whereas reticulocyte IF-3 bound globin mRNA.

An apparently analogous situation has been described for myoglobin biosynthesis in chick embryo red and white leg muscle (Thompson *et al.*, 1973). Although the initiation factors prepared from both red and white leg muscle are capable of stimulating myosin heavy-chain synthesis, only those from red muscle will produce myoglobin when RNA fractions containing myoglobin mRNA from red muscle are employed. When factors were fractionated, the specific factor was again found to be in fraction IF-3. Following upon the observation of Low and Rich (1973) that chicken myoglobin begins to be synthesized very rapidly after 16 days of development, Heywood and Kennedy (1974) found a coincident appearance of the myoglobin-specific factor (red muscle IF-3). Indirect evidence suggested that the myoglobin messenger RNA was not preexistent in muscle before day 16, and it was inferred that concomitant transcriptional and translational control accounted for the appearance of myoglobin biosynthesis. The IF-3 fraction containing the specific properties for myosin and myoglobin translation has since been separated into a further four fractions, one possessing a selectivity for myosin translation and another a selectivity for myoglobin synthesis (Heywood *et al.,* 1974).

Although these experiments on initiation factor specificity are attractive, particularly in their application to the possibility of a preexistent myosin heavy-chain mRNA (Buckingham *et al.,* 1974a; Heywood *et al.,* 1975a), a certain number of criticisms can be applied. In general, the experiments in which the product myosin or myoglobin is assayed only as a complete molecule do not ensure that the effect seen is strictly due to initiation of protein synthesis. Since the initiation factor fractions used were not completely pure, the possibility exists that elongation factors, tRNA synthetases, or even tRNA contaminating the ribosome salt wash might act to selectively allow the completion of the intact molecule, which otherwise would be produced only as an undetected fragment. The problem of premature termination of polypeptide chains in cell-free systems is well known (Atkins *et al.,* 1975). Given this consideration, experiments studying the formation of an initiation complex (usually employing radioactive mRNA) can be cited as more direct evidence (Heywood, 1970b,c). However, these experiments are also subject to criticism. In the experiment where formation of an initiation complex with the 26 S myosin mRNA was studied by gradient analysis employing muscle or reticulocyte factors (Fig. 4, Heywood, 1970b), the criticisms can be advanced that radioactive rRNA also was partially bound to the 40 S ribosomal subunit and furthermore, tRNA was required for 80 S complex formation. Concerning this second point, evidence now exists showing that Met-tRNA binding very probably precedes mRNA binding to the 40 S subunit (Darnbrough *et al.,* 1973; Schreier and Staehelin, 1973b). Thus the fidelity of the myosin mRNA binding is suspect. Other experiments, studying 26 S myosin mRNA or mixed mRNA binding to ribosomes by a filter technique (Heywood, 1970a,c) did not characterize the putative initiation complex formed. All these experiments, which preceded much of what is the current understanding of eukaryotic protein synthesis, need to be reconsidered.

Unfortunately no work from any other laboratory has ever appeared to directly confirm or refute the experimental results consistently reported by Heywood and his colleagues. Mondal *et al.* (1974) and Przybyla and Strohman (1974), by apparently successfully translating chick myosin heavy chain in a heterologous rabbit reticulocyte lysate, have demonstrated the lack of an absolute requirement for muscle initiation factors. However, Heywood *et al.* (1974), using the same heterologous system, obtained a stimulation (2–4-fold) of heavy-chain synthesis by adding IF-3. The idea of specific translation factors for cellular eukaryotic mRNAs is in general disfavor, and a considerable number of mRNAs have been translated in heterologous cell-free systems without apparent specific requirements (see Brawermann, 1974; Lodish, 1974). In the absence of careful studies in efficient cell-free systems of yields of myosin HC per RNA molecule, the exact mode of selectivity of muscle IF-3 (and its subfractions) will remain unclear. Recently, we investigated (Whalen and Gros, 1977a) whether chicken embryo muscle initiation factors were capable of translating rabbit globin mRNA in the reconstituted heterologous system of Schreier and Staehelin (1973a). Although the muscle factors were only 15–30% as active as the homologous rabbit reticulocyte factors, the overall yield of globin synthesized by the muscle factors was greater than one molecule per molecule of RNA. Furthermore, parameters affecting overall synthesis (for example, ribosome concentration or polyamine levels) acted similarly on reticulocyte and muscle factors, suggesting that the control of globin synthesis in this system might be alike for both preparations. Experiments of this type directly treating the situations described by Heywood would be useful.

4. Translational Control RNAs (tcRNA)

A second proposal to account for control of protein synthesis, also derived from experiments of Heywood on chicken embryo leg muscle, is that of translational control RNAs (tcRNA).

Originally, a substance with some of the properties of RNA was isolated from dialysates of muscle initiation factors, and this material was found to inhibit globin translation in a rabbit reticulocyte lysate (Heywood *et al.*, 1974). Apparently, this effect on heterologous protein synthesis was due to an inhibition of mRNA and Met-tRNA binding to the small ribosomal subunit (Kennedy *et al.*, 1974). This material, when isolated from chicken erythroblasts or rabbit reticulocytes, had no effect on globin synthesis but effectively inhibited myosin and myoglobin translation in the cell-free system. A small RNA component, also found in dialyzates of reticulocyte initiation factors, has been described and partially characterized by Bogdanovsky *et al.* (1973), who found a requirement for this material in a fractionated globin-synthesizing system. Further studies with these preparations (Berns *et al.*, 1975; Salden *et al.*, 1975; Salden and Bloemendal, 1976) suggested that the stimulatory activity was not mRNA specific. However, Bester *et al.* (1975) have found two subfractions of tcRNA, one isolated from dialyzates of polysomes and another from dialyzates of mRNP particles. Briefly, the mRNP-tcRNA is rich in uridylate residues (about 50% of total) organized in stretches sufficient to form small hybrids to poly(A). It is capable of inhibiting the translation of mRNP-derived mRNA (but not polysome-derived mRNA) only when these mRNAs contain their poly(A) segments (Heywood *et al.*, 1975b). The tcRNA from polysomes is smaller than its mRNP counterpart, contains less oligo(U) and is less effectively hybridized to poly(A). It inhibits the translation neither of polysomal nor of mRNP-derived mRNA. The tcRNA component of the myosin mRNP (Heywood *et al.*, 1975a) is apparently specific in its inhibition of myosin translation, not affecting the translation of the other mRNP-derived mRNAs.

These experiments have led to the proposition of a very attractive model (Bester *et al.*, 1975) only partially supported by the facts. The major obstacle is the purity of the tcRNA preparation, in order to verify that the active component is indeed the RNA under study. Indeed, Raymondjean *et al.* (1977) have found that the polyamine spermidine, known to stimulate protein synthesis (Atkins *et al.*, 1975), was present in their RNA preparations (see Salden and Bloemendal, 1976). Other difficulties perhaps reflect the impurity of the preparations. For example, the inhibitory effect of mRNP–tcRNA on globin synthesis previously reported (Bester *et al.*, 1975) has in some experiments not been confirmed (Heywood *et al.*, 1975b), and the inhibition of putative myosin HC synthesis by mRNP–tcRNA once reported (Bester *et al.*, 1975) was not found when the mRNP–tcRNA was tested with purified fractions of myosin mRNA (Heywood *et al.*, 1975b). It is thus difficult to judge the reality of these entities and their effect, and these experiments and the proposed model await further confirmation.

A third possibility for translational control mechanisms is that of the function of messenger RNAs in ribonucleoprotein (RNP) particles. Although discussed in more detail in Section IV, C, 4, it is worth noting here that, in addition to aspects of mRNA stability, the proteins associated with RNPs may in fact contain initiation factors that could control the entry of such mRNAs into polysomes. Last, the tcRNAs described above seem to be associated with mRNPs, and thus these particles may contain the components required for the control of their utilization. Further work on these possibilities is expected.

V. The Genetic Approach: Muscle Cell Lines

The experimental results discussed in the preceding sections have concerned principally the study of differentiation in primary cultures of fetal muscle. However, several established muscle cell lines also exist that have retained the capacity to differentiate. These offer some advantages over primary cultures, especially the presence of a much more uniform cell population and the possibility of genetic manipulation on the muscle phenotype. The isolation of variants and of heterokaryons and hybrids between these and other cell lines should result in further information about the control of terminal differentiation. This section will include a brief description of the existing cell lines, both normal and variant with respect to differentiation. This will be followed by a short discussion of the effects of viral infection and transformation on the expression of the muscle phenotype. Finally, the few experiments of genetic manipulation carried out to date will be described and the potential of this approach discussed.

A. Cell Lines

Early experiments on isolated muscle cells were carried out by Konigsberg (1961), who showed that cloned myoblasts will form differentiated colonies. The first continuous cell lines were established by Yaffé (for review, see Yaffé, 1969) from uncloned primary cultures of fetal rat muscle after repeated cell passages. In the majority of cases, cell multiplication ceases after 3–5 passages and the line dies out. Treatment with the carcinogen 20(3)-methylcholanthrene during the first 2 passages resulted in the establishment of the first permanent muscle cell lines (Yaffé, 1968), e.g., L_6, M_{41}. Subsquently, lines were obtained without using a carcinogen (Richter and Yaffé, 1970), e.g., L_{63}, L_8. These cell lines multiply when maintained at low density, but when left to grow to high density they fuse to form myotubes, which in some cases clearly contain cross-striations and contract spontaneously (Richter and Yaffé, 1970). Morphological differentiation is accompanied by increases in muscle enzymes and contractile proteins (e.g., Shainberg *et al.,* 1971; Luzzati and Drugeon, 1972; Wahrmann *et al.,* 1973; Delain *et al.,* 1973; Patrick *et al.,* 1972) very similar to those observed in primary cultures (Yaffé, 1969). Most of the lines have a normal diploid number of chromosomes, but even one tetraploid line (L_6P) had similar differentiation properties (Richter and Yaffé, 1970). The myogenic lines were derived from noninbred strains of rats which made rigorous tests of tumorigenicity difficult, but injection of the cells did not result in tumors (Richter and Yaffé, 1970).

In addition to the rat myogenic lines, continuous cultures of muscle cells have been derived from the mixed cell population of embryoid bodies of mouse teratocarcinomas. Such mouse muscle lines differentiate to form myotubes, with concomitant increases in myosin, acetylcholine receptor (Boon *et al.*, 1974), and the M isozyme of creatine phosphokinase (M. E. Buckingham, unpublished observations). The karyotype of these cells is heterogeneous, varying between 60 and 70 chromosomes. Unlike primitive teratoma cell lines, the muscle cells are not tumorigenic (Boon *et al.*, 1974).

B. Variant Behavior

Clones isolated from the rat cell lines exhibited varying degrees of differentiation, as monitored by cell fusion, some even failing to fuse at all (Richter and Yaffé, 1970). Subclones of such cells, however, again exhibited a range of behavior with respect to fusion. Yaffé (1969) concluded that the capacity to differentiate is retained in the cell lines, but there is considerable lability in its expression. Our own experience when we have cloned teratoma muscle cell lines (J. P. Merlie, unpublished observations) or azaguanidine-resistant L_6 lines (W. E. Wright, unpublished observations) indicates a wide variability in the capacity of clones to fuse. Clones that do not differentiate morphologically may differentiate biochemically. Nonfusing teratoma clones, for example, nonetheless synthesize myosin and contain M-type creatine phosphokinase at confluence. Furthermore, some biochemical markers of differentiation may be expressed independently. Our azaguanidine-resistant strain of L_6 will fuse, with concomitant increase in myosin synthesis and appearance of the muscle type isozyme of creatine phosphokinase, but with no accompanying increase in the level of this enzyme, nor appearance of a detectable quantity of cholinergic receptor on the membrane.

The variants described above have arisen spontaneously from clones of normal phenotype. In addition, temperature-sensitive variants of the line L_6 have been induced by treatment with *N*-methyl-*N*-nitro-*N*′-nitrosoguanidine and screened with respect to the temperature sensitivity of growth and differentiation (Loomis *et al.*, 1973). One class of variants (e.g., clone E_3) fuses at 37°C but not at

41°C, while another class (e.g., H_6) fuses at 41°C but not at 37°C. In general, biochemical differentiation, estimated as changes in enzyme activity and myosin synthesis (Luzzati and Loomis, 1972; Luzzati *et al.*, 1973), correlates with the morphological behavior although some derangement of the normal mechanism is evident; for example, H_6 does not accumulate myosin at the permissive temperature of 41°C. Once differentiation has been initiated, the effects of change from permissive to nonpermissive temperatures differ: E_3 continues to differentiate, while H_6 is arrested. A potential difficulty with these temperature-sensitive lines lies in the high frequency of reversion after about eighty generations. The initial level of variants obtained after mutagenesis was also unusually high (about 30% of the 1–2% of cells surviving mutagen treatment) (Loomis *et al.*, 1973).

Apart from the selection of markers, such as HGPRT for hybridization experiments (Luzzati, 1974), strains of L_6 resistant to other drugs have been described. Ouabain-resistant clones of the $HGPRT^-$ line of L_6 have been isolated after exposure to the drug (Luzzati, 1974). After treatment with the mutagen ethyl methane sulfonate, L_6 grown in the presence of α-amanitin has given rise to clones resistant to the drug. One such clone, Ama 102, does not fuse, or synthesize M-type creatine phosphokinase, and the RNA polymerase II of these cells when examined *in vitro* is found to be partially resistant to the drug (Somers *et al.*, 1975a,b).

The interest in the different types of variants described lies in the information they offer about the coordination and regulation of differentiated functions. It would seem, for example, that the appearance of cholinergic receptor is not necessarily coordinated with the appearance of M-type creatine phosphokinase. The temperature-sensitive variants may possess heat-labile factors that control phenotypic expression, and, more specifically, the behavior of the amanitin-resistant line suggests the importance of a certain level of RNA polymerase II activity in differentiation. An obvious reservation about the study of variant cell lines lies in the extent to which their behavior is relevant to the normal processes of differentiation. Furthermore, the extreme sensitivity of myoblast differentiation to external factors, such as serum batch, should be borne in mind; variants may have changed serum factor requirements rather than a more fundamental lesion. However, normal and variant lines can give indications about regulatory controls and are potentially exploitable in cell hybridization-type experiments.

C. Viral Effects on Differentiation

The effects of viral infection and transformation on muscle cell differentiation have been included in this section because of the potential value of transformed lines, where differentiation can be induced under conditions that are nonpermissive for the virus. Experiments with temperature-sensitive strains of Rous sarcoma virus (RSV) have shown that myoblasts transformed at permissive temperatures retain the capacity to differentiate and do so normally when the cultures are shifted to a nonpermissive temperature for the virus (Fiszman and Fuchs, 1975; Holtzer *et al.*, 1975).

The potential interest of using viruses to probe the mechanisms of differentiation has been demonstrated in other systems (e.g., Humphries and Temin, 1974). In the case of muscle, it would appear that transformation acts reversibly on one of the controlling mechanisms of differentiation.* In the case of RSV, for example, transformation is most efficient when dividing myoblasts are infected with the virus. Viral infection of myoblasts does not prevent differentiation of the majority of incompletely transformed or nontransformed cells in the population, but the resultant myotubes rapidly vacuolate and degenerate (Easton and Reich, 1972). Myotubes are not permissive to RSV or to the DNA viruses polyoma and SV40. Polyoma virus when injected into myotubes (Graessmann *et al.*, 1973) synthesizes the T antigen, but does not induce cellular DNA synthesis in myotube nuclei, whereas myoblast nuclei are induced to synthesize DNA by the virus.

D. Heterokaryons, Hybrids, Reconstituted Cells

The study of abnormal behavior with respect to differentiation is one approach which it is possible to pursue with the muscle cell lines; another is the manipulation of different cell lines by cell hybridization-type experiments. Here, the study of phenotypic expression in the resultant progeny may provide information about its genetic control. Very few such experiments have as yet been carried out on myogenic cells.

The reactivation of chick erythrocyte nuclei in chick erythrocyte × rat myoblast heterokaryons has been examined (Carlsson *et al.*, 1974). Mixed cultures of myoblasts and heterokaryons will undergo normal myotube formation, with incorporation of the chick erythrocyte nuclei in the myotube. Although the synthesis of chick surface antigens is

* The extent of transformation depends on the stage of muscle cell development at which infection takes place and on the virus used.

directed by the reactivated chick nucleus, no chick-type myosin is detectable in the myotubes (Ringertz *et al.*, 1972). Mixed primary cultures of chick and rat myoblasts form hybrid myotubes where both types of myosin are synthesized. It is possible, as Ringertz *et al.*, (1972) suggested, that the erythrocyte nuclei were introduced too late during the development of the myoblast culture for reprogramming to have taken place. Alternatively, the myogenic part of the erythrocyte genome may be inaccessible to reactivation. Hybrids formed between fibroblast and myoblast cell lines (Buckingham *et al.*, 1974b) do not undergo muscle differentiation, and the synthesis of the peak of labeled 26 S RNA (see Section IV, C, 1) is suppressed, results similar to those obtained in other hybrids where loss of "luxury" functions is observed. Enucleation by cytochalasin B is another technique permitting a further type of cell manipulation, which results in the reconstitution of cells containing one or more nuclei and cytoplasm of different origins. This has been shown to work successfully in the case of L_6 myoblast lines (Ege *et al.*, 1974) and has potential applications in the study of the role of the nucleus in the terminal stages of muscle differentiation.

The future use of cell hybridization techniques, whether between normal and variant myoblasts or myoblasts and other cell types, depends on markers of muscle function, both of the end products of differentiation where myosin or creatine phosphokinase-M-type antibodies can be used, and more fundamentally of the initial transcription products of the muscle genome, where the development of specific cDNAs is of great importance. The sort of investigation to which the muscle system would then be susceptible is indicated by the work of Harrison *et al.* (1976) on the control of globin synthesis.

ACKNOWLEDGMENTS

We offer many thanks to our colleagues who have participated in the preparation of this review: Professor François Gros, whose interest in the muscle system and whose support of our research has made possible our participation; Gill Butler-Browne, Michel Weber, and Woody Wright for their helpful discussions and readings of the manuscript; Sataro Goto, Daniel Caput, Jean-Claude Lelong, Michel Jacquet, Arlette Cohen, and Noel Lamande for their participation in experiments described; Geneviève Antolini and Dominique Vitalyos for their help with the preparation of the manuscript.

J. P. Merlie was a fellow of the Jane Coffin Childs Memorial Fund for Medical Research and the Muscular Dystrophy Associations of America. R. G. Whalen was a fellow of the Fondation Philippe and the Damon Runyon–Walter Winchell Cancer Fund.

This work was supported by grants from the Fonds de Développement de la Recherche Scientifique et Technique, the Centre National de la Recherche Scientifique, the Institut National de la Santé et de la Recherche Médicale, the Commissariat à l'Energie Atomique, the Ligue Nationale Française contre le Cancer, the Fondation pour la Recherche Médicale Française, and the Muscular Dystrophy Associations of America.

REFERENCES

Almon, R. R., Andrew, C. G., and Appel, S. H. (1974). *Biochemistry* **13**, 5522–5528.

Atkins, J. F., Lewis, J. B., Anderson, C. W., and Gestland, R. F. (1975). *J. Biol. Chem.* **250**, 5688–5695.

Axelsson, J., and Thesleff, S. (1959). *J. Physiol. (London)* **149**, 178–193.

Bag, J., and Sarkar, S. (1975). *Biochemistry* **14**, 3800–3807.

Beranek, R., and Vyskocil, F. (1967). *J. Physiol. (London)* **188**, 53–66.

Berg, D. K., and Hall, Z. W. (1974). *Science* **184**, 473–475.

Berg, D. K., and Hall, Z. W. (1975). *J. Physiol. (London)* **252**, 771–789.

Berg, D., Kelly, R. B., Sargent, P. B., Williamson, P., and Hall, Z. W. (1972). *Proc. Natl. Acad. Sci. U.S.A.* **69**, 147–151.

Berns, A., Salden, M., Bogdanovsky, D., Raymondjean, M., Schapira, G., and Bloemendal, H. (1975). *Proc. Natl. Acad. Sci. U.S.A.* **72**, 714–718.

Bester, A. J., Kennedy, D. S., and Heywood, S. M. (1975). *Proc. Natl. Acad. Sci. U.S.A.* **72**, 1523–1527.

Betz, W. (1976). *J. Physiol. (London)* **254**, 63–73.

Blobel, G. (1973). *Proc. Natl. Acad. Sci. U.S.A.* **70**, 924–928.

Bogdanovsky, D., Hermann, W., and Schapira, G. (1973). *Biochem. Biophys. Res. Commun.* **54**, 25–32.

Boon, T., Buckingham, M. E., Dexter, D. L., Jakob, H., and Jacob, F. (1974). *Ann. Microbiol. (Paris)* **125b**, 13–28.

Brawerman, G. (1974). *Annu. Rev. Biochem.* **43**, 621–642.

Brockes, J. P., and Hall, Z. W. (1975a). *Biochemistry* **14**, 2092–2099.

Brockes, J. P., and Hall, Z. W. (1975b). *Biochemistry* **14**, 2100–2106.

Brockes, J. P., and Hall, Z. W. (1975c). *Proc. Natl. Acad. Sci. U.S.A.* **72**, 1368–1372.

Brockes, J. P., Berg, D. K., and Hall, Z. W. (1976). *Cold Spring Harbor Symp. Quant. Biol.* **40**, 253–263.

Buckingham, M. E., and Gros, F. (1975). *In* "The Use of Iodinated Density Gradient Media for Biological Separations" (D. Rickwood, ed.), p. 71. Inform. Retrieval.

Buckingham, M. E., Caput, D., Cohen, A., and Gros, F. (1973). *In* "Normal and Pathological Protein Synthesis in Higher Organisms" (G. Schapira *et al.*, eds.), pp. 457–474. INSERM, Paris.

Buckingham, M. E., Caput, D., Cohen, A., Whalen, R. G., and Gros, F. (1974a). *Proc. Natl. Acad. Sci. U.S.A.* **71**, 1466–1470.

Buckingham, M. E., Cohen, A., Gros, F., Luzzati, D., Charmot, D., and Drugeon, G. (1974b). *Biochimie* **56**, 1571–1573.

Buckingham, M. E., Goto, S., Whalen, R. G., and Gros, F. (1975). *Proc. FEBS Meet., 10th* **38**, 325–336.

Buckingham, M. E., Cohen, A., and Gros, F. (1976). *J. Mol. Biol.* **103**, 611–626.

Burridge, K., and Bray, D. (1975). *J. Mol. Biol.* **99**, 1–14.

Campo, M. S., and Bishop, J. O. (1974). *J. Mol. Biol.* **90**, 649–663.

Carlsson, S. A., Ringertz, N. R., and Savage, R. E. (1974). *Exp. Cell Res.* **84**, 255–266.

Catterall, W. A. (1975). *J. Biol. Chem.* **250**, 1776–1781.

Chang, C. C., and Huang, M. C. (1975). *Nature (London)* **253**, 643–644.

Changeux, J. P. (1975). *Handb. Psychopharmacol.* **6**, 235–301.

Changeux, J. P., Kasai, M., and Lee, C. V. (1970). *Proc. Natl. Acad. Sci. U.S.A.* **67**, 1241–1247.

Changeux, J. P., Benedetti, L., Bourgeois, J. P., Brisson, A., Cartaud, J., Devaux, P., Grunhagen, H., Moreau, M., Popot, J. L., Sobel, A., and Weber, M. (1976). *Cold Spring Harbor Symp. Quant. Biol.* **40**, 211–230.

Chi, J. C., Rubinstein, N., Strahs, K., and Holtzer, H. (1975a). *J. Cell Biol.* **67**, 523–537.

Chi, J. C., Fellini, A., and Holtzer, H. (1975b). *Proc. Natl. Acad. Sci. U.S.A.* **72**, 4999–5003.

Cohen, S. A., and Fischbach, G. P. (1973). *Science* **181**, 76–78.

Colbert, D. A., Edwards, K., and Coleman, J. R. (1976). *Differentiation* **5**, 91–96.

Coleman, J. R., and Coleman, A. W. (1968). *J. Cell. Physiol.* **72**, Suppl. 1, 19–34.

Crain, S. M., and Peterson, E. R. (1974). *Ann. N.Y. Acad. Sci.* **228**, 6–34.

Darnbrough, C., Legon, S., Hunt, T., and Jackson, R. J. (1973). *J. Mol. Biol.* **76**, 379–403.

Delain, D., Meienhofer, M. C., Prox, D., and Schapira, F. (1973). *Differentiation* **1**, 349–354.

Del Castillo, J., and Katz, B. (1955). *J. Physiol. (London)* **128**, 157–181.

Devreotes, P., and Fambrough, D. M. (1975). *J. Cell Biol.* **65**, 335–358.

Devreotes, P., and Fambrough, D. M. (1976). *Proc. Natl. Acad. Sci. U.S.A.* **73**, 161–164.

Diamond, J., and Miledi, R. (1962). *J. Physiol. (London)* **162**, 393–408.

Dolly, J. O., and Barnard, E. A. (1975). *FEBS Lett.* **57**, 267–271.

Drachman, D. B., and Witzke, F. (1972). *Science* **176**, 514–516.

Easton, T. G., and Reich, E. (1972). *J. Biol. Chem.* **247**, 6420–6431.

Edelman, G., Yohara, I., and Wang, J. L. (1973). *Proc. Natl. Acad. Sci. U.S.A.* **70**, 1442–1446.

Ege, T., Krondahl, U., and Ringertz, N. R. (1974). *Exp. Cell Res.* **88**, 428–432.

Elzinga, M., Maron, B. J., and Adelstein, R. S. (1976). *Science* **191**, 94–95.

Emerson, C. P., Jr., and Beckner, S. K. (1975). *J. Mol. Biol.* **93**, 431–447.

Eppenberger, H. M., Eppenberger, M., Richterich, R., and Aebi, H. (1964). *Dev. Biol.* **10**, 1–16.

Etlinger, J. D., and Fischman, D. A. (1973). *Cold Spring Harbor Symp. Quant. Biol.* **37**, 511–522.

Fambrough, D., and Rash, J. E. (1971). *Dev. Biol.* **26**, 55–68.

Fambrough, D. M., and Hartzell, H. C. (1972). *Science* **176**, 189–191.

Fambrough, D. M., Hartzell, H. C., Rash, J. E., and Ritchie, A. K. (1974). *Ann. N.Y. Acad. Sci.* **228**, 47–62.

Fine, R. E., and Blitz, A. L. (1975). *J. Mol. Biol.* **95**, 447–454.

Fischbach, G. D. (1970). *Science* **169**, 1331–1333.

Fischbach, G. D. (1972). *Dev. Biol.* **28**, 407–429.

Fischman, D. A. (1970). *Curr. Top. Dev. Biol.* **5**, 235.

Fiszman, M. Y., and Fuchs, P. (1975). *Nature (London)* **254**, 429–431.

Gearhart, J., and Mintz, B. (1975). *Cell* **6**, 61–66.

Goto, S., Buckingham, M. E., and Gros, F. (1977). Submitted for publication.

Gozes, I., Schmitt, H., and Littauer, U. Z. (1975). *Proc. Natl. Acad. Sci. U.S.A.* **72**, 701–705.

Graessmann, A., Graessmann, M., and Fogel, M. (1973). *Dev. Biol.* **35**, 180–186.

Greenberg, J. R., and Perry, R. P. (1972). *J. Mol. Biol.* **72**, 91–98.

Gross, K. W., Jacobs-Lorena, M., Baglioni, C., and Gross, P. R. (1973). *Proc. Natl. Acad. Sci. U.S.A.* **70**, 2614–2618.

Gruenstein, E., and Rich, A. (1975). *Biochem. Biophys. Res. Commun.* **64**, 472–477.

Guth, L. (1968). *Physiol. Rev.* **48**, 645–687.

Gutmann, E., and Young, J. Z. (1944). *J. Anat.* **78**, 15–43.

Hall, Z. W. (1972). *Annu. Rev. Biochem.* **41**, 925–952.

Harris, A. J. (1974). *Annu. Rev. Physiol.* **36**, 251–306.

Harris, A. J., Heinemann, S., Schubert, D., and Tarakis, H. (1971). *Nature (London)* **231**, 296–301.

Harrison, P. R., Affara, N. A., Conkie, D., Rutherford, T., Sommerville, J., and Paul, J. (1976). *Prog. Differ. Res., Proc. Int. Conf. 2nd, 1975* p. ■■■.
Hartzell, H. C., and Fambrough, D. (1973). *Dev. Biol.* **30**, 153–165.
Hauschka, S. D. (1972). *In* "Growth, Nutrition, and Metabolism of Cells in Culture" (G. H. Rothblat and V. J. Cristofalo, eds.), Vol. 2, pp. 67–131. Academic Press, New York.
Heywood, S. M. (1970a). *Cold Spring Harbor Symp. Quant. Biol.* **34**, 799–803.
Heywood, S. M. (1970b). *Nature (London)* **225**, 696–698.
Heywood, S. M. (1970c). *Proc. Natl. Acad. Sci. U.S.A.* **67**, 1782–1788.
Heywood, S. M., and Kennedy, D. S. (1974). *Dev. Biol.* **38**, 390–393.
Heywood, S. M., and Nwagwu, M. (1968). *Proc. Natl. Acad. Sci. U.S.A.* **60**, 229–234.
Heywood, S. M., and Nwagwu, M. (1969). *Biochemistry* **8**, 3839–3845.
Heywood, S. M., and Rich, A. (1968). *Proc. Natl. Acad. Sci. U.S.A.* **59**, 590–597.
Heywood, S. M., and Thompson, W. C. (1971). *Biochem. Biophys. Res. Commun.* **43**, 470–475.
Heywood, S. M., Dowben, R. M., and Rich, A. (1967). *Proc. Natl. Acad. Sci. U.S.A.* **57**, 1002–1009.
Heywood, S. M., Kennedy, D. S., and Bester, A. J. (1974). *Proc. Natl. Acad. Sci. U.S.A.* **71**, 2428–2431.
Heywood, S. M., Kennedy, D. S., and Bester, A. J. (1975a). *FEBS Lett.* **53**, 69–72.
Heywood, S. M., Kennedy, D. S., and Bester, A. J. (1975b). *Eur. J. Biochem.* **58**, 587–593.
Holtzer, H., Sanger, J. W., Ishikawa, H., and Strahs, K. (1973). *Cold Spring Harbor Symp. Quant. Biol.* **37**, 549–566.
Holtzer, H., Biehl, J., Yeoh, G., Meganathan, R., and Kaji, A. (1975). *Proc. Natl. Acad. Sci. U.S.A.* **72**, 4051–4055.
Hooisma, J., Slaaf, D. W., Meeter, E., and Stevens, W. F. (1975). *Brain Res.* **85**, 79–85.
Humphries, E., and Temin, H. (1974). *J. Virol.* **14**, 531–538.
Huszar, G. (1972). *Nature (London) New Biol.* **240**, 260–264.
Jacob, F., and Monod, J. (1963). *In* "Cytodifferentiation and Macromolecular Synthesis" (M. Locke, ed.), pp. 30–64. Academic Press, New York.
Katz, B. (1966). "Nerve Muscle and Synapse." McGraw-Hill, New York.
Kaufman, S. J., and Gross, K. W. (1974). *Biochim. Biophys. Acta* **353**, 133–145.
Kennedy, D. S., Bester, A. J., and Heywood, S. M. (1974). *Biochem. Biophys. Res. Commun.* **61**, 415–423.
Kidokoro, Y. (1975a). *J. Physiol. (London)* **244**, 129–143.
Kidokoro, Y. (1975b). *J. Physiol. (London)* **244**, 145–159.
Kidokoro, Y., and Heinemann, S. (1974). *Nature (London)* **252**, 593–594.
Konigsberg, I. R. (1961). *Proc. Natl. Acad. Sci. U.S.A.* **47**, 1868–1872.
Kwan, S. W., and Brawerman, G. (1972). *Proc. Natl. Acad. Sci. U.S.A.* **69**, 3247–3250.
Lindstrom, J., Singer, S. J., and Lennox, E. S. (1973). *J. Membr. Biol.* **11**, 217–226.
Lodish, H. (1974). *Nature (London)* **251**, 385–388.
Lømo, F., and Westgaard, R. H. (1975). *J. Physiol. (London)* **252**, 603–626.
Loomis, W. F., Jr., Wahrmann, J. P., and Luzzati, D. (1973). *Proc. Natl. Acad. Sci. U.S.A.* **70**, 425–429.
Low, R. B., and Rich, A. (1973). *Biochemistry* **12**, 4555–4559.
Low, R. B., Vournakis, J. N., and Rich, A. (1971). *Biochemistry* **10**, 1813–1818.
Luzzati, D. (1974). *Biochimie* **56**, 1567–1569.
Luzzati, D., and Drugeon, G. (1972). *Biochimie* **54**, 1157–1167.
Luzzati, D., and Loomis, W. F. (1972). *In* "Cell Differentiation" (R. Harris, P. Allin, and D. Viza, eds.), pp. 335–384. Munksgaard, Copenhagen.

Luzzati, D., Loomis, W. F., Drugeon, G., and Wahrmann, J. P. (1973). *In* "Normal and Pathological Protein Synthesis in Higher Organisms" (G. Schapira *et al.*, eds.), pp. 475–485. INSERM, Paris.
Marchok, A. C., and Wolff, J. M. (1968). *Biochim. Biophys. Acta* **155**, 378–393.
Merlie, J. P., Sobel, A., Changeux, J. P., and Gros, F. (1975). *Proc. Natl. Acad. Sci. U.S.A.* **72**, 4028–4032.
Merlie, J. P., Changeux, J. P., and Gros, F. (1976). *Nature (London)* **264**, 74–76.
Merlie, J. P., Changeux, J. P., and Gros, F. (1977). Submitted for Publication.
Milcarek, C., Price, R., and Penman, S. (1974). *Cell* **3**, 1–10.
Miledi, R. (1960). *J. Physiol. (London)* **154**, 190–205.
Miledi, R., and Potter, L. T. (1971). *Nature (London)* **233**, 599–603.
Molinaro, M., Zani, B., Martinozzi, M., and Monesi, V. (1974). *Exp. Cell Res.* **88**, 402–405.
Mondal, H., Sutton, A., Chen, V. J., and Sarkar, S. (1974). *Biochem. Biophys. Res. Commun.* **56**, 988–996.
Morris, G. E., Buzash, E., Rourke, A., Tepperman, K., Thompson, W., and Heywood, S. M. (1973). *Cold Spring Harbor Symp. Quant. Biol.* **37**, 535–541.
Murphy, L., and Attardi, G. (1973). *Proc. Natl. Acad. Sci. U.S.A.* **70**, 115–119.
Nelson, P., Christian, C., and Nirenberg, M. (1976). *Proc. Natl. Acad. Sci. U.S.A.* **73**, 123–127.
Nurse, C. A., and O'Lague, P. H. (1975). *Proc. Natl. Acad. Sci. U.S.A.* **72**, 1955–1959.
O'Farrell, P. H. (1975). *J. Biol. Chem.* **250**, 4007–4021.
Palacios, R., Palmiter, R. D., and Schimke, R. T. (1972). *J. Biol. Chem.* **247**, 2316–2321.
Paterson, B., and Prives, J. (1973). *J. Cell Biol.* **59**, 241–245.
Paterson, B., and Strohman, R. C. (1972). *Dev. Biol.* **29**, 113–138.
Paterson, B., Roberts, B. E., and Yaffé, D. (1974). *Proc. Natl. Acad. Sci. U.S.A.* **71**, 4467–4471.
Patrick, J., Heinemann, S. F., Lindstrom, J., Schubert, D., and Steinbach, J. H. (1972). *Proc. Natl. Acad. Sci. U.S.A.* **69**, 2762–2766.
Pollard, T. D., and Weihing, R. R. (1974). *Crit. Rev. Biochem.* **2**, 1–65.
Porter, C. W., Barnard, E. D., and Chin, T. H. (1973). *J. Membr. Biol.* **14**, 383–402.
Przybyla, A., and Strohman, R. C. (1974). *Proc. Natl. Acad. Sci. U.S.A.* **71**, 662–666.
Raymondjean, M., Bogdanousky, D., Bachner, L., Kneip, B., and Shapira, G. (1977). *FEBS Lett.* **76**, 311–315.
Rash, J. E., and Fambrough, D. (1973). *Dev. Biol.* **30**, 166–186.
Reiter, M. J., Cowburn, D. A., Prives, J. M., and Karlin, A. (1972). *Proc. Natl. Acad. Sci. U.S.A.* **69**, 1168–1172.
Richter, C., and Yaffé, D. (1970). *Dev. Biol.* **23**, 1–22.
Ringertz, N. R., Carlsson, S. A., and Savage, R. E. (1972). *Adv. Biosci.*
Ritchie, A., and Fambrough, D. (1975). *J. Gen. Physiol.* **66**, 327–355.
Rosbash, M., and Ford, P. J. (1974). *J. Mol. Biol.* **85**, 87–103.
Rourke, A. W., and Heywood, S. M. (1972). *Biochemistry* **11**, 2061–2066.
Salden, M., and Bloemendal, H. (1976). *Biochem. Biophys. Res. Commun.* **68**, 157–161.
Salden, M., Bisseling, T., Berns, A., and Bloemendal, H. (1975). *Biochem. Biophys. Res. Commun.* **65**, 317–322.
Sarkar, S., and Cooke, P. H. (1970). *Biochem. Biophys. Res. Commun.* **41**, 918–925.
Sarkar, S., Mukherjee, S. P., Sutton, A., Mondal, H., and Chen, V. (1973). *Prep. Biochem.* **3**, 583–598.
Schimke, R. T. (1974). *Biochem., Ser. One* **9**, 183–221.
Schreier, M. H., and Staehelin, T. (1973a). *J. Mol. Biol.* **73**, 329–349.
Schreier, M. H., and Staehelin, T. (1973b). *Nature (London), New Biol.* **242**, 35–38.

Schudt, C., Gaertner, U., Pölken, G., and Pette, G. (1975). *Eur. J. Biochem.* **60**, 579–586.
Shainberg, A., Yagil, G., and Yaffé, D. (1971). *Dev. Biol.* **25**, 1–29.
Shimada, Y., Fischman, D. A., and Moscona, A. A. (1969). *Proc. Natl. Acad. Sci. U.S.A.* **62**, 715–721.
Singer, R. H., and Penman, S. (1972). *Nature (London)* **240**, 100–102.
Somers, D. G., Pearson, M. L., and Ingles, C. J. (1975a). *J. Biol. Chem.* **250**, 4825–4831.
Somers, D. G., Pearson, M. L., and Ingles, C. J. (1975b). *Nature (London)* **253**, 372–374.
Spirin, A. S. (1969). *Eur. J. Biochem.* **10**, 20–35.
Sreter, F. A., Balint, M., and Gergely, J. (1975). *Dev. Biol.* **46**, 317–325.
Steinbach, J. H., Harris, A. J., Patrick, J., Schubert, D., and Heinemann, S. (1973). *J. Gen. Physiol.* **62**, 255–270.
Sytkowski, A. J., Vogel, Z., and Niremberg, M. W. (1973). *Proc. Natl. Acad. Sci. U.S.A.* **70**, 270–274.
Thompson, W. C., Buzash, E. A., and Heywood, S. M. (1973). *Biochemistry* **12**, 4559–4565.
Tomkins, G. M., Gelehrter, T. D., Granner, D., Martin, D., Jr., Samuels, H. H., and Thompson, E. B. (1969). *Science* **166**, 1474–1480.
Turner, D. C., Maier, V., and Eppenberger, H. M. (1974). *Dev. Biol.* **37**, 63–89.
Vogel, Z., Sytkowski, A. J., and Niremberg, M. W. (1972). *Proc. Natl. Acad. Sci. U.S.A.* **69**, 3180–3184.
Wahrmann, J. P., Gros, F., and Luzzati, D. (1973). *Biochimie* **55**, 457–463.
Whalen, R. G., and Gros, F. (1977a). *Biochim. Biophys. Acta* **475**, 393–402.
Whalen, R. G., and Gros, F. (1977b). In preparation.
Whalen, R. G., Butler-Browne, G. S., and Gros, F. (1976a). *Proc. Natl. Acad. Sci. U.S.A.* **73**, 2018–2022.
Whalen, R. G., Buckingham, M. E., and Gros, F. (1976b). *Prog. Nuc. Acid Res. Mol. Biol.* **19**, 485–489.
Whalen, R. G., Buckingham, M. E., Goto, S., Merlie, J. P., and Gros, F. (1977). *Proc. Muscular Dystrophy Assn., 5th Int. Sci. Conf.*, in press.
Williamson, R. (1973). *FEBS Lett.* **37**, 1–6.
Wilson, B. W., and Walker, C. R. (1974). *Proc. Natl. Acad. Sci. U.S.A.* **71**, 3194–3198.
Wilson, B. W., Nieberg, P. S., Walker, C. R., Linkhart, T. A., and Fry, D. W. (1973). *Dev. Biol.* **33**, 285–299.
Yaffé, D. (1968). *Proc. Natl. Acad. Sci. U.S.A.* **61**, 477–483.
Yaffé, D. (1969). *Curr. Top. Dev. Biol.* **4**, 37–77.
Yaffé, D., and Dym, H. (1973). *Cold Spring Harbor Symp. Quant. Biol.* **37**, 543–547.
Yaffé, D., Yablonka, Z., Kessler, G., and Dym, H. (1975). *Proc. 10th FEBS Meet.*, **38**, 313–323.
Young, R. B., Goll, D. E., and Strohmer, M. H. (1975). *Dev. Biol.* **47**, 123–135.
Zalin, R. J., and Montague, W. (1974). *Cell* **2**, 103–108.

CHAPTER 4

ORIGIN AND ESTABLISHMENT OF EMBRYONIC POLAR AXES IN AMPHIBIAN DEVELOPMENT

P. D. Nieuwkoop

HUBRECHT LABORATORY,
UTRECHT, THE NETHERLANDS

I. Introduction

The development of a spherical egg is essentially a four-dimensional process, with time as the fourth dimension. A four-dimensional process, however, is difficult to visualize by the human mind, which has a tendency to single out certain phenomena and to follow them in a two-dimensional "projection," e.g., as a quantitative change in a certain variable with time, or as the relation between two variables considered as not being mutually dependent. The development of the spherical egg is thus reduced to a number of "perpendicular" projections. It must nevertheless be realized that a resynthesis of these projections is required for complete understanding of the process of development. The question therefore arises how far the customary distinction between perpendicular embryonic axes is due merely to this tendency toward reducing the whole to two-dimensional projections, or whether, in fact, it finds its basis in essential features of the developing system. As we shall see below, in vertebrate development the various axes are established during different phases of development; this pleads strongly in favor of the second alternative.

In a spherical body that becomes anisotropic, perpendicular axes can be distinguished, the first two of which are determinative, the third following automatically from these. The term "axis" does not imply any definite polarity, and, since embryonic development is typically polarized, I will use the terms "polarity" and "polar axis," instead of just "axis"; polarity and polar axis are vectorial entities, whereas axis is only a geometrical entity.

The mesodermal mantle, which is the most essential feature of vertebrate development, is characterized by cephalocaudal polarity on the one hand, and by a combination of dorsoventral and mediolateral polarity on the other. We speak either of its dorsoventral or its mediolateral differentiation, depending on whether the projection is on a sagittal or a frontal plane, the two projections showing essentially the same features.

In the growing oocyte or the mature egg, cephalocaudal and dorsoventral polarities cannot yet be distinguished. Usually only a single primary, animal–vegetative polarity is evident from the very beginning. The primary dorsoventral polarization of the egg often becomes manifest only shortly before cleavage. The relationships between these primary polarities of the unicellular egg and the ultimate polar axes of the developing embryo will be elucidated in this chapter, and the origin and establishment of the various polarities will be discussed.

II. Morphological and Experimental Evidence for the Distinction of Two Primary Polar Axes in the Amphibian Egg prior to the Onset of Cleavage

A. Animal–Vegetative Polarity; Morphological Evidence

All amphibian eggs exhibit a distinct animal–vegetative polarity. In the immature oocyte this is expressed in the eccentric positions of the germinal vesicle (toward the animal pole) and the yolk mass (toward the vegetative pole). In the maturing oocyte the animal pole is, by definition, represented by the position of the maturation spindle, and slightly later by that of the first polar body, the vegetative pole being situated in the outer surface of the egg in the center of the vegetative yolk mass. In some eggs the vegetative pole is marked by a separate pigment spot, as in the *Xenopus* egg. Internally the animal–vegetative polarity is expressed *inter alia* in the spatial distribution of the yolk platelets. Dalcq and Pasteels' (1937, 1938) notion of a continuous animal–vegetative gradient in yolk distribution is certainly not correct, for the distribution is clearly discontinuous (however, also see Pasteels, 1948). The animal portion of the egg contains a relatively large amount of small to medium-sized yolk platelets embedded in rather abundant cytoplasm. On the other hand, the vegetative portion of the egg is composed of a very high quantity of mainly large yolk platelets, the amount of cytoplasm present being scanty. There actually is an intermediate zone of varying width between the two major components of the egg—the so-called transitional zone—in which the yolk platelets are of various sizes. This zone, however, is not essentially different from the animal component, so that it suffices to distinguish two different moieties or distinct components, animal and vegetative. Finally, in some eggs, such as those of *Rana fusca* (see Ancel and Vintemberger, 1948), a separate central cytoplasm—the so-called brown yolk—can be distinguished by its different pigmentation. Like the material of the transitional zone, it belongs to the animal moiety of the egg, later becoming incorporated into the animal cap, not into the vegetative yolk mass. Among the various amphibian species the proportion between the animal and vegetative moieties in the mature egg may vary considerably; in small eggs that are relatively poor in yolk, e.g., those of *Xenopus,* the vegetative yolk occupies a markedly smaller part of the egg volume than in large and yolky eggs, e.g., those of *Megalobatrachus* or *Salamandra*.

In many amphibian eggs the animal moiety is more or less strongly pigmented, in contrast to the vegetative moiety, which is nearly unpigmented. This embryonic pigment is located mainly in the outer, cortical layer of the egg, but pigment granules are also scattered in the internal cytoplasm. In the animal moiety of the egg, the cortical layer, which functions as a physiological unit, comprises the plasmalemma, a layer of dense cytoplasm with microfibrils and pigment granules, and a layer of cytoplasm with small yolk platelets (the latter varying in thickness according to location and stage of development). In the vegetative moiety the cortical layer is much thinner; moreover, its actual composition is insufficiently known.

B. Animal-Vegetative Polarity; Experimental Evidence

Experiments involving the isolation of animal and vegetative portions of early blastulae (Harrison stage 7) of *Ambystoma mexicanum* show that the amphibian egg essentially consists of only two moieties, which have different developmental capacities. The animal moiety develops cilia (Grunz, 1973) as a first step toward ectodermal differentiation, whereas the vegetative moiety tends to develop in an endodermal direction. However, the development of isolates soon stops and disintegration sets in (Nieuwkoop, 1969a). In a more advanced blastula (stage 8 and older) a separate equatorial region can be distinguished, which upon isolation exhibits extensive mesodermal and endodermal, and sometimes also ectoneurodermal differentiation tendencies. Experiments involving recombination of animal cap and vegetative yolk material (Nieuwkoop, 1969a) demonstrate that mesodermal differentiation tendencies are actually induced in the animal moiety by an inductive influence emanating from the vegetative moiety during blastulation. This holds for both urodeles and anurans; in the latter, Sudarwati and Nieuwkoop (1971) could likewise demonstrate that the entire mesodermal marginal zone develops epigenetically.

These observations are supported by Nakamura and Matsuzawa's (1967) isolation experiments involving individual blastomeres or small groups of blastomeres. Nakamura and Takasaki (1970) suggest that mesodermal differentiation already sets in at stage 6 (Harrison). Isolation experiments at that stage are difficult to interpret, however, because of the still incomplete segregation of the two moieties into separate blastomeres, so that equatorial blastomeres may contain animal as well as vegetative material. Isolation of such blastomeres will lead to mesodermal differentiation due to a subsequent inductive interaction between the two components.

The effects have been tested of vegetalizing agents, such as LiCl (Nieuwkoop, 1970), and of animalizing agents, such as $ZnCl_2$ and $NaJC_2O_4$ (P. D. Nieuwkoop, unpublished), upon recombinates of animal and vegetative material of blastulae of *Ambystoma mexicanum*. It became clear that the animal, ectodermal moiety of the blastula may be partially or completely transformed into mesodermal and endodermal structures (various degrees of vegetalization, according to Ogi, 1961), whereas the differentiation of the vegetative moiety apparently cannot be affected. In lower concentrations animalizing agents have no effect at all on this moiety, whereas at higher concentrations they are simply toxic (P. D. Nieuwkoop, unpublished observations). It must therefore be concluded that the vegetative moiety of the amphibian blastula is already irrevocably determined for endodermal development (first steps only), whereas the animal moiety is still totipotent at the blastula stage.

The experimental evidence therefore clearly corroborates the descriptive observations: the amphibian egg initially consists of only two different moieties, the interaction of which leads to the formation of the third, mesodermal component. Recombination experiments of ventral vegetative yolk material of the urodele blastula with different regions of the animal moiety have shown that within the latter there exists an animal–vegetative gradient in mesodermal competence (Sutasurya and Nieuwkoop, 1974).

C. Dorsoventral Polarity; Morphological and Experimental Evidence

In the unfertilized egg of several amphibian species, e.g., that of *Rana fusca* (see Ancel and Vintemberger, 1948), the pigment cap takes up a radially symmetrical position with respect to the animal–vegetative polar axis (see Fig. 1a). In other amphibian eggs, e.g. that of *Rana esculenta* (see Pasteels, 1937), and in some batches of *Xenopus laevis* eggs (personal observations) the pigment cap may be situated eccentrically with respect to the animal–vegetative polar axis, possibly foreshadowing later bilateral symmetry. Wittek (1952), moreover, has called attention to the fact that oocytes of *Rana fusca* may show a clear bilateral symmetry (see also Devillers, 1961), whereas according to

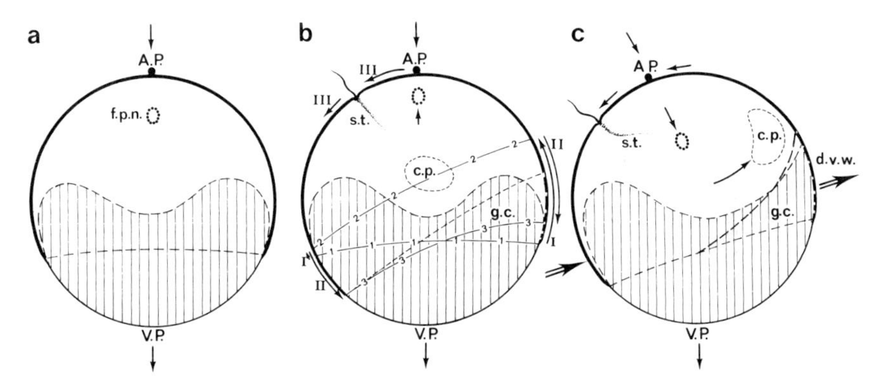

Fig. 1. Diagrammatic representation of events leading to gray crescent formation in the amphibian (here anuran) egg. (a) Initial configuration; radially symmetrical position of pigment cap around animal pole (A.P.), and vegetative yolk mass (hatched) with vegetative pole (V.P.); f.p.n. = female pronucleus. (b) Contraction (I) and subsequent relaxation (II) of pigment cap around point of sperm entrance; displacement of edge of pigment cap from initial position (1) to contracted position (2) and subsequent reexpanded position (3), leading to first step in dorsoventral polarization; internal appearance of area of clear cytoplasm (c.p.) in center of egg. Subsequent ventral displacement of A.P. and of sperm tract (s.t.) (III) and appearance of dorsal gray crescent (g.c.). (c) Dorsoventral polarization of egg; definitive gray crescent formation, accompanied by pulling out of yolk mass into "dorsal vitelline wall" (d.v.w.) and displacement of clear cytoplasm toward dorsal side.

Ancel and Vintemberger (1948) bilateral symmetry becomes manifest in *Rana fusca* only with the appearance of the gray crescent. According to Ancel and Vintemberger the ultimate formation of the gray crescent is due to a directive displacement of the pigment cap with respect to the vegetative yolk mass, that is, with respect to the animal–vegetative polar axis. Gray crescent formation occurs also in the eggs of *Rana esculenta,* but there, according to Pasteels (1937), it shows a distinct relation to the original eccentricity of the pigment cap. The latter is a rather inconstant phenomenon, however, and may vary considerably in extent among eggs of the same species and even more strongly among eggs of different species. We shall return to this phenomenon later (see pp. 126 and 127). Summarizing, gray crescent formation may be taken as the externally visible manifestation of the dorsoventral polarization of the egg. It runs more or less perpendicular to the animal–vegetative polarity of the egg (see further p. 125 and Fig. 1c).

Experiments of Ancel and Vintemberger (1948) have shown that the dorsoventral polarization of the anuran egg becomes irrevocably fixed with the appearance of the gray crescent. They could demonstrate that in the egg of *Rana fusca* the penetration of the sperm normally determines the future dorsoventral polarity, the gray crescent appearing on the side opposite to the sperm entrance point, at the boundary of the animal and vegetative moieties of the egg. Gravitational rotation of the egg within the egg membranes through more than 135° may, however, overrule the symmetrization by the sperm, whereas eggs that are artificially activated (no sperm entry) while oriented with the animal pole upward (no rotation of the egg under the influence of gravity) nevertheless always show dorsoventral polarization. This may be due either to an already existing deviation from radial symmetry (see pp. 126 and 127) or to an intrinsic tendency toward the development of bilateral symmetry. The latter may result from an unstable equilibrium in tangential contractile forces within the cortical layer of the egg in particular in the animal moiety (see p. 126 and Fig. 2a). Wounds made in the cortical layer of the fertilized egg initially widen, showing the existence of tangential tensions in the cortical layer (Holtfreter, 1943). The wounds afterward close owing to a secondary wound-closing reaction (Bluemink, 1972). Shortly after sperm entry or artificial activation, the entire pigmented cap of the egg contracts (contraction of activation) and gradually expands again, never returning to its original position, however (Rzehak, 1972) (see Fig. 1b). These observations clearly show that gray crescent formation is an active process taking place in the cortical layer of the egg (see also Løvtrup, 1958).

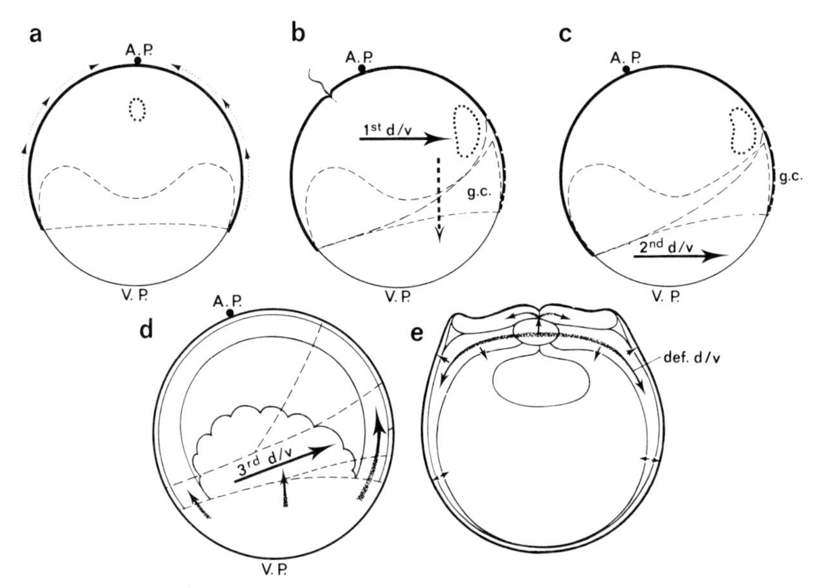

FIG. 2. Successive phases in the dorsoventral (d/v) polarization of the amphibian egg and embryo. A. P., animal pole; V.P., vegetative pole. (a) Initial radially symmetrical configuration of the egg, with balanced tangential contractile forces in cortical layer (· · · · · · >). (b) Primary d/v polarization of the animal moiety of the egg by means of dorsal displacement of clear inner cytoplasm and (subsequent) gray crescent formation (g.c.) and probable transfer to vegetative moiety (----- >). (c) Secondary d/v polarization of the vegetative moiety. (d) Transfer of d/v polarization from vegetable yolk mass to the presumptive mesoderm induced in the animal moiety (tertiary d/v polarization). (e) Definitive d/v polarization of the entire embryo by induction by the mesodermal mantle of d/v polarization in overlying ectoneurodermal and underlying endodermal layers of neurula.

It should be realized, however, that dorsoventral polarization is not restricted to a displacement of the pigmented cortical layer with respect to the vegetative yolk mass. Extensive interior material displacements occur within the animal moiety of the egg and even affect the vegetative yolk. The displacement of the original sperm track during gray crescent formation already shows that also cytoplasmic material deeper than the cortical layer is affected (Ancel and Vintemberger, 1948). Recent observations made by Klag and Ubbels (1975) in *Discoglossus pictus* and by Hengst and Ubbels (1977) in *Xenopus laevis* demonstrate that around the time of gray crescent formation an area of clear cytoplasm (yolk-free or poor in yolk) appears in the center of the egg, which subsequently becomes displaced toward the future dorsal side (see Fig. 1, b and c). Pasteels (1951, 1964), moreover, has described the formation of a dorsal "vitelline wall" in the gray crescent region.

All these observations indicate that cytoplasmic displacements involve the entire animal moiety of the egg, even influencing the shape and position of part of the heavy yolk, which is slightly displaced toward the future dorsal side. The dorsoventral polarization of the animal moiety of the egg may be called the *primary dorsoventral polarization* of the egg (see Fig. 2b). Further analysis is required to obtain a true insight into the complex cytoplasmic movements and their possible relationship to dorsoventral polarization.

III. The Formation of the Definitive Polar Axes of the Embryo

A. Dorsoventral Polarity

Experiments in which animal and vegetative material of *Ambystoma mexicanum* blastulae was recombined upon rotation through various angles (Nieuwkoop, 1969b) showed that at the blastula stage the dorsoventral polarity no longer resides in the animal moiety, since no polarizing influence of the gray crescent region could be demonstrated, but now resides in the vegetative yolk material. This polarization of the vegetative yolk mass has the character not so much of a continuous dorsoventral gradient as of a dorsal center of dominance (Boterenbrood and Nieuwkoop, 1973). The reinterpretation of Pasteels' (1951) forced position *(Umkehr)* experiments by Nieuwkoop (1973, pp. 27–28) suggests that the yolk mass may already be polarized in the symmetrized, uncleaved egg. This would mean that the polarization is transferred from the animal to the vegetative moiety at a very early stage. The polarization of the endodermal yolk mass may be called the *secondary dorsoventral polarization* of the egg (see Fig. 2c).

The recombination experiments of animal and vegetative material already mentioned (Nieuwkoop, 1969a,b; Sudarwati and Nieuwkopp, 1971; Nieuwkoop and Ubbels, 1972; Boterenbrood and Nieuwkoop, 1973; review by Nieuwkoop, 1973) have shown, moreover, that the entire mesoderm, together with the pharyngeal endoderm, is induced in the animal moiety of the blastula by an inductive influence emanating from the vegetative yolk mass, in particular from its dorsal portion. In the blastula mesoderm induction is restricted to the periphery, where the animal and vegetative moieties are in direct contact with each other. During this induction process the dorsoventral polarity of the egg is transferred back, so to speak, from the vegetative yolk mass to the animal, ectodermal moiety of the egg, i.e., to the presumptive endomesodermal marginal zone. The resulting dorsoventral polarity of the mesoderm may, therefore, be called the *tertiary dorsoventral polarization* of the developing embryo (see Fig. 2d). It is the polarization of the mesoderm that is responsible for the *ultimate dorsoventral organization* of the embryo, since the regional organization of both the ectoneuroderm and the endoderm depends upon that of the mesodermal mantle (see Fig. 2e) (Saxén and Toivonen, 1962; Nieuwkoop, 1966; Balinsky, 1948; Okada, 1960).

B. Mediolateral Polarity

As already mentioned, the dorsoventral and mediolateral polarities of the embryo are very closely related, since before the formation of the coelomic cavity both polarities refer only to the regional differentiation of the mesodermal mantle.

Slight differences in mesoderm-inducing capacity between the lateral portions of the yolk mass seem to be responsible for the characteristic left-right asymmetry of the definitive embryo (von Kraft, 1971; Boterenbrood and Nieuwkoop, 1973).

C. Craniocaudal Polarity

Only during the process of mesoderm induction does the craniocaudal polar axis of the embryo become manifest, viz., in the regional craniocaudal organization of the induced mesoderm. The induced meso- and endoderm bordering on the original yolk mass represents the presumptive most anterior region of the future endomesoderm, while the mesoderm formed at increasing distances away from the yolk mass corresponds to the future more posterior mesoderm (see Nieuwkoop, 1973). Within the animal moiety the mesoderm-inducing action apparently spreads with decrement from the vegetative yolk mass in the direction of the animal pole. This decline parallels the decrease in mesodermal competence within the animal moiety, from the equator toward the animal pole [Sutasurya and Nieuwkoop, 1974; cf. Spemann, 1936, p. 59, and 1962, p. 92, concept of double assurance *(doppelter Sicherheit)*].

The primary regional segregation of the marginal zone into areas with different differentiation tendencies (see Holtfreter-Ban, 1965) must be based upon quantitative differences in the inductive action exerted by the vegetative yolk mass (see Boterenbrood and Nieuwkoop, 1973; review by Nieuwkoop, 1973). This inductive influence, which may also be called a vegetalizing influence, apparently reaches the level needed for endodermal differentiation only in the direct vicinity of the dorsal yolk mass. On the dorsal side the endodermal differentiation

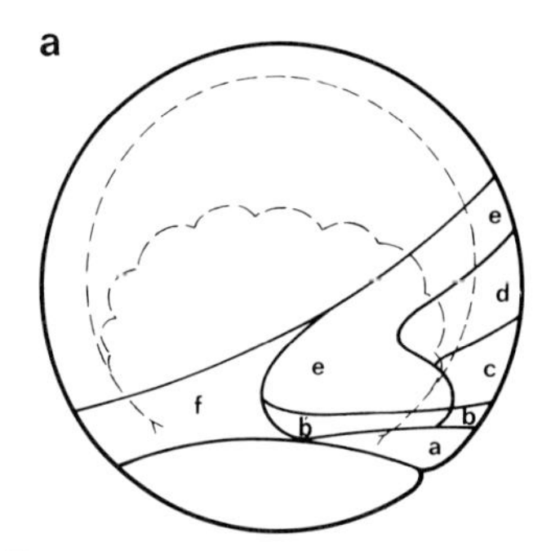

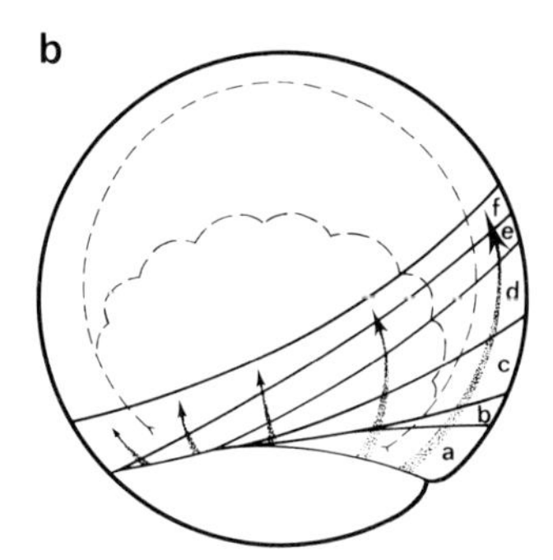

FIG. 3. (a) Anlage map of presumptive organ rudiments in the marginal zone of the amphibian (here urodelan) early gastrula according to Vogt (1929), Nakamura (1942), and Pasteels (1942, 1949). a, pharynx endoderm; b, prechordal mesoderm; b′, parachordal mesoderm, c, anterior notochord; d, posterior notochord; e, somites of trunk and tail; f, lateroventral mesoderm. (b) Various postulated threshold values for regional mesodermal differentiation within the presumptive marginal zone due to different quantitative inductive action by dorsal, lateral, and ventral yolk mass. Labels a–f as in diagram (a).

tendencies are followed consecutively by differentiation tendencies for notochord, somites, and tail mesoderm (see Fig. 3a). A similar but less pronounced anteroposterior sequence of differentiation tendencies is found in the lateral and ventral marginal zone. It must be emphasized, however, that this primary pattern in the unvaginated marginal zone, which also emerges from computer simulation experiments (see Fig. 3b) (C. J. Wier, unpublished data), is still labile and only partially corresponds to the ultimate pattern in the mesoderm as represented in the anlage map (Vogt, 1929; Nakamura, 1942; Pasteels, 1942, 1949). This is probably mainly due to (1) additional, enhancing influences for notochord and somite differentiation exerted during gastrulation by the invaginated anterior endomesoderm upon the still uninvaginated posterior marginal zone (T. Hama, personal communication) and (2) a reciprocal influence of the overlying neural plate upon the differentiation of the archenteron roof (Kato and Okada, 1956; Kurrat, 1974; C. J. Wier, unpublished data).

During gastrulation the position of the cephalocaudal polar axis of the presumptive mesoderm becomes reversed, the phayngeal endoderm and prechordal mesoderm which are responsible for head formation ultimately being situated anteriorly. The induction of the central nervous system by the underlying archenteron roof—particularly by the median notochordal and prechordal meso- and endoderm anlagen—gives the embryo its *final craniocaudal organization* (Nieuwkoop *et al.*, 1952, Nieuwkoop, 1966; Saxén and Toivonen, 1962).

IV. Relationships between the Primary Polar Axes of the Uncleaved Egg and the Definitive Polar Axes of the Embryo

A. Animal–Vegetative versus Craniocaudal Polarity

The craniocaudal polarity of the embryo has often been erroneously identified with the animal–vegetative polarity of the uncleaved egg. It is true that in the urodele embryo the anterior extremity of the cephalocaudal polar axis coincides with the original animal pole of the egg (see Fig. 4), but this is only a coincidence. In contrast, in the anurans the original animal pole is found on the cranioventral side of the embryo in the vicinity of the heart anlage (see Fig. 4). The relationship between the animal-vegetative polarity of the uncleaved egg and the cephalocaudal polarity of the embryo is therefore only a *derivative* one. The animal–vegetative polarity of the egg is oriented perpendicular to the boundary between the animal and vegetative moieties of the egg. The craniocaudal polarity of the marginal zone of the blastula starts from the same boundary, but is initially oriented in the opposite direction (see Fig. 4a). Only after gastrulation, when the position of the cephalocaudal polar axis of the mesoderm has been reversed, do the two polar axes run more or less parallel. The craniocaudal polarity of the central nervous system, in which the craniocaudal organization of the embryo is expressed most clearly, coincides with the craniocaudal polarity of the invaginated mesoderm, under the influence of which it has developed (see Fig. 4b).

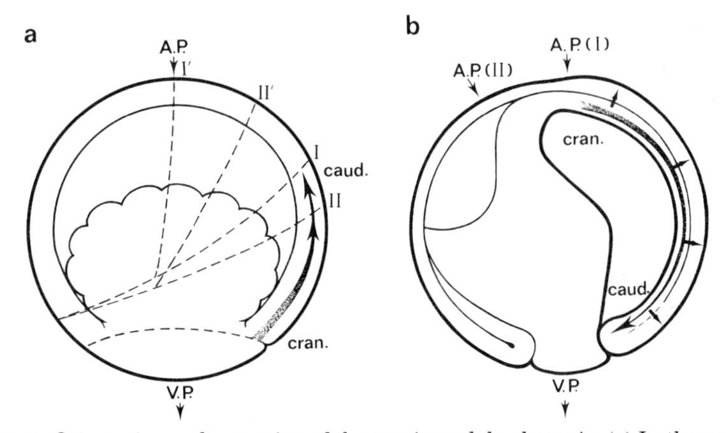

Fig. 4. Orientation and extension of the craniocaudal polar axis. (a) In the marginal zone of the urodelan (I) and anuran (II) early gastrula; I′ and II′: anterior border of presumptive neural area (after Vogt, 1929). (b) in the invaginated archenteron roof; ultimate position of the original animal pole (A.P.) and of the animal-vegetative polar axis in the two amphibian groups (I and II). V.P., vegetative pole.

B. Primary versus Definitive Dorsoventral Polarity

As we have seen, the initial dorsoventral polarization of the egg established during gray crescent formation is transferred through a still unknown, stepwise process from the animal moiety of the egg *(primary dorsoventral polarization)* to the vegetative yolk mass *(secondary dorsoventral polarization)*, and back again to the animal moiety in the form of the dorsoventral polarization of the induced mesoderm *(tertiary dorsoventral polarization)*, upon which the ultimate dorsoventral organization of the embryo depends *(definitive dorsoventral polarization)* (see Fig. 2).

C. Primary versus Definitive Mediolateral Polarity

The third, i.e., mediolateral, polar axis of the embryo is intimately bound up with the dorsoventral differentiation of the mesodermal mantle, and its establishment follows the same stepwise process; its left–right asymmetry is based upon slight differences in the induced left and right mesoderm.

V. Discussion

A. General Motivation

The difference in origin and development between the dorsoventral (and mediolateral) polarity on the one hand and the craniocaudal polarity on the other, strongly suggests that the distinction between them is not only due to the tendency of the human mind to reduce a four-dimensional process to a number of two-dimensional "projections," but is also based upon essential features of the developing system itself, features which are characteristic for the development of all vertebrates.

B. Origin of Primary Dorsoventral Polarization

As already mentioned, the origin of the primary dorsoventral polarization of the egg may be based upon a basically unstable equilibrium in the tangential forces acting in the cortical layer of the egg, particularly in the animal moiety; the vegetative moiety would act as a more massive "scaffolding," and thus as a "point of reference" for these forces. The fact that several eggs exhibit deviations from radial symmetry prior to fertilization—varying in extent in different species, in different batches, and also in individual eggs of one and the same batch—may be due to the equilibrium disturbing influence of gravity acting differentially upon the arbitrarily oriented oocytes in the wall of the sacklike ovary. Whereas fertilized eggs are more fluid (less viscous), so that the yolk can slide or sink down as a whole or in portions through the lighter animal cytoplasm when the egg is held in a forced position (Pasteels, 1951); in the much more viscous oocytes gravity may, however, have acted during a long lapse of time, leading nevertheless to a shift of the heavy yolk with respect to the pigmented cap. To test this hypothesis a careful comparison ought to be made of the positions of individual oocytes inside the ovary with the deviations from radial symmetry of the same oocytes after maturation.

C. Origin of Animal–Vegetative Polarity

The origin of the animal–vegetative polarity seems to be more mysterious. It certainly is not due to gravity (*at random* orientation of oocytes in the ovary) or to the direction from which the oocyte received its blood supply (Brøndsted and Meijer, 1950; Van Gansen and Weber, 1972). Although the animal-vegetative polarity is less evident at earlier stages of oogenesis, the eccentric position of the nucleus, the position of the so-called yolk nucleus of Balbiani, etc. indicate that a polarized state exists from the very beginning of oocyte formation (see also Van Gansen and Weber, 1972). When we realize that the primordial germ cells also show an anisotropic configuration of nucleus and cytoplasm—the germ plasm is situated unilaterally against the nucleus, while the nucleus is seldom spherical, but often bilobed—it may be suggested that the basic animal–vegetative polarity could be transferred from one generation to the next by cytoplasmic continuity through the germ line. In the anurans a continuity of the germinal cytoplasm has been demonstrated (Bounoure, 1939; Whitington and Dixon, 1975), and here it may act as the primary polarity-determining factor. This does not hold in the same way for the urodeles, where the primordial germ cells are induced along with other ventrocaudal mesodermal structures in the animal moiety of the egg during blastulation (Sutasurya and Nieuwkoop, 1974). K. Ikenishi and P. D. Nieuwkoop (unpublished data) found that a germinal cytoplasm is formed in the presumptive primordial germ cells of the urodeles only at a late tailbud stage, at which determination and initial differentiation of the primordial germ cells have already taken place.

We may now ask ourselves: What actually is polarity and where does it reside in the egg and embryo?

D. What Is Polarity?

Polarity is based upon a heterogeneity within the system concerned. Heterogeneity as such, however, is insufficient for determining polarity. It must include an arrangement in a directed way. Such a polarized heterogeneity may be in the form of either a *continuous* or a *discontinuous* change* in one or more properties; in the former case, the system is a *gradient* system; in the latter, a *mosaic* system consisting of a number of qualitatively different components.† An egg may, therefore, already be called "mosaic" when it consists of at least two separate components with different developmental properties. As we have seen, this holds for the amphibian egg, where animal and vegetative moieties can be clearly distinguished. We have also seen, however, that a continuous change in properties—i.e. an animal–equatorial gradient in mesodermal competence—exists within the animal moiety; therefore, both continuous and discontinuous heterogeneities can exist in one and the same system, along one and the same polar axis. If we assume that the discontinuous heterogeneity has developed from an initially continuous one, the former representing a further step in the differentiation process, development would be characterized by the early presence of continuous heterogeneities (gradients) and their subsequent transformation into discontinuous ones (mosaics). When this process occurs in two or more dimensions it may be called "pattern formation."

E. Where Does Polarity Reside?

A cell consists of three basic components—nucleus, cytoplasm and cell membrane. Although the nucleus is a very complex structure, it does not seem to have an intrinsic polarized organization: nuclear transplantation does not influence the polarity of the cell. It seems much more likely, therefore, that the polarization of the cell depends upon that of the cytoplasm and/or the cell membrane. Centrifugation of the unicellular egg of some invertebrates may lead to stratification of the cell constituents on the basis of differences in density, but this does not disturb the egg's preexisting polarity(ies). This has led to the conclusion that polarity can be localized only in the unaffected plasmalemma. It should be kept in mind, however, that stratification of the cell constituents does not necessarily imply that the dynamic ultrastructure of the cytoplasm is also entirely disturbed.

Recent studies (among others by Bluemink, 1970) have demonstrated that certain morphogenetic functions of the egg, like contractility and dilatation, are localized in the cortical layer (see Section II, C),

* The distinction between continuous and discontinuous heterogeneities more or less coincides with that between nonstructural and structural forms of heterogeneity.

† A system may also be called polarized when it consists of individually polarized elements, e.g., the slug stage of the cellular slime molds.

which acts as a functional unit. Although the cytoplasm shows a dynamic ultrastructure consisting of microtubules, membranous structures, etc., which may undergo drastic changes, e.g., during cytokinesis, it seems at present most likely that polarizing functions of the egg, such as its animal–vegetative and dorsoventral polarities, reside primarily in the cortical layer. It must however be realized that there are intricate interrelations between the cortical layer and the rest of the cytoplasm; but these may be of a secondary nature only.

There is still another argument for the view that the primary polarities mainly reside in the cortical layer of the egg. Since they either encompass the entire egg (animal–vegetative polarity) or at least a considerable portion of it (dorsoventral polarity), polarity is essentially a global property. During cleavage, through which the unicellular egg cell is subdivided into a logarithmically increasing number of daughter cells, polarity remains a global property of the developing embryo. In other words, cleavage does not affect the polarity(ies) of the egg. Theoretically, there are two possible mechanisms for maintaining polarity during cleavage: (1) during each cleavage cycle the original polarity is accurately transferred from the mother cell to each of the two daughter cells, or (2) the polarity of the original, unicellular egg becomes a pluricellular property of the developing embryo through the intermediary of some supracellular principle. According to the first alternative the unicellular egg should become transformed into a mosaic of individually polarized cells. The regulation phenomena observed under experimental conditions plead strongly against this notion. This holds for both "regulatory" and "mosaic" types of development, since also in the latter regulatory phenomena occur under particular experimental conditions. During cleavage the originally single and global cortical layer of the egg remains functional as a continuous layer in the pluricellular embryo by means of a network of interconnecting desmosomes. The latter link the cortical layers of the individual blastomeres together into a global system, despite the fact that it is cut up into ever smaller fragments. Therefore, although during cleavage the cytoplasm of the egg becomes organized into an increasing number of individual units, each with its own nucleus, the cortical layer maintains its global character. This strongly pleads in favor of the notion that the primary polarity(ies) of the egg mainly reside(s) in the cortical layer.

This situation probably continues as long as the cortical layer of the embryo maintains its individuality and no other structures are able to take over its unifying function. This is certainly the case during early development, and possibly even well into the postneurula stages. It seems, however, that the unifying function of the cortical layer begins to weaken as soon as mesodermal differentiation becomes manifest. In the mesodermal mantle the individual cells seem to be more loosely connected with each other; where in the mesodermal marginal zone of the blastula a continuous cortical layer existed previously, it seems to break down during or after invagination and endodermal tube formation.

There is no reason to assume that the embryonic polarities function only during early development and disappear as soon as the main embryonic features are established. The phenomena of repair after wounding, and particularly of regeneration upon loss of considerable parts of the body, such as the limb, tail, or snout, strongly suggest that the polarities remain active as guiding principles throughout the entire life of the individual, irrespective of its age and ultimate size (see also Chandebois, 1975). Although it may be assumed that the polarities of the adult animal do not differ essentially from those of the developing embryo, they no longer seem to reside in any particular layer or structure, but form part of the complex structural organization of the adult organism.

VI. Summary

A distinction must be made between the *primary polarities* of the unicellular egg (the animal–vegetative and the dorsoventral polar axes) and the *definitive polarities* of the developing embryo (the craniocaudal, dorsoventral, and mediolateral polar axes).

Experimental evidence and theoretical considerations support the view that the primary polarities of the egg reside in the cortical layer, which acts as a functional unit.

In the amphibians the primary animal–vegetative polarity of the egg has the character partially of a discontinuous heterogeneity (the egg consists of an animal and a vegetative moiety) and partially of a continuous heterogeneity (gradient of mesodermal competence within the animal moiety). Whereas the vegetative moiety seems to be determined from the very beginning as endoderm, the animal moiety is still totipotent. It is suggested that the primary animal–vegetative polarity is transferred from one generation to the next by means of cytoplasmic continuity through the germ line.

The primary dorsoventral polarization of the egg may already be foreshadowed in the unfertilized egg but is normally determined by the place of entrance of the sperm or by the rotation of the egg within its membranes. It may find its physical basis in a disturbance of an unstable equilibrium of tangential contractile forces within the cortical layer, as well as in internal cytoplasmic displacements within the animal moiety of the egg. Possibly already before cleavage, this primary dorsoventral polarization becomes transferred from the animal moiety to the vegetative yolk mass, in the dorsal portion of which a center of dominance of mesoderm-inducing capacity arises. This secondary dorsoventral polarity is then transferred back to the animal moiety during mesoderm induction leading to the tertiary dorsoventral polarization.

The definitive polarities of the embryo become established only during gastrulation. The dorsoventral and mediolateral polarities arise as a result of the regional distribution of the mesoderm-inducing activity along the periphery of the vegetative yolk mass, the craniocaudal polarity as a result of the decremental extension of the mesoderm-inducing action into the animal, ectodermal moiety. The position of the latter polarity becomes reversed during gastrulation. All three polarities are finally transferred from the mesodermal mantle to the overlying ectoneurodermal as well as the underlying endodermal layer. The relationships between the definitive polar axes of the embryo and the primary polarities of the egg are discussed.

Repair and regeneration phenomena in adult animals point strongly toward the persistence of the definitive polarities throughout the life of the individual.

REFERENCES

Ancel, P., and Vintemberger, P. (1948). *Bull. Biol. Fr. Belg.* **31**, Suppl., 1.

Balinsky, B. I. (1948). *Wilhelm Roux' Arch. Entwicklungsmech. Org.* **143**, 365.

Bluemink, J. G. (1970). *J. Ultrastruct. Res.* **32**, 142.

Bluemink, J. G. (1972). *J. Ultrastruct. Res.* **41**, 95.

Boterenbrood, E. C., and Nieuwkoop, P. D. (1973). *Wilhelm Roux' Arch. Entwicklungsmech. Org.* **173**, 319.

Bounoure, L. (1939). "L'origine des cellules reproductrices et le problème de la ligne germinale." Gauthiers-Villars, Paris.

Brøndsted, H., and Meijer, H. (1950). *Vidensk. Medd. Dan. Naturhist. Foren. Kjobenhavn* **112**, 253.

Chandebois, R. (1976). "la Morphogénétique des animaux pluricellulaires Maloine, Paris."

Dalcq, A., and Pasteels, J. J. (1937). *Arch. Biol.* **48**, 669.

Dalcq, A., and Pasteels, J. J. (1938). *Bull. Acad. R. Med. Belg.* [VI] **3**, 261.

Devillers, C. (1961). *In* "Germ Cells and Development," pp. 81–118. Baselli, Paria.

Grunz, H. (1973). *Wilhelm Roux' Arch. Entwicklungsmech. Org.* **173**, 283.

Hengst, R. T. M., and Ubbels, C. A. (1977). In preparation.

Holtfreter, J. (1943). *J. Exp. Zool.* **93**, 251.

Holtfreter-Ban, H. (1965). Thesis, University of Michigan, Ann Arbor.

Kato, K., and Okada, T. S. (1956). *Mem. Coll. Sci., Univ. Kyoto, Ser. B* **23**, 1.

Klag, J., and Ubbels, G. A. (1975). *Differentiation* **3**, 15.

Kurrat, H. J. (1974). Thesis, University of Cologne.

Løvtrup, S. (1958). *J. Embryol. Exp. Morphol.* **6**, 15.
Nakamura, O. (1942). *Annot. Zool. Jpn.* **21**, 169.
Nakamura, O., and Matsuzawa, T. (1967). *Embryologia* **9**, 223.
Nakamura, O., and Takasaki, H. (1970). *Proc. Jpn. Acad.* **46**, 546.
Nieuwkoop, P. D. (1966). *Cell Differ. Morphog., Int. Lect. Course, 1965* pp. 120–143.
Nieuwkoop, P. D. (1969a). *Wilhelm Roux' Arch. Entwicklungsmech. Org.* **162**, 341.
Nieuwkoop, P. D. (1969b). *Wilhelm Roux' Arch. Entwicklungsmech. Org.* **163**, 298.
Nieuwkoop, P. D. (1970). *Wilhelm Roux' Arch. Entwicklungsmech. Org.* **166**, 105.
Nieuwkoop, P. D. (1973). *Adv. Morphog.* **10**, 1.
Nieuwkoop, P. D., and Ubbels, G. A. (1972). *Wilhelm Roux' Arch. Entwicklungsmech. Org.* **169**, 185.
Nieuwkoop, P. D. *et al.* (1952). *J. Exp. Zool.* **120**, 1.
Ogi, K. (1961). *Embryologia* **5**, 384.
Okada, T. S. (1960). *Wilhelm Roux' Arch. Entwicklungsmech. Org.* **152**, 1.
Pasteels, J. (1937). *Arch. Anat. Microsc.* **33**, 279.
Pasteels, J. (1942). *J. Exp. Zool.* **89**, 255.
Pasteels, J. (1948). *Folia Biotheor. (Leiden)* **3**, 83.
Pasteels, J. (1949). *Arch. Biol.* **60**, 235.
Pasteels, J. (1951). *Bull. Soc. Zool. Fr.* **76**, 231.
Pasteels, J. (1964). *Adv. Morphog.* **3**, 363.
Rzehak, K. (1972). *Folia Biol. (Krakow)* **20**, 409.
Saxén, L., and Toivonen, S. (1962). "Primary Embryonic Induction." Academic Press, New York.
Spemann, H. (1936). "Experimentelle Beiträge zu einer Theorie der Entwicklung." Springer-Verlag, Berlin and New York.
Spemann, H. (1962). "Embryonic Development and Induction." (transl.), 2nd ed. Hafner, New York.
Sudarwati, S., and Nieuwkoop, P. D. (1971). *Wilhelm Roux' Arch. Entwicklungsmech. Org.* **166**, 189.
Sutasurya, L. A., and Nieuwkoop, P. D. (1974). *Wilhelm Roux' Arch. Entwicklungsmech. Org.* **175**, 199.
Van Gansen, P., and Weber, A. (1972). *Arch. Biol.* **83**, 215.
Vogt, W. (1929). *Wilhelm Roux' Arch. Entwicklungsmech. Org.* **120**, 384.
von Kraft, A. (1971). *Naturwiss. Rundsch.* **24**, 142.
Whitington, P. Mac D., and Dixon, K. E. (1975). *J. Embryol. Exp. Morphol.* **33**, 57.
Wittek, M. (1952). *Arch. Biol.* **63**, 134.

CHAPTER 5

AN OLD ENIGMA: THE GRAY CRESCENT OF AMPHIBIAN EGGS

J. Brachet

LABORATOIRE DE CYTOLOGIE ET EMBRYOLOGIE MOLÉCULAIRES, DÉPARTEMENT DE BIOLOGIE MOLÉCULAIRE, UNIVERSITÉ LIBRE DE BRUXELLES, BRUSSELS, BELGIUM, AND LABORATORIO DI EMBRIOLOGIA MOLECOLARE, C.N.R. ARCO FELICE, (NAPLES), ITALY

DEDICATION

This paper is dedicated to the memory of Albert Brachet, who published an important paper on the gray crescent exactly 70 years ago. In March 1909, the frog's spawning season in Belgium was late, and thus short (there were no refrigerators at that time and egg laying could not be delayed by keeping the females in the cold). On the 19th, his wife gave birth to a boy called Jean. But Albert Brachet was too busy pricking the gray crescent of frog eggs to go to see mother and newborn baby before the following day. The boy grew up to respect Science and . . . the gray crescent.

I. General Introduction to the Problem

Visual examination of oocytes and eggs of many amphibian species immediately shows that there is a pigmented half and a white one; they correspond to the animal and the vegetal poles of the egg, respectively. A cytological or cytochemical examination of amphibian oocytes and eggs always shows that this animal–vegetal *polarity* corresponds to a *gradient* distribution of the cytoplasmic constituents:

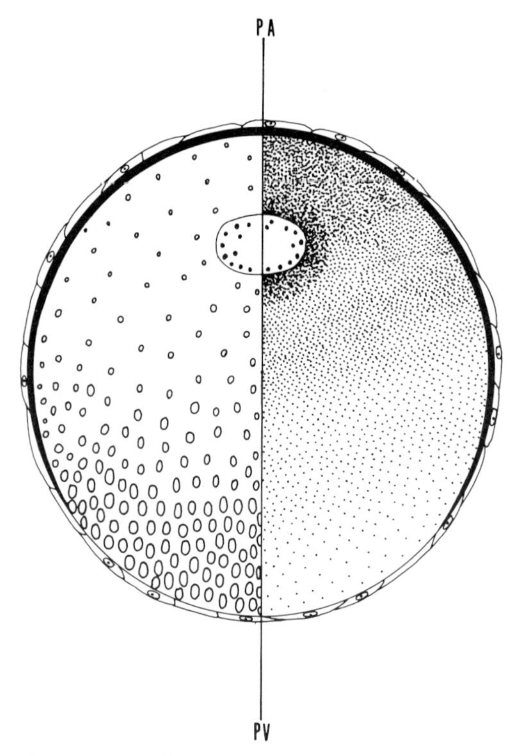

FIG. 1. Schematic representation of polarity gradients in a full-grown amphibian oocyte. Left: yolk platelets; right: ribosomes and glycogen granules. PA, animal pole; PV, vegetal pole.

yolk platelets are larger and more numerous at the vegetal than at the animal pole; conversely, ribosomes, glycogen particles, fatty inclusions (lipochondria), mitochondria, etc., are more abundant at the animal pole; the content of these organelles gradually decreases toward the vegetal pole, where it reaches a minimum (Fig. 1). This polarity gradient is extremely important for development: the cephalocaudal axis of the tadpole bears direct and causal relationships with the animal–vegetal gradient. If the polarity gradient did not exist, the embryo would have neither head or tail*; indeed, upsetting the polarity gradient, by slight centrifugation, leads to microcephaly (Pasteels, 1940, 1953).

---

* This is not quite true: the material present at the vegetal pole contains the "germ plasm"; without a polarity gradient, eggs or spermatozoa would be produced all over the body with disastrous consequences (for instance, gametogenesis in the brain!).

There is no straightforward explanation of the establishment of the polarity gradient during oogenesis: it is certainly not due to such simple factors as gravity (although the yolk platelets are heavier than the other cytoplasmic organelles) or a differential blood supply—there are no more blood capillaries at the animal than at the vegetal pole of the growing oocyte (Van Gansen and Weber, 1972). It might be that polarity results from local differences in the properties of the cell surface in the vitellogenic oocytes: we know, from the work of Wallace *et al.* (1973), that vitellogenin, the precursor for the yolk phosphoproteins, penetrates into the cells by pinocytosis; it first binds to positive sites of the microvilli, which greatly increase the cell surface of the oocyte (Brummett and Dumon, 1976); sialomucous substances, which might be part of the plasma membrane itself or be present in an extracellular surface coat (glycocalix), seem to be responsible for the binding of vitellogenin. But we do not know whether the distribution of the charged sites varies at the two poles when vitellogenesis begins. Another, perhaps more likely, possibility is that animal–vegetal polarity is genetically determined: already at the pachytene stage, the ribosomal genes accumulate into a cap, which establishes a polarity axis in the very young oocyte; it would be interesting to know whether this very early polarity coincides with the animal–vegetal polarity of the full-grown oocyte and the unfertilized egg. Figure 1 represents, in a schematic way, the little we know about the establishment of the polarity gradient during oogenesis and the changes that follow until the appearance of the gray crescent.

Maturation does not alter the situation very much: a "white spot," where the pigmented layer has lost some of its thickness, can now be seen at the animal pole (at least in species where, as in *Xenopus laevis,* the eggs are only moderately pigmented); it is due to the migration toward the animal pole of the nuclear sap from the broken-down huge germinal vesicle. The changes that follow *fertilization* are much more important and will be presented in greater detail in the next section. Briefly, the breakdown of the cortical granules results in the formation of the fertilization membrane; between the egg surface and this membrane lies the perivitelline space, which is filled with fluid. When the fertilization membrane has completely separated from the plasma membrane, the egg undergoes, under the influence of gravity, a rotation: the animal pole now lies upward and the vegetal pole downward (Fig. 2). About 2 hours later, a half-moon crescent, of intermediate pigmentation, makes its appearance on one side of the egg: it is the *gray crescent,* which is clearly visible only in a limited number of species and in favorable batches of eggs. It has been particularly

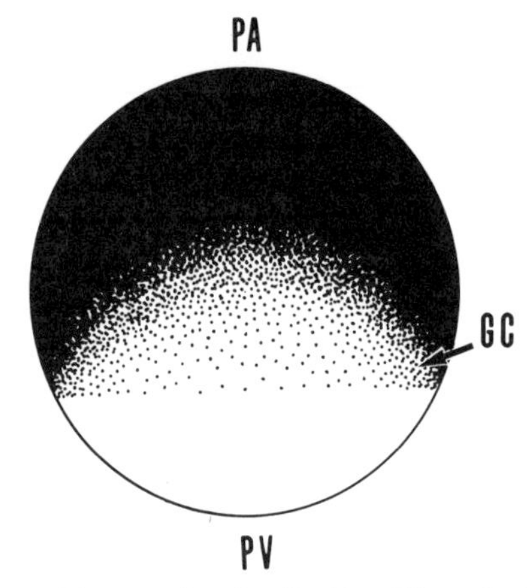

FIG. 2. Frog egg about 2 hours after fertilization. PA, animal pole; PV, vegetal pole; GC, gray crescent.

studied in the eggs of *Rana temporaria* (previously called *Rana fusca*). *Rana pipiens, Xenopus laevis, Discoglossus pictus,* and *Ambystoma mexicanum.* The gray crescent (Figs. 2 and 3) becomes particularly visible, in eggs where pigmentation is favorable, at the time of first cleavage.

The gray crescent is a *"germinal localization,"* and it is a marker of the *dorsal side* of the fertilized egg, the future embryo, and the adult. Thus, in the fertilized egg (and still better at the 2-cell stage), it is already possible to see, by simple observation with a lens,* all the major coordinates of the future adult; the animal pole will become the head, the vegetal pole the gonads, the gray crescent containing half the dorsal side (with nervous system and notochord); the opposite side will become ventral. Already in 1904, experiments where A. Brachet destroyed, by pricking with a hot steel needle, one of the two blastomeres at the 2-cell stage demonstrated that the bilateral symmetry of the fertilized egg remains intact during the entire embryogenesis. *Bilateral symmetry,* which is marked by the plane that cuts the gray crescent into two equal halves, is not affected by cleavage; coincidence between the first cleavage plane and the plane of bilateral symmetry is found in only 60–70% of frog eggs (A. Brachet, 1904, 1906). Of course,

* Early embryologists did not possess dissecting microscopes and proper illumination. I remember seeing my father, around 1927, pricking the gray crescent of frog eggs with a hot steel needle; all he had for observation were watchmaker's spectacles with thick lenses and an ordinary electrical bulb. Nevertheless, he could see the gray crescent much better than the majority of our graduate students provided with modern optical equipment.

bilateral symmetry exists even in eggs where no gray crescent can be seen because they are either too pigmented *(Bufo)* or unpigmented; this is the case for *Triturus cristatus* eggs, for instance; but experiments with localized vital staining (Banki, 1929) have clearly shown that *Triturus* eggs possess an invisible equivalent of the gray crescent. The pigment is thus nothing more than a useful marker: in *Xenopus,* a very interesting albino mutant has been recently described by Hoperskaya (1975); electron microscopy shows that it possesses neither melanosomes, nor premelanosomes (Bluemink and Hoperskaya, 1975). Nevertheless the homozygous albino mutants develop very well: they have dorsal and ventral sides and perfect bilateral symmetry: the

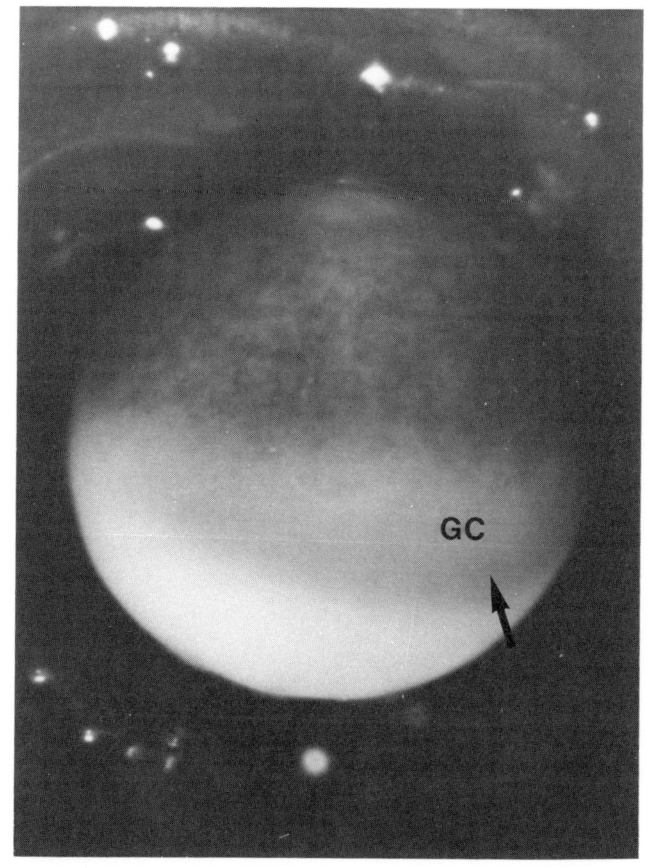

FIG. 3. The gray crescent (GC) shown in this photograph was induced precociously by placing an axolotl egg at 35.5°C for 10 minutes. (Courtesy of Dr. M. Namenwirth.)

fertilized eggs which gave rise to them thus possessed a cryptic, invisible equivalent of the gray crescent.

In summary, the gray crescent is a very useful morphological marker, visible in certain favorable amphibian species, for the prospective dorsal side of the embryo and the adult; the plane that cuts it into two equal halves is the plane of bilateral symmetry, which will be retained by the adult.

Eggs that, for some reason, have not acquired a dorsoventral organization and have thus neither a visible nor a cryptic gray crescent, develop into *anidian* embryos: such anidians are occasionally found among frog eggs which have been artificially fertilized and, more frequently, among *Xenopus* eggs where the gray crescent has been injured (Fig. 4); they remain like ciliated spheres, which whirl around at great speed and finally die, perhaps of exhaustion. As one can see from Fig. 4, there is no other differentiation than irregular strands of cells at a time when the embryo should have reached the tailbud stage and possess a well defined neural tube, a notochord, and somites.

The gray crescent problem has been ably discussed in the past by

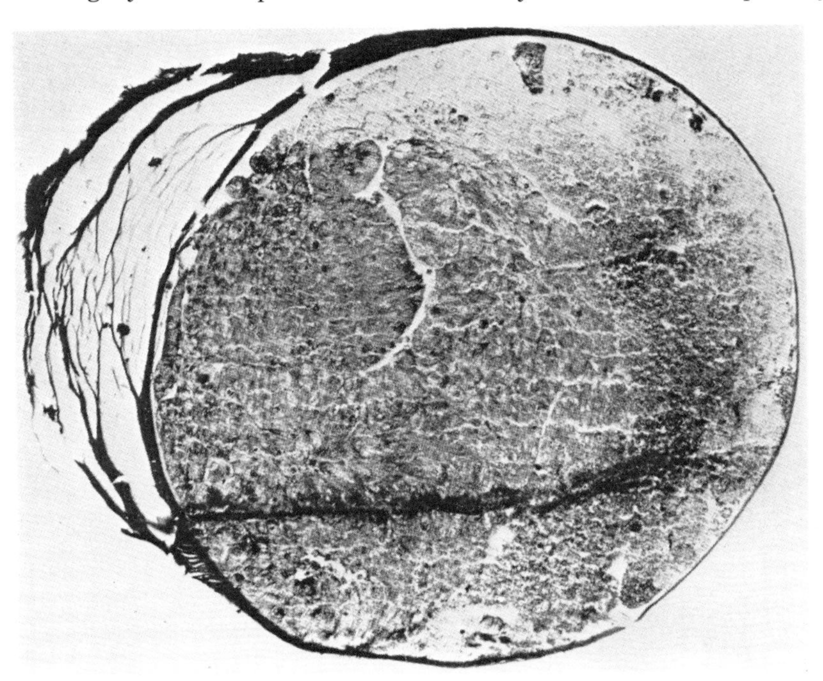

FIG. 4. Anidian embryo. Note almost complete absence of differentiation, 36 hours after injury of the dorsal cortex. From Brachet and Hubert (1972). Reproduced with permission.

several workers and has been the subject of many excellent reviews: the most important are those of A. Brachet (1931), Holtfreter and Hamburger (1955), Dollander (1961), Pasteels (1964), and Løvtrup (1965). The question has also been discussed, briefly but interestingly, by Nieuwkoop (1973). A major piece of work on the subject, which should be consulted by those who wish to find more details than in the present review, is that of Ancel and Vintemberger (1948).

II. Changes Following Fertilization or Parthenogenetic Activation of Frog Eggs

A. Observations Made on Living Eggs or Histological Sections

The morphological changes that occur in frog *(R. temporaria, R. pipiens)* eggs after fertilization can be divided artificially into three different phases.

1. *First Phase*

At 5 to 15 minutes after insemination, *cortical granule breakdown* (Fig. 5) begins at the place where the plasma membranes of the two gametes have fused; the breakdown is propagated starting from the entry point of the spermatozoon, from one cortical granule to the next. The site of sperm entry has been recently reinvestigated, in *R. pipiens,* by Elinson (1975), who found that spermatozoa can enter anywhere in the animal half, but with a preference within 60° from the animal pole. The second polar body is expelled after 25–30 minutes. During that period, a contraction of the animal pole *cortex* (the cytoplasmic layer that lies immediately under the plasma membrane, which will be discussed in the next section) occurs at the animal pole; as a result, the white spot present at the animal pole since germinal vesicle breakdown disappears. Later on, the pigmentation returns to normal; the speed of this relaxation varies from species to species (from 10 to 60 minutes). Elinson (1975) has shown that this temporary contraction of the cortex toward the animal pole allows an upward movement of the sperm nucleus that brings it closer to the female pronucleus.

Cortical granule breakdown and contraction of the cortex begin earlier (3–4 minutes instead of 10 minutes) when the egg is activated by pricking with a needle because penetration of the mucous jelly by the sperm takes some time; otherwise, the two phenomena are identical. However, the cortical response is different when agents such as urethane (Wolf, 1974c) and especially the divalent cation ionophore A23187 (Steinhardt and Epel, 1974; Hanocq *et al.,* 1974) are used for the induction of activation: all the cortical granules explode together

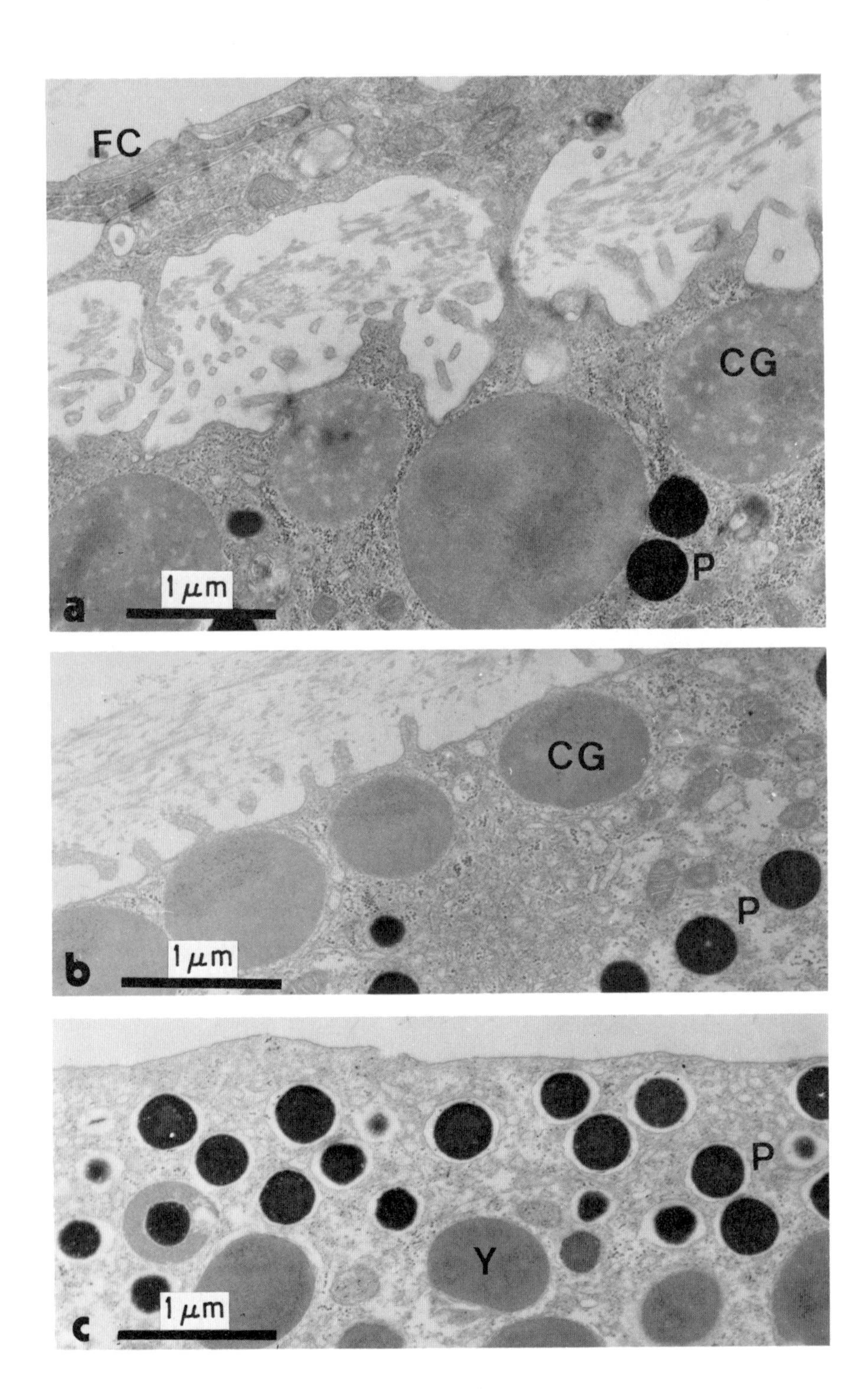

FC
CG
P
1 μm
a
CG
P
1 μm
b
P
Y
1 μm
c

and the rotation of the egg inside the fertilization membrane is much faster. There is good evidence that both fertilization and cortical response to pricking require the presence of Ca^{2+} ions in the surrounding medium. According to Wolf (1974c), the requirement for Ca^{2+} is restricted to the 5–10 seconds that immediately follow pricking. The contraction of the cortex is also Ca^{2+}-dependent (Gingell, 1970); the ionophore A23187, in the presence of Ca^{2+}, induces a massive and general contraction of the egg cortex (Schroeder and Strickland, 1974). It has also been reported that, during this initial phase of cortical contraction, permeability to water increases; it then comes back to its initial value (Løvtrup, 1962). Thus permeability changes, in particular to water and divalent ions (Morrill and Murphy, 1972; Morrill *et al.*, 1971), are probably important biochemical factors in the control of this first phase of postfertilization events, which is characterized morphologically by cortical granules opening and cortex contraction.

2. *Second Phase*

About 45 minutes after insemination or pricking with a glass needle, fusion of the pronuclei (amphimixy) takes place. By that time, DNA replication has taken place and the zygote nucleus has thus the 4c value. The perivitelline space increases in volume and reaches its maximum size after 90 minutes. Relaxation of the cortex has already taken place and permeability to water is dropping to its low initial value.

3. *Third Phase*

A *symmetrization rotation* takes place 1–2 hours after insemination: bilateral symmetry is now established in a definitive way, and in many species the *gray crescent,* becomes visible; as already mentioned, it is a marker for the dorsal side and thus the bilateral symmetry plane.

There is still a good deal of discussion about the mechanics of this symmetrization rotation (called by Pasteels, 1964, *cortical reaction of symmetrization*). For Ancel and Vintemberger (1948), the cortex of the egg would rotate 30° around an axis perpendicular to the plane of symmetry: this would lift the pigment, on the dorsal side, toward the animal pole (Fig. 6). This ascension of the dorsal cortex (but not of the ventral one) is in agreement with the observations of Banki (1929); as shown in Fig. 7, the egg cortex is stretched on the dorsal side, but not

---

FIG. 5. Electron micrographs of the cortical region in *Xenopus laevis:* (a) ovarian oocyte; (b) unfertilized egg; (c) fertilized egg. CG, cortical granules; FC, follicular cells; P, pigment; Y, yolk platelets. (Courtesy of G. Steinert.)

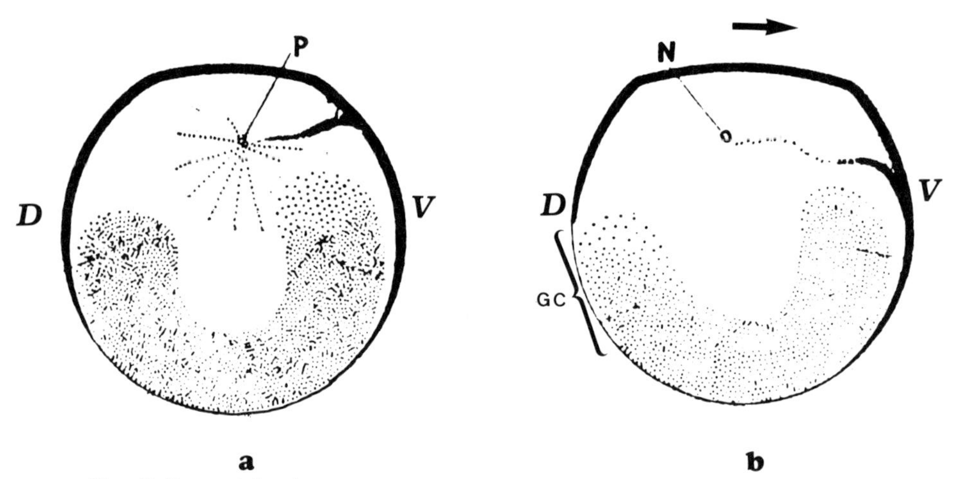

FIG. 6. Symmetrization rotation according to Ancel and Vintemberger (1948). (a) Fertilized egg before gray crescent formation. (b) Fertilized egg after gray crescent (GC) formation due to cortical contraction in the direction of the arrow. Reproduced with permission.

on the ventral one. As shown in Fig. 6, the yolk undergoes a displacement, under the influence of gravity, at the same time: the result is that a close contact is established between large yolk platelets from the vegetal pole and the dorsal cortex; the latter, as a result of the symmetrization rotation, has become thinner than its ventral counterpart. On

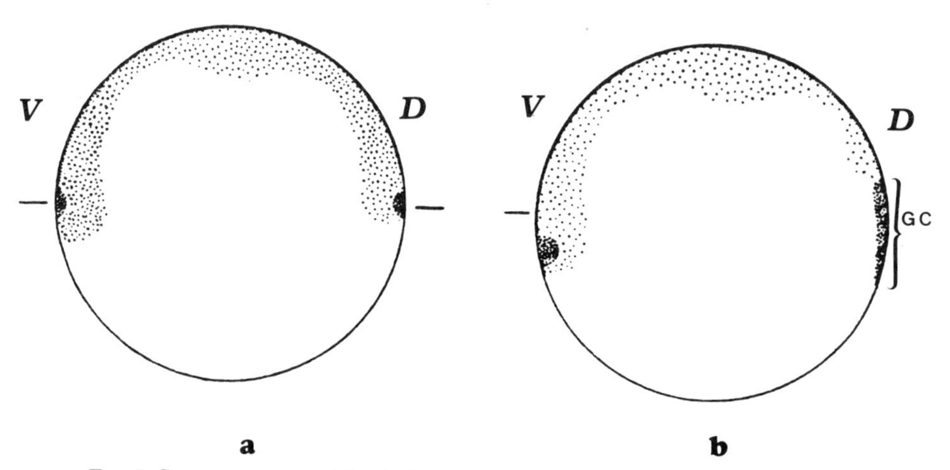

FIG. 7. Symmetrization of the fertilized egg according to Banki (1929). (a) Fertilized egg before gray crescent formation. (b) Fertilized egg after gray crescent formation (GC): stretching of the dorsal cortex is evidenced by localized vital staining.

the other hand, Løvtrup (1965) has proposed that there is no rotation of the cortex around the yolk mass and that symmetrization is the result of a stretching or contraction of the dorsal cortex. Since there are no important recent data bearing on this problem, and since the question has already been discussed in great detail by Ancel and Vintemberger (1948), Clavert (1962), Pasteels (1964), and Løvtrup (1965), it would be pointless to enter a long discussion here. The purpose of the present review is to try to revive interest in the gray crescent problem (i.e., in the symmetrization of the amphibian eggs); one can only deplore that the workers who have treated eggs with the bivalent ions ionophore A23187, colchicin, cytochalasin B, etc., have not had the curiosity to look at the appearance of the gray crescent in the treated eggs. It is well known, for instance, that the gray crescent is more visible in eggs when the rotation inside the fertilization membrane has been slow; but nobody knows whether a gray crescent is present in eggs where this rotation is very fast, because all the cortical granules have broken down almost simultaneously (for instance, after treatment with A23187).

Of potential interest for the solution of this still mysterious problem of symmetrization rotation is the recent finding by Benford and Namenwirth (1974) that a heat shock (10 minutes at 35°–65°C) produces a very distinct gray crescent in axolotl eggs in a very short time; in controls, the gray crescent does not appear until 4–6 hours after insemination and is much fainter. This artificially produced gray crescent is, as in controls, closely correlated with the appearance of the dorsal lip of the blastopore: localized vital staining has shown that, in 20 out of 21 eggs, the midpoint of the dorsal lip fell within the gray crescent's border. These interesting results agree with the view, to be discussed later, that there might already be a hidden tendency toward bilateral symmetry in the newly fertilized, if not in the unfertilized, egg. There is no doubt that the unexpected finding of Benford and Namenwirth (1974) deserves closer scrutiny.

Another phenomenon, which occurs much later in unfertilized eggs and also deserves closer scrutiny, is *"pseudogastrulation":* as first described by Holtfreter (1943b), when unfertilized *R. pipiens* eggs are kept in Ringer for 36 hours or more, a groove resembling a blastopore makes its appearance near the vegetal pole (Fig. 8). This pigmented groove progresses with time and often assumes a circular shape surrounding a white "yolk plug." These curious findings of Holtfreter (1943b) have been entirely confirmed by Smith and Ecker (1970) and by Baltus *et al.* (1973), who found that "pseudogastrulation" regularly occurs when *R. pipiens* (but rarely *X. laevis*) oocytes are induced to

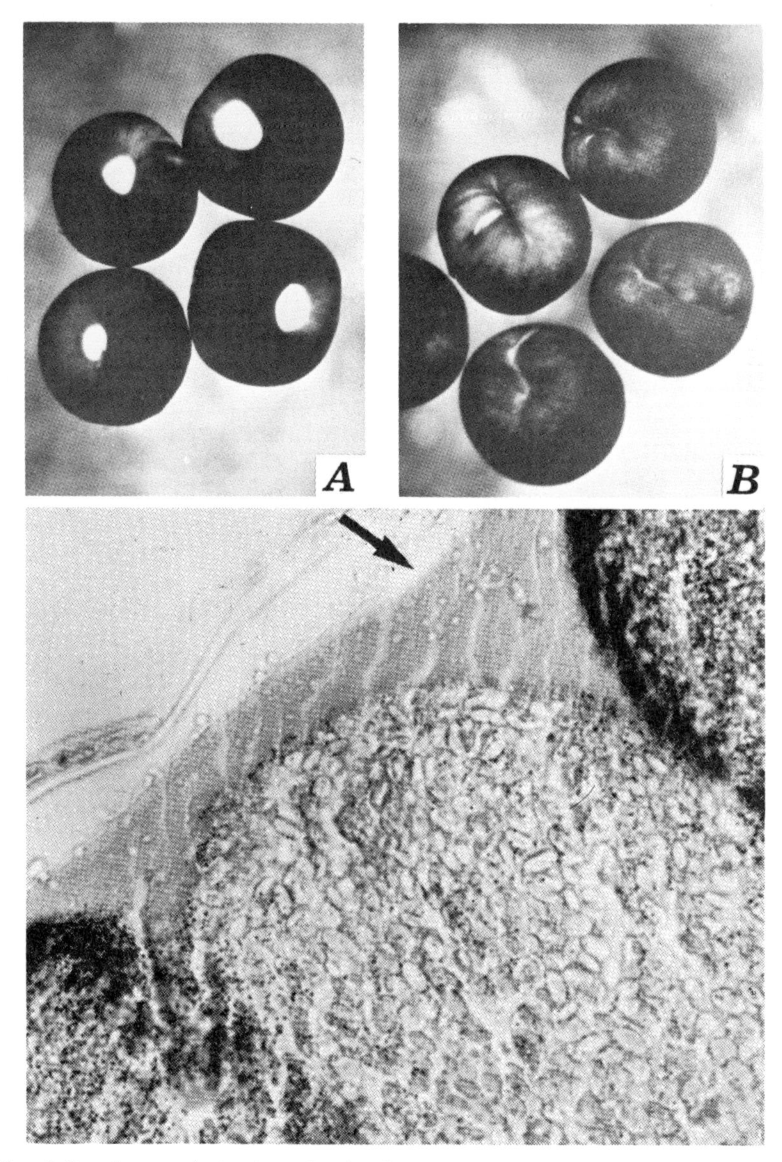

FIG. 8. Pseudogastrulation in unfertilized eggs of *Rana pipiens*. (A) Progression of the pseudoblastoporal lip (from A to B). From L. D. Smith and Ecker (1970). Reproduced with permission. (B) Section through the pseudo yolk plug. From Baltus *et al.* (1973). Reproduced with permission.

undergo maturation *in vitro* by progesterone treatment and kept for many hours in Ringer. Pseudogastrulation occurs even when the oocyte has been enucleated, before progesterone treatment; it does not occur in oocytes where maturation has not been induced by *in vitro* progesterone treatment; it is reversibly inhibited by anaerobiosis and thus requires energy (Smith and Ecker, 1970). Cytologically, pseudogastrulation is linked to a local segregation, followed by an overflow of basophilic hyaloplasm, which finally accumulates at the vegetal pole: in fact, the "yolk plug" does not contain yolk platelets, but is made of basophilic material (Baltus *et al.*, 1973) (Fig. 8B). These curious morphological changes show that the egg cortex displays contractile properties even when the nucleus has been removed. It would be rewarding to study the effects of various substances (cytochalasin B, colchicin, ionophores, cycloheximide, etc.) on eggs undergoing pseudogastrulation and to study their ultrastructure. Still more important for our present purpose would be to look for a correlation between the "blastoporal lip" of the uncleaved eggs and dorsoventral organization; this might be possible if the "pseudogastrulae" still responded to parthenogenetic agents.

B. Electron Microscope Studies

There have been many recent studies about the ultrastructure of the amphibian egg surface; but unfortunately very few people have paid attention to possible ultrastructural differences between dorsal and ventral sides in fertilized eggs or early cleavage stages.

We shall mention here the observations dealing with the formation of the *fertilization membrane* only briefly despite their interest: the studies of Grey *et al.* (1974), Wolf (1974a), and Wyrick *et al.* (1974) show that, in *Xenopus*, the fertilization membrane originates from the vitelline membrane (chorion) which surrounded the unfertilized egg, by the apposition of two different materials: on the inner side, an exudate from the broken-down cortical granules and, on the outer side, the innermost layer (J1) of the jelly that surrounds amphibian eggs. According to Wolf (1974b), the cortical granules of the *Xenopus* egg (in contrast with those of sea urchin eggs: review by Epel, 1975) do not possess protease activity; part of their content remains in the perivitelline space and the remaining part combines with the J1 layer of the jelly. The main constituent of the cortical granules is of mucopolysaccharidic (acidic glycoprotein) nature; recent biochemical analyses (Wolf *et al.*, 1976) have confirmed that the fertilization membrane results from the Ca^{2+}-dependent binding of glycoproteins and proteins originating from the vitelline membrane, the cortical granules and the J1 layer.

The physiological properties of the vitelline and fertilization membranes are very different, as shown by Grey *et al.* (1976): they have succeeded in isolating these membranes from, respectively, unfertilized and fertilized *Xenopus* eggs, and they have treated them with spermatozoa activated by treatment with an extract of the jelly which surrounds the eggs; they found that while the spermatozoa easily penetrate into isolated vitelline membranes from both outer and inner sides, they do not penetrate at all into isolated fertilization membranes. The vitelline membrane thus contains sperm receptors on both sides; these receptors have been broken down or they are masked in the fertilization membrane.

Several papers have described the ultrastructure of the amphibian egg surface, especially in relation with changes at fertilization or furrow formation during early cleavage (Balinsky, 1960; Wartenberg and Schmidt, 1961; Dollander, 1961; Baker, 1965; Hebard and Herold, 1967; Selman and Perry, 1970; Kalt, 1971; Sanders and Zalik, 1972). They have been inspired by the pioneer work of Holtfreter (1943a, 1948), who was the first to study in detail the adhesive and contractile properties of embryonic amphibian cells: he ascribed these properties to a "surface coat," which would form a continuous extracellular contractile envelope and would contain pigment granules. The present picture, arising from electron microscopy (Fig. 9) of the cell surface is different: just beneath the *plasma membrane* (plasmalemma), there is an electron dense layer; it is fairly homogeneous and probably contains a fibrillar network. This layer is the *cortex* and is very probably responsible for the contractility of the surface when Ca^{2+} ions or polycations are locally applied (Gingell, 1970). Only Dollander (1961) and Hebard and Herold (1967) have been interested in its possible relationships with the gray crescent; they state that, in *Xenopus,* the thickness and continuity of this superficial layer vary: it is thickest and mostly continuous at the animal pole and is thinner and continuous at the vegetal pole; the thickness is intermediate in the dorsal and ventral sides, where the layer is quite discontinuous; it is thinner and more discontinuous on the dorsal side, in agreement with what has been said in the preceding section about a probable stretching of the dorsal cortex during the symmetrization rotation. A similar structure has been observed in *Triturus* and *Hynobius* eggs by Ikushima and Maruyama (1971): under the plasmalemma, they found an alveolar layer 0.5–1.0 μm thick. Underneath is a pigmented layer devoid of yolk platelets, which is about 5 μm thick and corresponds to the cortex. The Japanese work-

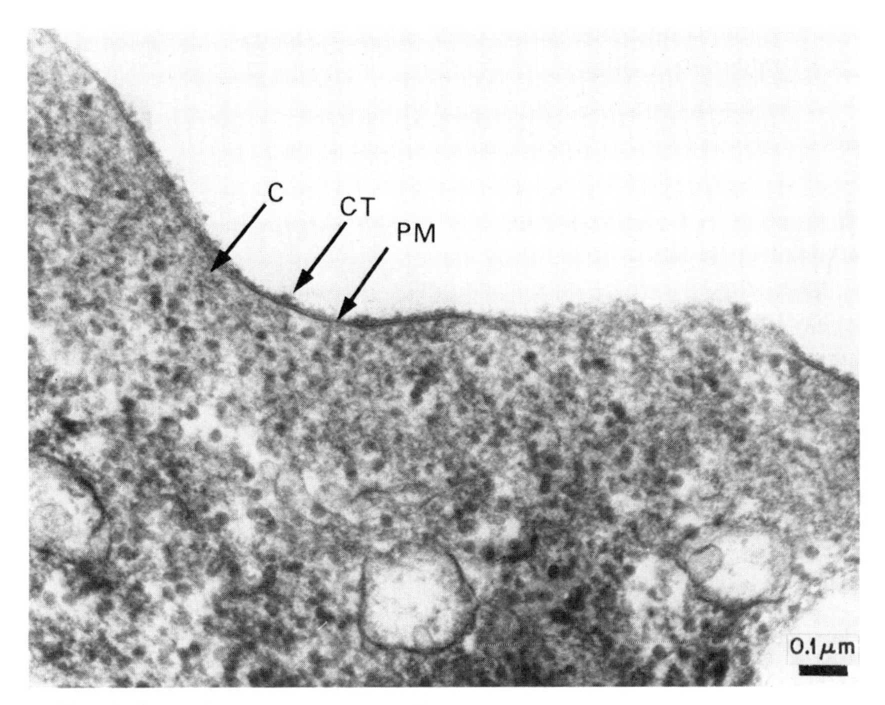

FIG. 9. Cortical region of a stage-2 *Xenopus* egg after removal of the fertilization membrane. PM, plasma membrane; C, cortex; CT, coat (thin and diffuse). (Courtesy of Dr. M. Geuskens.)

ers have isolated small pieces of the cortex manually and found that it contains mainly pigment granules and mitochondria. Similar results have been obtained by Bluemink (1972) and by Luckenbill (1971), who studied wound healing in fertilized, uncleaved *Xenopus* eggs; Bluemink (1972) isolated fragments, about 5 μm thick, of the cortex of the animal pole and found that they contained, in addition to the plasma membrane, a feltlike (presumably contractile) material, pigment granules, vesicles of various size, mitochondria, lipid droplets, and small yolk platelets.

The presence of contractile microfilaments and actin molecules in the cortex of amphibian oocytes from several species has recently been beautifully demonstrated by Franke *et al.* (1976). Using immunofluorescence methods, they have proved that isolated cortices contain large amounts of actin molecules. It would be of great interest to study, with the same techniques, the distribution of actin in fertilized and cleaving eggs.

There is thus a general agreement about the existence of a cortex just beneath the plasma membrane, although the question of its thickness is more debatable since it largely depends upon a question of definition: should one call cortex only the thin superficial layer (less than 1 μm thick) or include in it the underlying pigmented layer? For operational reasons, in this review, we shall call cortex the material that can be manually isolated and contains the various inclusions described by Ikushima and Maruyama (1971) and by Bluemink (1972).

Still under discussion remains the question whether amphibian eggs are surrounded by an *extracellular surface coat:* the majority of electron microscopists, starting with Wartenberg and Schmidt (1961), have concluded that Holtfreter's (1943a, 1948) surface coat does not exist. However, Bluemink and de Laat (1973) have described, in *Xenopus,* the presence of extracellular material stainable with Ruthenium Red. This material can also be seen in Fig. 9, which depicts a stage-2 blastomere *Xenopus* egg devoid of its fertilization membrane: there is a continuous, but thin, coat outside the cell surface; if these eggs are treated with wheat germ agglutinin (WGA), the coat becomes more irregularly distributed (Fig. 10). Although these findings favor the existence of a thin extracellular surface coat in *Xenopus* eggs, it is not clear, at the present time, whether one is dealing with a genuine egg constituent (i.e., a glycocalix) or with material normally present in the perivitelline space, which has precipitated upon the egg surface as a result of fixation.

Little will be said about the changes that occur during furrowing of cleaving eggs, since a long discussion would take us too far from the subject of this review: we already know that there is a good deal of evidence against the view that cleavage plane and bilateral symmetry plane coincide (A. Brachet, 1904, 1906) in more than 60–70% of the eggs. The work of Bluemink (1970), Bluemink and de Laat (1974), de Laat *et al.* (1973, 1974, 1975), and Bluemink *et al.* (1976) is a thorough analysis of early cleavage in *Xenopus* eggs and *Ambystoma* eggs, based on the use of electron microscopy, measurements of the membrane potential and permeability of K^+ ions, effects of cytochalasin B (which disrupts the actin microfilaments), etc. The general conclusion is that the newly formed membrane has different physiological properties from the "old" one; it probably arises from the large reserve of membrane material that is present in the cytoplasm. In particular, the permeability to K^+ ions of the new membrane that forms the furrow is much higher than that of the preexisting membrane (de Laat *et al.,* 1975); the new membrane contains fewer intramembrane particles than the old one (Bluemink *et al.,* 1976).

Another major factor in furrowing is the intervention of actin mic-

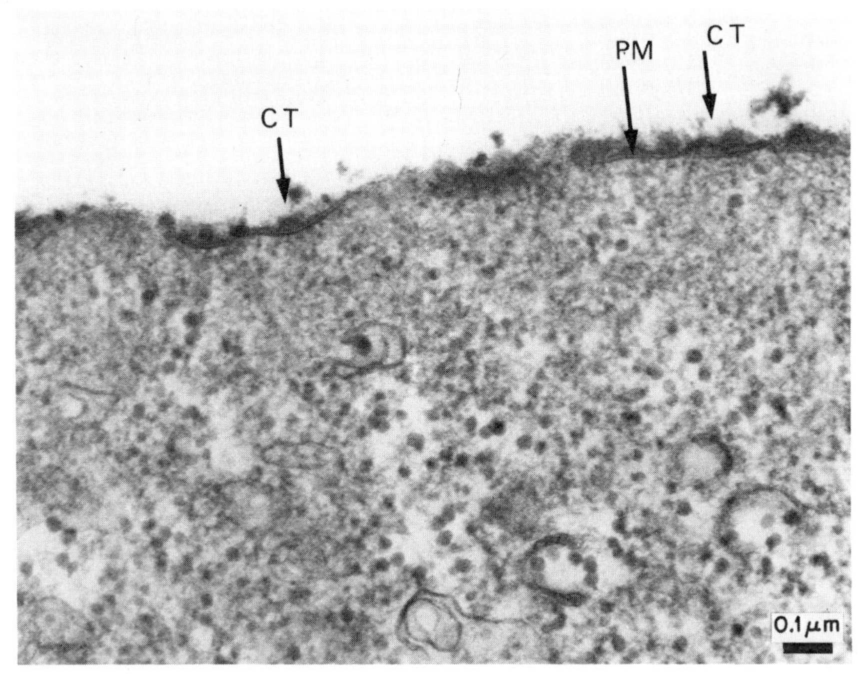

FIG. 10. Cortical region of a stage-2 *Xenopus* egg after removal of the fertilization membrane and treatment during 30 minutes with wheat germ agglutinin. PM, plasma membrane; CT, coat (irregularly distributed). (Courtesy of Dr. M. Geuskens.)

rofilaments and microtubules: both cytochalasin B and vinblastin inhibit furrowing. That the microfilaments present in the cleavage furrow of amphibian eggs are really made of actin has been established by Perry *et al.* (1971): amphibian eggs microfilaments bind with heavy meromyosin, forming "arrowhead complexes." The number of these organized actin microfilaments is small in just-fertilized *Triturus* and *Xenopus* eggs; they are present during the whole development in *Xenopus,* but are not easily seen before neurulation in the newt (Perry, 1975). The effects of cytochalasin B on furrow formation in cleaving amphibian eggs have been studied in greater detail by Selman *et al.* (1976) who followed, among other things, the uptake of the labeled drug by autoradiography. Application of the elegant immunofluorescent techniques for actin detection developed by Franke *et al.* (1976) to the same material should give an unequivocal answer to the question of the role played by contractile actin microfilaments in furrowing. The distribution of the pigment granules also changes during cleavage in *Xenopus* (suggesting that important changes occur in the organization of the egg cytoskeleton in relation to aster formation) (Fig. 11).

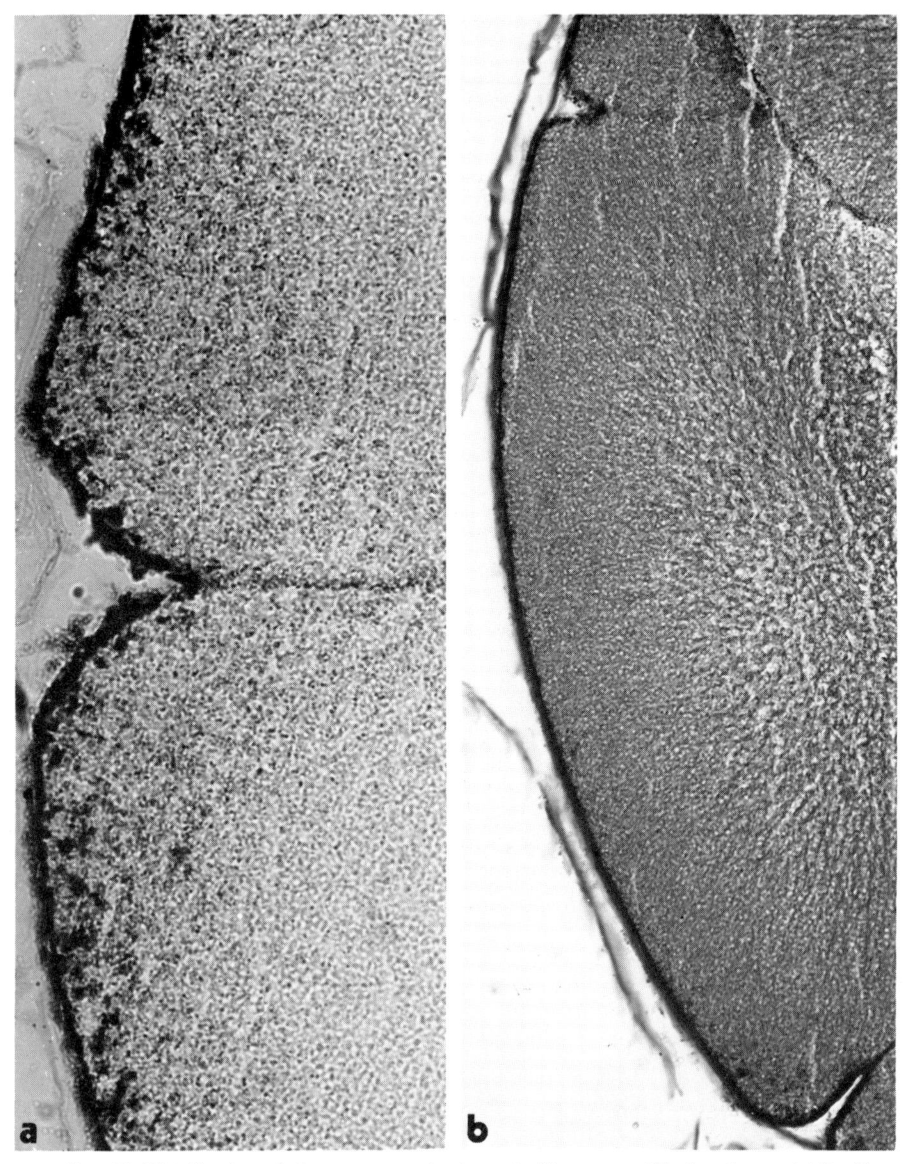

FIG. 11. Distribution of pigment granules in early *Xenopus mülleri* embryos: (a) 2-cell stage; (b) 8-cell stage. The pigment has a more superficial localization in (b) than in (a); this is probably due to the presence of asters in the 8-cell stage egg. (Courtesy of Professor A. Ficq.)

Other approaches to the study of the cell surface are the binding of fluorescent (or radioactive) lectins and scanning electron microscopy (SEM). There is very little binding of fluorescent concanavalin A (Con A) to fertilized *Xenopus* eggs (O'Dell *et al.*, 1974), and the gray crescent does not stand out by increased staining; Con A has no effect upon cleavage in *Xenopus* eggs. On the other hand, fertilized and cleaving *Xenopus* eggs strongly bind wheat germ and soybean agglutinins; if these lectins are added to recently fertilized eggs that have been freed from their fertilization membrane, arrest of cleavage is immediate (unpublished observations by our colleague, Dr. R. Tencer). However, there is no obvious differential staining of the gray crescent by these two fluorescent lectins.

The SEM studies of Monroy and Baccetti (1975) show that the organization of the plasma membrane is different at the animal and the vegetal poles and that extensive reorganization of the cell surface takes place after fertilization; no significant difference could be found between the surfaces of the future dorsal and ventral regions.

Very kindly, Professor J. Signoret (University of Caen) agreed to examine, at our request, the surface of *Pleurodeles* and *Ambystoma* eggs by SEM. His unpublished results (Figs. 12 and 13) confirm the

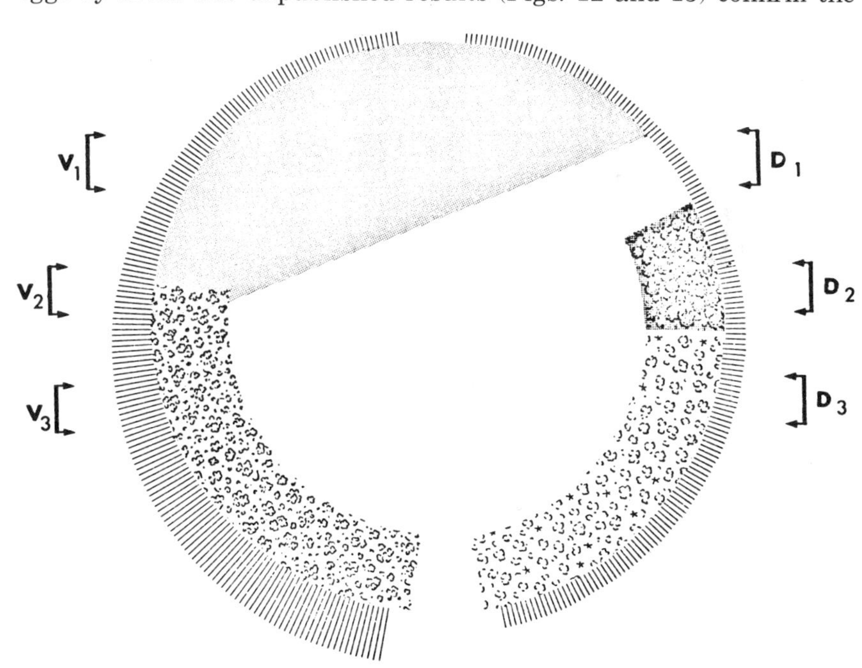

FIG. 12. Schematic representation of the distribution of microvilli (stripes), pigment (gray area) and yolk platelets in a cleaving amphibian egg. V, ventral side; D, dorsal side; D_2, gray crescent. (Courtesy of Professor J. Signoret.)

a

b

conclusion of Monroy and Baccetti (1975) that there are differences in the surface structure of the animal and vegetal poles. But he also found differences between the dorsal and ventral sides at the 4-cell stage, where the gray crescent region is particularly visible. This region is poor in pigment and characterized by a very strong "*gaufrage*" (honeycomb structure), whose significance is not clear: it is probably an artifact that makes the yolk platelets underlying the thin dorsal cortex visible with the SEM. But the fact that the differences between the various regions of the egg are perfectly reproducible shows that there are regional differences in the properties of the membrane or cortex. There are also local differences in the shape and size of the microvilli (Figs. 12 and 13); the analysis, in this respect, is more difficult because, according to Professor Signoret and to Denis-Donini *et al.* (1976), the size and morphology of the microvilli change during the cell cycle.

III. Determination at Will of the Gray Crescent

The classical observations and experiments of Roux (1887, 1903a,b,c) have clearly shown that there is a correlation between the entry point of the spermatozoon and the position of the gray crescent: the gray crescent makes its appearance opposite the pigmented trail left by the spermatozoon (Fig. 14). By ingenious and simple experiments, Roux (1903a,b,c) succeeded in what he called "localized fertilizations": the position of the entry point of the sperm could be established at will by the experimenter; again the gray crescent always appeared on the opposite side of the egg. Thus the entry point of the sperm is found in the ventral half of the egg; but the experiments of Roux on localized fertilization, as well as the recent observations of Elinson (1975), show that there is no "predestined" fertilization meridian: in Nature, fertilization occurs at random and there is little doubt that the symmetrization of the egg (evidenced by the appearance of the gray crescent on the dorsal side) is a consequence of fertilization.

Things become more complex when the egg is submitted to various experimental conditions. As shown by A. Brachet (1904, 1931) polyspermic eggs have a gray crescent; the latter is also formed when an egg is activated by pricking, and, in this case, there is no correlation between the localization of the needle and that of the gray crescent; this means that there is no correlation between the point where cortical granule breakdown begins and the localization of the gray crescent and

FIG. 13. Early cleavage stage *(Pleurodeles)* seen under a scanning electron microscope: (a) ventral side (region V_2 of Fig. 12). (b) dorsal side (region D_2 of Fig. 12—gray crescent). (Courtesy of Professor J. Signoret.)

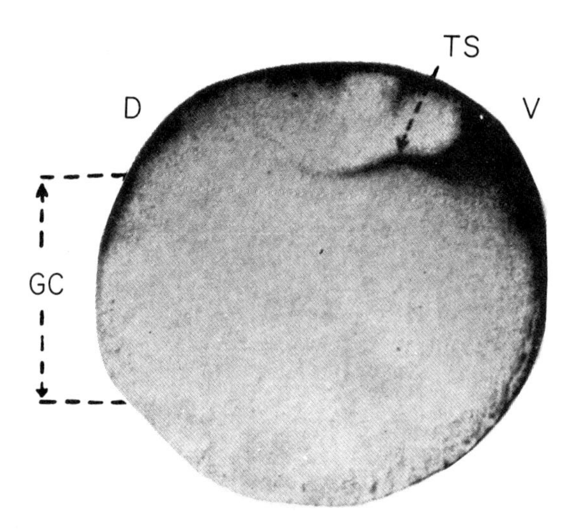

FIG. 14. Formation of the gray crescent (c.g.) in a fertilized egg of *Rana fusca*. The penetration path of the sperm (T.S.) is visualized by an accumulation of pigment. The gray crescent lies opposite the entrance point of the sperm. After Ancel and Vintemberger (1948). Reproduced with permission.

the plane of symmetry. Even when an unfertilized egg is pricked with a needle while it is maintained in a vertical position and thus cannot rotate inside the vitelline membrane, a gray crescent will form (A. Brachet, 1904, 1911). If the egg is slightly compressed and then fertilized, there is no correlation between the entry point of the sperm and the position of the gray crescent (Weigmann, 1927).

How the entry point of the spermatozoon controls the bilateral symmetry is not known. It has been suggested by Kubota (1967) that the spermaster might play a role in the determination of the gray crescent: he found that a region of high rigidity appears around the point of sperm entry and that this regional pattern is correlated with the proximity of a spermaster or cytaster. Similar observations have been made by Kubota (1967) on eggs activated by pricking in the presence of frog's blood. Very recently, Manes and Barbieri (1976) have shown that injection of a sperm homogenate (obtained with a French pressure press) in a subcortical region of the animal pole induces, in *Bufo arenarum*, the appearance of the gray crescent at the side opposite the injection point; as in the experiments of A. Brachet (1911), control injections of Ringer solution had no such effects. These preliminary experiments sound promising, but a few words of caution seem necessary: the correct identification of the gray crescent is difficult in toad eggs because of their heavy pigmentation; furthermore, when the sperm homogenate was added to unfertilized eggs, a low (1‰) percentage of fertilization was obtained, showing that a few spermatozoa had remained intact. Manes and Barbieri (1976) suggest that the active constituent in the sperm homogenate might be a centriole, which would induce the polymerization of tubulin molecules in aster microtubules; but unfortunately they give no cytological evidence for this very plausible hypothesis. These experiments should be repeated on species that display a well marked gray crescent, and it would be interesting to know whether their outcome would be modified if the eggs are treated with drugs that inhibit microtubule assembly (colchicin, *Vinca* alcaloids, etc.).

The work of Ancel and Vintemberger (1948) has largely clarified the apparent discrepancies by showing the importance of the "orientation rotation" due to gravity in the establishment of bilateral symmetry. Figure 15 describes schematically their most important experiment: if an unfertilized frog egg is placed in the position indicated on the figure and then fertilized at random, it will rotate in the direction shown by the arrow; its gray crescent will always appear on the side opposite to the observer, thus on the side of the lamp used for the observation (whether the light is switched on or off, of course). Similar results have been obtained with *Triturus cristatus* eggs, which have no gray crescent: if the egg remains unmoved after its rotation, the dorsal lip of the blastopores will form on the side of the "light," not on that of the observer. This experiment confirms that the gray crescent is nothing more than a valuable marker of dorsoventral polarity and of the bilateral symmetry plane: melanosomes have apparently nothing to do in these fundamental processes. Ancel and Vintemberger (1948) have

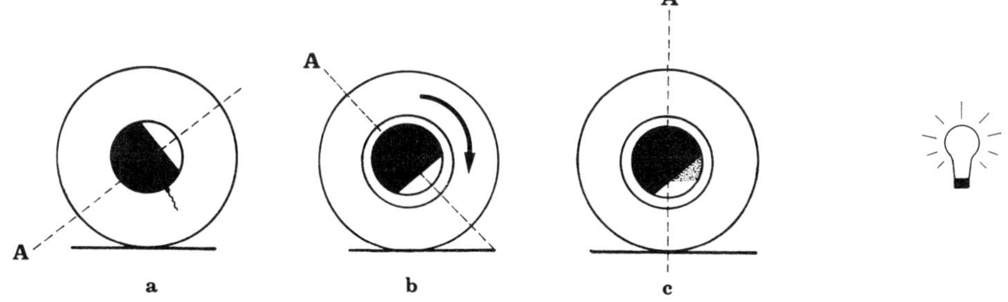

FIG. 15. A classical experiment of Ancel and Vintemberger (1948). (a) An unfertilized frog egg is placed in an oblique position and then fertilized (A = animal pole). (b) The egg rotates, under the influence of gravity, after the uplifting of the fertilization membrane, as indicated by the arrow. (c) The gray crescent always appears on the side facing the lamp. Reproduced with permission.

also demonstrated that a forced rotation 45 minutes after insemination, when the spermatozoon has already penetrated into the egg, is still efficient; later on, the rotation is no longer effective, and the position of the gray crescent is determined by the entry point of the spermatozoon. A rotation through 360° will nullify the effect of the spermatozoon: the latter will now be in the dorsal side, like the gray crescent (Fig. 16). These experiments clearly lead to the conclusion that symmetrization is a progressive, epigenetic process.

However, experiments of A. Brachet (1904, 1906, 1931), Banki (1929), Pasteels (1932), and especially Tung (1933), which mainly dealt with the localized destruction with a hot steel needle of *unfertilized* frog eggs, have led to the conclusion that they might already possess some kind of bilateral symmetry. As already mentioned, the very fast appearance of a gray crescent after a heat shock is also taken by Benford and Namenwirth (1974) as evidence for the preexistence of some form of latent bilateral symmetry in unfertilized axolotl eggs. For Ancel and Vintemberger (1948), the position given to the unfertilized egg would create a preferential meridian for sperm entry in contradiction with Roux's conclusions. Clearly, the whole question of the possible existence of dorsoventral polarity in unfertilized eggs remains in an unsatisfactory state and requires new investigations.

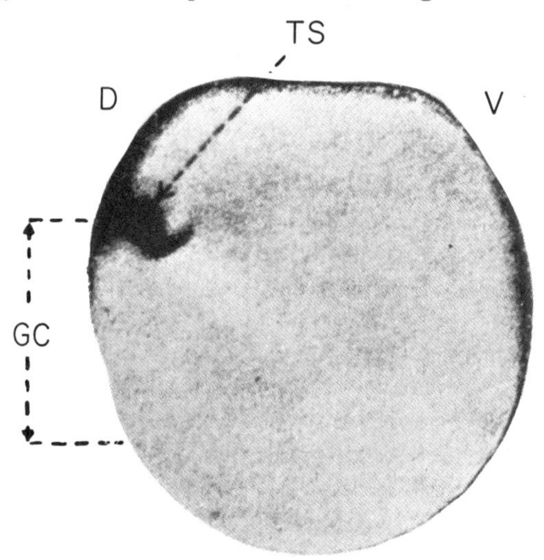

FIG. 16. Inversion of the dorsoventral axis in a normally fertilized egg of *Rana temporaria* after directed rotation through 360°. c.g., gray crescent; T.S., penetration path of the sperm. In contrast to the normal situation shown in Fig. 14, the gray crescent has formed on the same side as the entrance point of the sperm. After Ancel and Vintemberger (1948). Reproduced with permission.

In a recent discussion of the gray crescent problem, Nieuwkoop (1973) agrees that it results from a thinning out of the pigmented cortex and from closer contact of the yolk platelets with the plasma membrane: this closer contact probably explains the "gaufrée" (honeycomb) morphology of the gray crescent shown in Fig. 13. Nieuwkoop (1973) also admits that the gray crescent apparently plays an important role in the initial phases of the symmetrization of the egg and in the further formation of the embryonic axis; but he points out, on the basis of his own experimental results, that the gray crescent has lost its importance at the blastula stage: by that time, the dorsoventral polarity of the embryo would no longer reside in the cortex, but in the endoderm. There would thus be an epigenetic change in the determination of dorsoventral polarity, which would shift from the surface of the egg toward its interior. Whether the dorsoventral polarization of the endoderm at the blastula stage is related to the initial formation of the gray crescent remains, according to Nieuwkoop (1973), an open question.

There are some indications that the proteins present in the nuclear sap of the germinal vesicle might play a role in the establishment of dorsoventral polarity. We found (J. Brachet, 1938, 1950a) that these proteins give a strong nitroprusside reaction for —SH groups after denaturation; after maturation, the —SH-containing proteins, as expected, accumulate at the animal pole. When the egg undergoes its first cleavage, the sulfhydryl proteins become localized in an equatorial crescent on one side of the egg; since this work was done on *Triturus* eggs, which have little pigment and no visible gray crescent, the suggestion that the crescent of nitroprusside-reacting material and the gray crescent are identical remains hypothetical. A more precise cytological and cytochemical analysis of the cytoplasmic changes that lead to the formation of the gray crescent in the eggs of *Discoglossus pictus* (an interesting material, because it shows a well-defined gray crescent despite the fact that the spermatozoon enters the egg very close to its animal pole) has been recently carried on by Klag and Ubbels (1975). Their main results can be summarized as follows: the unfertilized and freshly fertilized egg contains a column of light cytoplasm mixed with nuclear sap of the germinal vesicle; it is poor in yolk, but rich in RNA and glycogen. About 1 hour after fertilization, the pigmented cortical layer moves ventrally; the gray crescent becomes visible between 75 and 90 minutes after insemination. By that time (90 minutes) the mixture of germinal vesicle nuclear sap and clear cytoplasm rich in glycogen and RNA moves toward the cortex of the gray crescent (Fig. 17) and becomes very close to it, except for a thin layer of

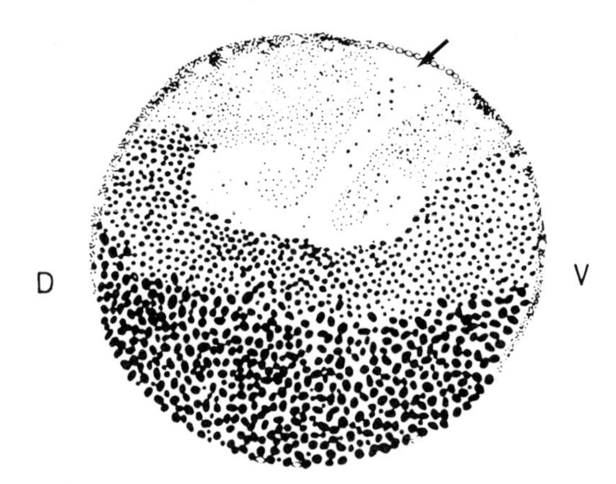

FIG. 17. Regional morphological differentiation of the egg of *Discoglossus pictus,* 75 minutes after fertilization. The arrow points to the column of light cytoplasm (rich in RNA and glycogen) mixed with nuclear sap of the germinal vesicle. The distribution of small, medium-sized, and large yolk platelets is represented by small, medium-sized and large dots. From Klag and Ubbels (1975). Reproduced with permission.

large and medium-sized yolk platelets. These observations show that the cytoplasmic changes that lead to the formation of the gray crescent are not exclusively cortical: there is a cytoplasmic movement toward the dorsal side, which might favor closer contact between yolk platelets and gray crescent, or affect the symmetrization of the yolky endoderm postulated by Nieuwkoop (1973). It also brings material originating from the germinal vesicle in contact with the dorsal cortex.

Intervention of proteins originally present in the nuclear sap of the germinal vesicle in the establishment of dorsoventral polarity might have important implications for future development: it has been shown by Waddington (1938) that grafting a killed germinal vesicle into the blastocoel of a young *Triturus* grastrula can induce a nervous system; we observed (J. Brachet, 1938), in similar experiments, that fresh germinal vesicles induce the formation of huge suckers in *Discoglossus.* More recently, Huff (1962) and Malacinski (1974) have shown that injection into fertilized frog eggs of nuclear sap from the germinal vesicle produces hyperdevelopment of the head (brain and sucker). However, similar experiments by Namur (1974) led, on the contrary, to microcephaly in axolotl eggs.

One could suggest two kinds of experiments for making progress in the field discussed in this section: it would be interesting to see whether a gray crescent forms when *anucleate* frog or *Xenopus* oocytes are treated with progesterone and then activated by pricking or addition of the ionophore A23187; the cytology of such eggs would be worth investigating in relation with the work of Klag and Ubbels (1975). Such an experiment should prove or disprove the possibility that nuclear sap from the germinal vesicle plays a role in the establishment of the gray crescent and bilateral symmetry.

Another experiment (which, if it has been done, is still a "top secret") would be to study gray crescent formation in the absence in gravity: it would be interesting to repeat the experiments of Roux (on localized fertilization), and those of Ancel and Vintemberger, in a "Skylab."

IV. Inversion Experiments. The Dalcq and Pasteels Theory

These questions have been so ably reviewed by Pasteels (1964), who played a leading role in the experiments themselves, that there is nothing that we could add. The interested reader should thus consult his excellent and detailed review; only a brief summary will be given here.

It is known, since the work of Schultze (1894), that inverting slightly compressed fertilized frog eggs results in the formation of double embryos. As shown later by Penners and Schleip (1928a,b) and by Pasteels (1938, 1939), formation of such double monsters is closely linked to a flow of yolk from the vegetal toward the animal pole of the inverted eggs. A detailed analysis led Pasteels (1938, 1939) to the conclusion that the position of the dorsal lip, in gastrulae originating from inverted eggs, is determined by the interaction of two factors: the migration of the yolk under the influence of gravity (there is another experiment for Skylab biologists) and some influence coming from the gray crescent area.

When frog eggs are kept in an oblique position, the heavy yolk will be displaced by gravity in an abnormal position; in such experiments, as shown by Born in 1885, a second, "artificial" gray crescent can be seen on the ventral side. From his very careful analysis of these experiments, Pasteels (1964) concludes that Born's crescent "is a rather good imitation of the gray crescent, not only in its external appearance, but also as regards its morphogenetic properties." In Born's crescent, as in the genuine gray crescent, rather large yolk platelets are in close contact with a poorly pigmented cortex.

These observations and extensive experiments on centrifuged eggs have led Pasteels to the conclusion that the gray crescent cortex, in contrast to the yolk, is not displaced by moderate centrifugation. Dalcq and Pasteels (1938) have proposed, on the basis of these facts, that embryonic development would be initially controlled by an interaction between two factors: an animal–vegetal gradient in *yolk* content and a *cortical field* that has its center in the gray crescent. While the yolk gradient can be easily modified by gravity (in inversion or centrifugation experiments), the cortex would keep its architecture unimpaired in such experiments. Morphogenesis would occur, in normal or in inverted eggs, whenever heavy yolk platelets from the vegetal pole come into close contact with the cortex. The latter would contain a hypothetical component c, whose concentration would be maximal in the center of the gray crescent and would decrease progressively from this focal point of the cortical field, and a component v present in the yolk. The concentration of c would be maximal in the center of the gray crescent and that of v at the vegetal pole. The product cv of their interaction would control morphogenesis; it has been called "organisine" by Dalcq and Pasteels (1938). Regional differentiation would be due to quantitative differences in the concentration of this morphogenetic substance; it could be explained by assuming that it depends upon threshold values of organisine concentration as shown in Fig. 18.

The Dalcq and Pasteels (1938) theory is now almost 30 years old. It has been criticized many times, but I think that it remains a very good model for explaining what happens during the *early* stages of develop-

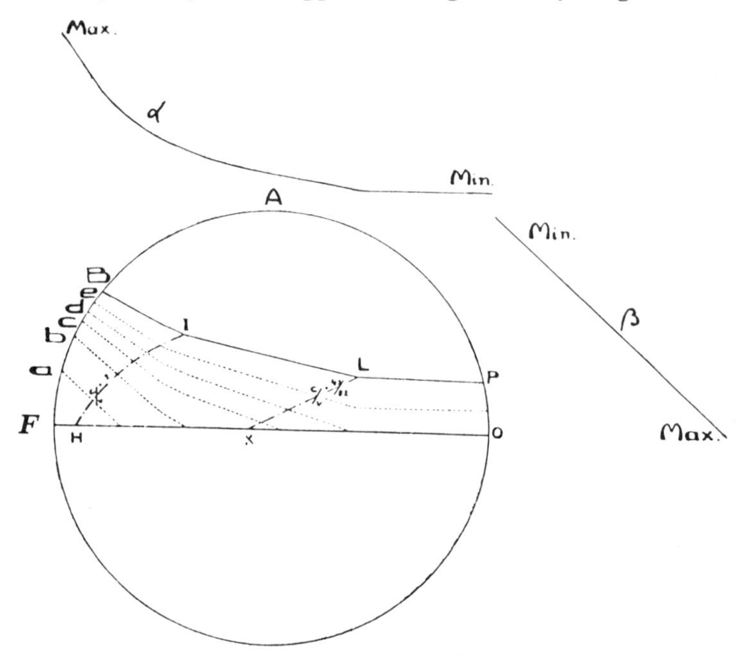

FIG. 18. Graphic representation of the double gradient theory of Dalcq and Pasteels (1938). α are arbitrary values for the cortical field with its maximum in F. β are arbitrary values for yolk gradient. Reproduced with permission.

ment, which are the subject of this review. In fact, we have already pointed out that the formation of the gray crescent is already an epigenetic phenomenon; we should not expect a theory based on experiments made on fertilized or early-cleaving eggs to apply equally well to gastrulae or neurulae: too many other epigenetic changes occur during cleavage and gastrulation to make that possible. For instance, Nieuwkoop's (review in 1973) experiments show that there is a symmetrization of the endoderm, a fact that could not be included in the Dalcq and Pasteels (1938) theory since it was not known; but he points out himself that this symmetrization of the endoderm has been demonstrated at the blastula stage, and he accepts that, at earlier stages, the gray crescent might be important. If there is an interaction between dorsal cortex and yolk platelets, it is conceivable that the reaction product could diffuse or even spread autocatalytically from the cortex to the endoderm mass during cleavage.

In favor of the Dalcq and Pasteels theory are the following facts: the structure (Brachet, 1948a, 1972) and ultrastructure (Hebard and Herold, 1967) of the cortex of amphibian eggs are not visibly affected by centrifugation. There is no doubt that very large yolk platelets underlie the gray crescent cortex, and this is confirmed by the SEM micrographs of Professor Signoret (Fig. 13). It is still not known whether there is a chemical interaction between yolk platelets and cortical material, but this is by no means impossible: yolk platelets are much less inert than was thought 30 years ago. We know (for a review, see Brachet, 1975) that they contain many enzymes (proteases, phosphoprotein phosphatase, acid phosphatase) and even inhibitors of their own proteases (Slaughter and Triplett, 1976); they also contain some DNA and RNA, as well as glycoproteins localized in their outer layer. More important for our present context is the finding by Faulhaber and Lyra (1974) that this outer layer of the yolk platelets from *Xenopus* contains inducing substances and that their activity changes during development: extracts of yolk platelets, as well as of microsomes, from cleavage stages have an archencephalic and weak deuterencephalic inducing activity; extracts of yolk platelets from gastrulae and neurulae have a much stronger deuterencephalic and spinocaudal inducing activity than those from morulae.

One cannot thus exclude the possibility that interactions between the gray crescent cortex and the yolk platelets release or activate inducing substances from the latter (and possibly the microsomal fraction). Of interest, because they also demonstrate epigenetic changes in inducing activity during the cleavage period, are the recent results of Amashima (1975): he found that endoderm induces mesoderm in ectodermic "sandwiches" at all stages from the uncleaved egg to the larva; but the inducing activity of the endoderm from uncleaved eggs is weak—it induces only red blood cells, whereas endoderm taken from later stages also induces somites and pronephros. These findings reinforce Nieuwkoop's (1973) conclusions about the role played by the endoderm in amphibian morphogenesis and establish that there are epigenetic changes in its inducing activity. Only further experiments will show whether these changes result from interactions between yolk and dorsal cortex. As will be shown in the next section, the latter has also inducing activity.

The weakest part of the Dalcq and Pasteels theory (1938) lies in the hypothesis that regional differentiation can be ascribed to threshold differences in the concentration of a single morphogenetic substance, the "organisine." It is this purely quantitative interpretation of morphogenesis that explains why an otherwise still valid theory is almost forgotten: we now know, from the work of Toivonen, Yamada, and especially Tiedemann (reviewed by Tiedemann, 1975, 1976) that it is possible to isolate, from various tissues and even from various biochemical fractions of chick embryos, proteins that exert either neuralizing or mesodermizing (vegetalizing) effects on isolated gastrula ectoderm. That such substances are present in the amphibian eggs and embryos themselves (although they have not yet been biochemically well characterized) is clear from the work of Faulhaber (1972), Faulhaber and Lyra (1974), and Wall and Faulhaber (1976). It is no longer possible, at the present time, to explain amphibian morphogenesis on the basis of quantitative differences of a single substance: the existence of two distinct factors (neuralizing and mesodermizing) must now be considered as very probable, if not certain.

It is clear, in conclusion, that we are still badly in need of biochemical work on the chemical nature of the inducing factors present in the amphibian eggs themselves. If they could be isolated and well characterized, it would be possible to study their biosynthesis and to establish their localization at the various stages of development (by immunofluorescence, by instance). Such studies would allow us to know whether, as proposed by Dalcq and Pasteels (1938), the inducing substances that control amphibian development arise from an interaction between the gray crescent and the yolk platelets that lie underneath.

V. Destruction, Removal, Grafting of the Gray Crescent. Effects upon Morphogenesis

A. Brachet (1906) destroyed, by pricking with a hot steel needle, large areas of unfertilized or fertilized *Rana temporaria* eggs. He obtained almost perfect regulation (i.e., normal development) if the eggs were pricked during the first 45 minutes following fertilization. The result of the pricking experiments changed dramatically 1½ hour after insemination: at that time, the eggs had turned to the "mosaic" type and were provided with germinal localizations, since pricking of the dorsal half led to deficiencies that could no longer be corrected by regulation. The gray crescent does not become visible before 2 hours after fertilization in this species: pricking thus efficiently destroys a germinal localization before it can be seen by pigmentation changes; thus bilateral symmetry already precedes the appearance of a visible gray crescent, demonstrating that its establishment is a progressive, epigenetic process. As already mentioned, these experiments also proved that cleavage does not modify the bilateral symmetry, which has been fixed forever before the egg divides; they further showed that the plane of bilateral symmetry and that of first cleavage coincide in only 60–70% of the eggs.

As already mentioned, repetition of these experiments by Pasteels (1932) and Tung (1933) suggested that the unfertilized egg already possesses some kind of labile bilateral organization, which fertilization stabilizes. Pasteels (1932) pointed out that, in order to be efficient, the hot needle used for pricking should penetrate deep into the egg; this suggested that the morphogenetic territories lie deep inside the egg.

This problem took a very different orientation when Curtis published, in 1960 and 1962, the results of his experiments on *cortical grafting* in *Xenopus* eggs. In order to test the validity of the ideas proposed by Dalcq and Pasteels (1938) about the existence of a cortical field, he tried to graft small pieces of cortex removed at early stages of development—and succeeded; the pieces measured about 150 μm in diameter and their thickness varied from 0.5 to 3.0 μm. Electron microscopy showed that, as confirmed later by Bluemink (1972) on somewhat thicker fragments (5 μm), the pieces contained the cell membrane, a thin hyaline layer, mitochondria, and pigment granules. Here are the main results obtained by Curtis in 1960: development was normal when the grafts are transplanted, during first cleavage, to the same site as that from which they were derived. But, if pieces obtained from the gray crescent area were transplanted to the ventral margin of the egg, a secondary "dorsal lip" and a secondary embryonic axis were induced (Fig. 19). The inverse transplantation (a piece of cortex excised from the animal pole or from the ventral margin of the egg grafted into the gray crescent) caused a splitting of the dorsal lip at gastrulation and later the formation of "double embryos." Animal pole cortex grafted to the vegetal pole produced exogastrulation. Graft of cortical

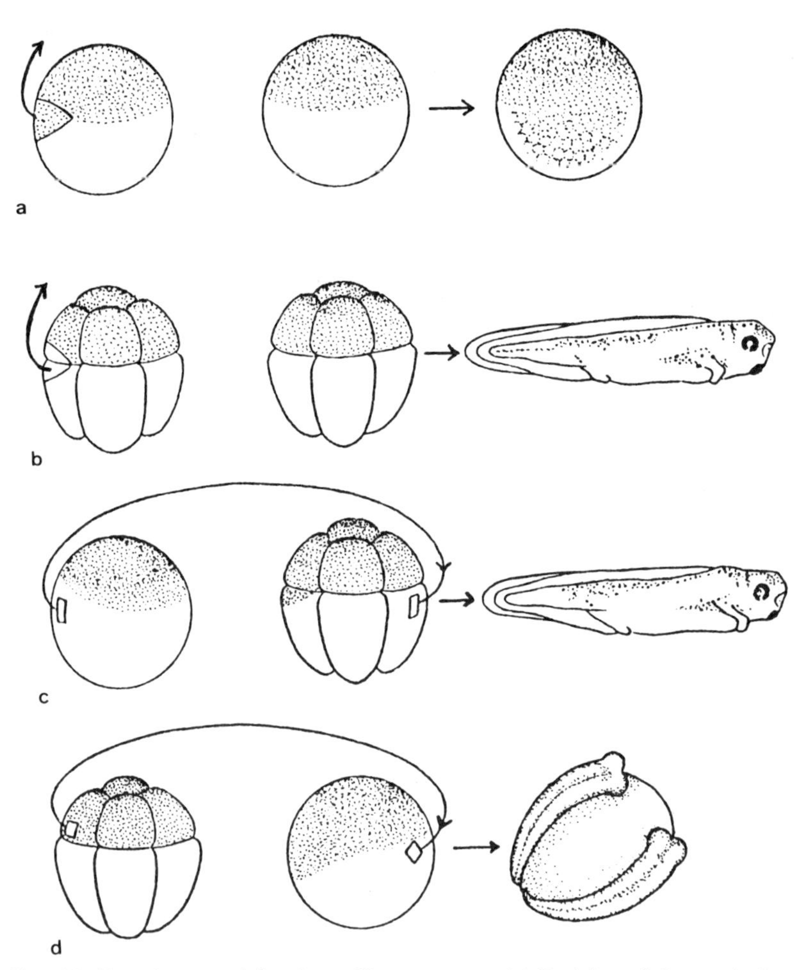

FIG. 19. Experiments of Curtis on *Xenopus* eggs. (a) Excision of the cortical gray crescent area at the 1-cell stage: no gastrulation. (b) Same experiment at the 8-cell stage: normal embryo. (c) Graft of the gray crescent cortex of the 1-cell stage to the ventral part of the 8-cell stage: it does not result in the induction of a secondary embryonic axis. (d) Graft of the gray crescent cortex from the 8-cell stage to the ventral margin of the 1-cell stage: induction of a secondary embryonic axis. After Curtis (1962), redrawn by J. J. Pasteels (1964). Reproduced with permission.

material from unfertilized eggs into cleaving embryos inhibited further development. It was concluded from these experiments that the cortical material possesses morphogenetic properties that especially affect gastrulation. These experiments indicated that the properties of the cortex are different in unfertilized and fertilized eggs: taken out from the unfertilized egg, it inhibits cleavage in the recipient egg; graft of cortex taken from fertilized eggs has no such inhibitory effect. These findings are in agreement with more recent work by Masui (1974): he found that unfertilized *Xenopus* eggs contain a "cytostatic factor," which inhibits cleavage if it is injected into a recipient egg at the 2-blastomere stage. This cytostatic activity is Ca^{2+} dependent, and its apparent disappearance, after fertilization, might be due to an efflux of Ca^{2+} following insemination of the eggs.

The main results reported in the second paper of Curtis (1962) are shown in Fig. 19 and can be summarized in the following way: excision of cortex from the region of the gray crescent of uncleaved fertilized eggs arrested development at the blastula stage; morphogenesis stops, suggesting that the gray crescent cortex is indispensable for gastrulation and morphogenesis. However, when the same experiment was done at the 8-cell stage, development was normal. Therefore, a fundamental change takes place in the properties of the dorsal cortex between the recently fertilized egg and the 8-blastomere stage. This has been confirmed by other experiments of Curtis (1962): grafting of gray crescent cortex from 8-cell stage eggs to an uncleaved fertilized egg induced a secondary axis, while grafting the same material to an 8-blastomere embryo had no such effect. Grafting a piece of dorsal cortex from uncleaved fertilized eggs to the ventral half of an 8-cell-stage embryo also had no effect.

Curtis (1962) concluded that the cortical field, at the 8-blastomere stage, has undergone a stabilization: removal of cortex can be corrected by regulatory processes; addition of more dorsal cortex does not affect development. In the uncleaved fertilized egg, the situation is much more labile: there is only an accumulation of a morphogenetic factor in the gray crescent, which will somehow activate or promote the establishment of the organized cortical field that is present at the 8-cell stage. Morphogenetic interactions within the cortex thus occur before the embryo reaches the stage of 8 blastomeres, when regulation becomes possible.

In summary, a series of epigenetic changes occur during the acquisition of bilateral symmetry: there seems to be already a vague tendency toward bilateral symmetry in the unfertilized egg; bilateral symmetry becomes apparent a short time before the appearance of the gray crescent; it is stabilized at the 8-cell stage and resides in the endoderm at the blastula stage.

Unfortunately, nobody has so far been able to repeat the experiments of Curtis (1960, 1962), which represent, from the technical viewpoint, a true *tour de force.* This lack of independent confirmation remains a matter of considerable concern. However, the related experiments by Tomkins and Rodman (1971) appear to be confirmatory of the main conclusions of Curtis. These workers isolated cortex material from either the gray crescent or the animal pole of the egg by dissection with fine tungsten needles and introduced this material, through a small hole at the animal pole, into the blastocoel of a mid-blastula embryo in order to test its inducing capacities. They found that only the gray crescent cortex had significant inducing activity; this activity increased between the 1-cell and the 8-cell stages.

There is an important discrepancy between these results and those of Curtis (1962); Tomkins and Rodman (1971) did not obtain induction of a secondary axis when the gray crescent cortex of the 8-blastomere stage was grafted on the ventral part of eggs at the same stage. However, it might be argued that, in such delicate experiments, negative results could carry less weight than positive ones. The essential point is that the gray crescent cortex seems to contain inducing activity that is not present in the animal pole cortex. Whether this activity is identical to the inducing factors isolated by Faulhaber and Lyra (1974) from yolk platelets and microsomes is unfortunately unknown.

We have so far considered the gray crescent as a purely *cytoplasmic* germinal localization, where factors required for gastrulation and differentiation of an embryonic axis are located. But nobody, until 1972, had the curiosity to examine the nuclear cytology of amphibian eggs *shortly* after operating upon them. We have therefore studied the cytological appearance of *Xenopus* eggs in which the gray crescent cortex had been mechanically injured (Brachet and Hubert, 1972) in order to determine whether nuclear and mitotic abnormalities were produced.

Slight injury of the dorsal or ventral cortex in 1- or 2-cell *Xenopus* eggs resulted in very frequent mitotic abnormalities (pluricentric and polyploid mitoses: Fig. 20): slight pricking of the cortex thus affects the organization of the mitotic spindles and DNA replication (Brachet and Hubert, 1972). These mitotic abnormalities are about twice as frequent after partial destruction of the dorsal than of the ventral cortex by slight injury with a needle at the 1- to 2-blastomere stage. They resulted, as one would expect, in *aneuploidy,* a condition known to be lethal and to arrest development at the late blastula or early gastrula stage (Fankhauser, 1934). Cytophotometric measurements of the DNA content per nucleus showed that aneuploidy is much more frequent after injury of the dorsal than of the ventral cortex; in embryos that can go beyond the gastrula stage, it is more important in the mesentoderm than in the neurectoderm.

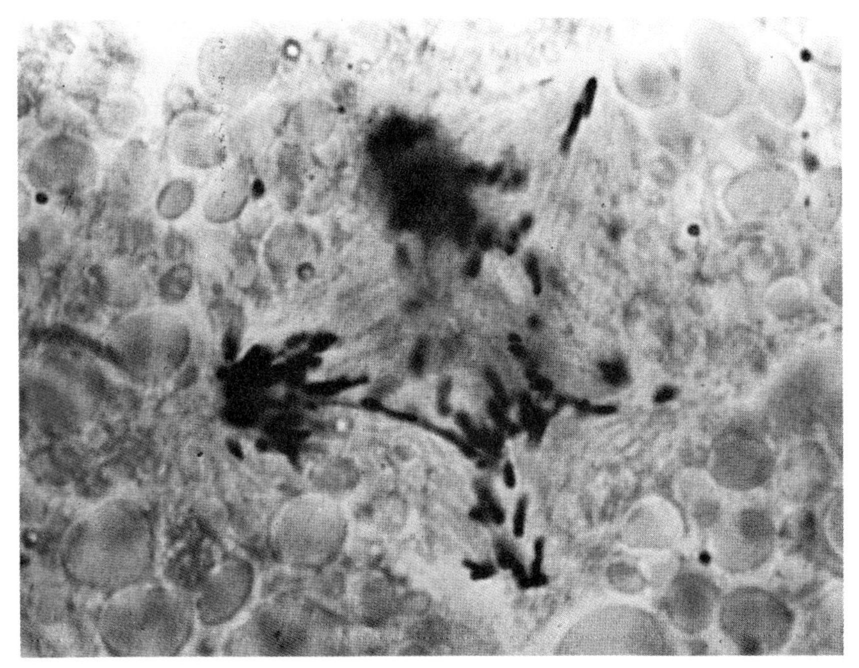

FIG. 20. Multipolar mitosis resulting from slight injury of the cortex (embryo fixed 4 hours after injury). From Brachet and Hubert (1972). Reproduced with permission.

These unexpected results, which demonstrated that cleavage mitoses often becomes abnormal when the cell surface is mechanically injured, do not invalidate the main conclusions of A. Brachet (1906) and Pasteels (1932), since these investigators studied embryos fixed many hours after the destruction of the gray crescent; moreover, they discarded those embryos that displayed irregular cleavage (as a result of abnormal assembly of the mitotic apparatus or incomplete furrowing) or which were arrested during gastrulation. Furthermore, our observations confirmed that developmental abnormalities are at least twice as frequent after injury to the dorsal than the ventral cortex of fertilized eggs. However, it should be kept in mind that nearly all the embryos that originated from dorsally wounded eggs showed some signs of aneuploidy by cytophotometric analysis; one of them was even almost anidian (Fig. 4), and it is impossible, in such a case, to rule out a genomic effect as the cause of poor development. Such a possibility strongly comes to mind in the case of the experiments in which Curtis (1962) removed pieces of the dorsal cortex and obtained an arrest of development at the late blastula stage; since the arrested blastulae were not cytologically analyzed, one cannot say whether the developmental arrest was due to lack of a morphogenetic stimulus resulting from the removal of part of the dorsal cortex, or to mitotic abnormalities that could lead to lethal aneuploidy. Thus, slight injury of the cortex often can produce aneuploidy, and this possibility must be kept in mind. Only a thorough cytological analysis, substantiated by quantitative cytophotometric measurements of the DNA content of individual nuclei, would allow one to conclude whether the effects observed by Curtis were really cortical-cytoplasmic, and not the result of injury and consequent disturbances to the genome.

The same warning holds for experiments where tissue extracts or proteins are injected into eggs, as pointed out by Markert and Ursprung (1963) and Melton (1965). It might also hold for the more recent studies of Anservin and Williams (1974), who claimed that injection of cytoplasm taken from different blastomeres into the various blastomeres of frog eggs at the 8- 16-cell stage had different effects: there was no effect if the cytoplasm from a given blastomere is injected into the same blastomere at the same stage; in other cases, abnormalities of development were found, suggesting differences in the chemical composition of the various blastomeres. While this is a very likely possibility, it should, of course, be confirmed by chemical analysis of the proteins present in the different blastomeres; but it would also be important to know whether the observed abnormalities were not due to secondary effects on the mitotic processes that might lead to aneuploidy.

VI. Is There a "Cortical Inheritance"?

As mentioned above, injury to the gray crescent results in arrested development, at the blastula or early gastrula stages in some of the eggs, and in various developmental abnormalities at the neurula, tailbud, or tadpole stages in others; the rest continue to develop and can reach the adult state. Curtis (1965) mated females that developed from eggs whose gray crescent had been injured with normal males or with males developed from injured eggs. He found that in a small number of the resulting embryo development was arrested just before gastrulation, while others continued to develop. When the adults derived from this first generation were mated, the percentage of lethals (arrest of development) in the descendants increased; in the third generation, 85% of the eggs from the females originating from eggs injured two generations earlier showed pregastrular arrest (even 100% for certain females, against only 0.5% in the controls). The source of the sperm (from a normal male, or from a male originating from an injured egg) made no difference, raising the possibility of cytoplasmic inheritance. Curtis (1965) proposed several hypotheses in order to explain these unexpected results: (1) Deletion of a part of the cortex may prevent its correct replication and result in the absence of essential cortical properties in subsequent generations. (2) The operation sets up a population of replicating molecules responsible for the inhibitory effect on gastrulation. In this case, the cortex of the gray crescent would have properties of self-replication, possibly due to the presence of particles endowed with genetic continuity.

This second hypothesis, although it might strike one as a fantasy of classical geneticists, could appeal to those who, some 30 years ago participated (like myself), to a very limited extent (Brachet, 1948b) in the enthusiasm for *plasmagenes*, i.e., self-replicating cytoplasmic particles. However, all the plasmagenes studied at that time have turned out to be viruses, so that this theory is now completely discredited and forgotten. One should point out, however, that, in view of the major importance of cytoplasm during early embryonic development, it is impossible to discount the hypothetical existence of such particles in eggs. However, the only argument in favor of their possible existence are the curious results of Curtis (1965), which remain to be explained and independently confirmed.

A less attractive, but not unrealistic, explanation is that the results of Curtis (1965) were simply due to chance: pregastrular arrest of embryonic development is not a specific morphogenetic abnormality and can hardly be taken as a reliable marker of specific genetic effects. Embryologists who have been working with *Xenopus laevis* (a domesticated animal generally reared in laboratories) know that there are periods of the year when there are "bad eggs" and "bad females." During these periods, "strange" results are obtained—artificial fertilization fails to succeed, many embryos die at early stages of development, etc. This is probably due to some inadequate physiological conditions that affect the quality of the eggs in an adverse way. Most likely, it is the egg cytoplasm, rather than the genome, that is abnormal; probably, oogenesis does not proceed normally, due to seasonal environmental factors or to poor control of the pH, chlorine content, ionic balance, temperature of water in the aquaria, inadequate feeding, too frequent injections of pituitary hormones to induce egg laying, etc. There is no indication that this seasonal, general type of lethality has a genetic basis, but this has never been studied in detail.

Another possibility resides in the fact that, as said before, slight injuries of the fertilized egg cortex easily induce aneuploidy (Brachet and Hubert, 1972). This aneuploidy will lead to pregastrular arrest if it is extensive, but it might persist, at a subtler level, in females that can reach the adult state. One could consider, for instance, the existence of slight chromosomal aberrations in the germ-line cells, which might affect oogenesis or egg viability, like the *o* mutation in the axolotl (recent review by Brothers, 1976). As a result, eggs unable to develop normally would be produced. In the axolotl, a number of genes that affect oogenesis has been discovered. The *o* mutation can be corrected (Briggs and Cassens, 1966) by the injection of cytoplasm, or, better, of nuclear sap from the germinal vesicle of normal oocytes. Similar "correction" experiments on the eggs laid by the females obtained by Curtis would certainly be worth trying.

We do not think that our nuclear–cytological studies on *Xenopus* eggs whose gray crescent has been injured (Brachet and Hubert, 1972) suffice to imply that the explanations proposed by Curtis (1965) for his observations are incorrect. However, they have shown that even slight injuries of the egg cortex can be followed by chromosomal abnormalities; this, and the seasonal variations in egg viability mentioned above, may make it difficult, if not impossible, to prove whether "cortical inheritance" in *Xenopus* actually exists and if it is cytoplasmic or genetic. In order to complete the picture of this problem, one might mention still another phenomenon in amphibian embryology, which may bear a remote similarity to the notion of cortical inheritance. It is the existence in the cytoplasm of maturing oocytes, of a *maturation-promoting factor* (MPF of Masui and Markert, 1971; Wasserman and Masui (1976). If this factor is injected into an immature oocyte, the latter undergoes maturation; infection of cytoplasm from this oocyte into another immature one causes its maturation. Such serial transfers of MPF can be continued repeatedly. It thus appears that MPF may be capable of "self-amplification" or "autocatalysis", although other interpretations are conceivable. In this respect, this phenomenon bears perhaps some resemblance to the "self-replicative" properties hypothesized to exist in the egg cortex by Curtis (1965).

VII. Inactivation of the Gray Crescent Morphogenetic Substance by Ultraviolet (UV) Irradiation

It is a well documented fact that UV irradiation decreases the inducing activity of the dorsal lip of the blastopore (organizer); inactivation is greatest at wavelengths where UV absorption is maximal for nucleic acids (around 2600 Å) (Dürken, 1937; Reith, 1937, 1941; Brandes, 1940, 1941). Comparable experiments, but on recently fertilized eggs instead of gastrulae, have been done recently by Grant and by Malacinski; they demonstrate a UV sensitivity of the gray crescent region and confirm its morphogenetic importance.

Grant and Wacaster (1972) have irradiated with UV (at 2537 Å) the vegetal pole of *R. pipiens* fertilized eggs; the gray crescent is unfortunately difficult to see in this species and could thus not be selectively irradiated. They obtained microcephalic or even acephalic embryos, suggesting that the inducing ability had been impaired by UV irradiation (Fig. 21). These morphogenetic defects could be due to irreversible damage to the nuclei, not to an injury of the cortex, presumably that of the gray crescent. This possibility could be ruled out by nuclear transplantation experiments: development of anucleate unfertilized eggs was the same whether the transplanted nucleus came out of an irradiated or a control donor. Thus the nuclei were not irreversibly damaged either directly or by interactions with irradiated cytoplasm or cortex. Injection of cytoplasm (but not of nuclear sap from the germinal vesicle of oocytes) from normal fertilized eggs reversed the inhibitory effects of UV in 30% of the cases: thus the injected material contains factors essential for neural differentiation.

Trying to obtain more precise information, Grant and Wacaster (1972) used a UV microbeam and compared the effects of irradiation on the marginal (equatorial) zone and on the vegetal pole: they obtained, in the first case, 30% microcephalic embryos and only 13% in the second. Irradiated cytoplasm is not markedly inhibitory when it is in-

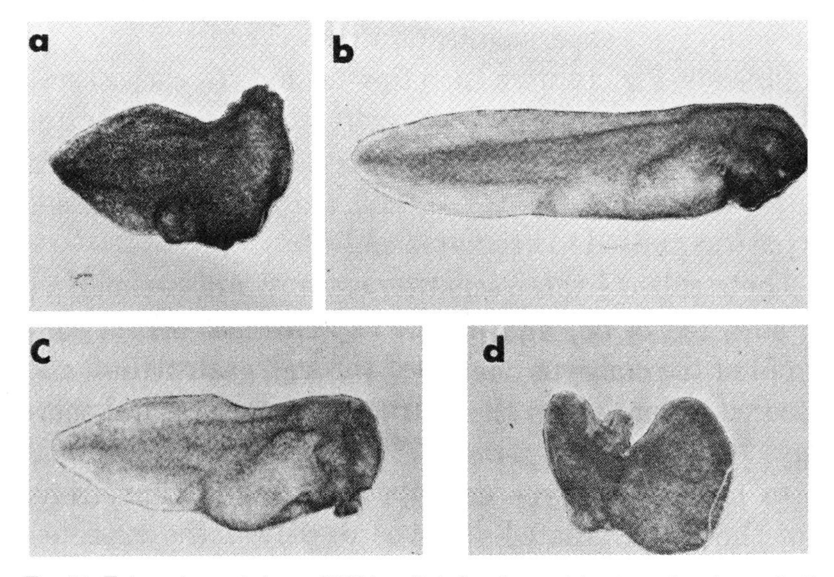

FIG. 21. External morphology of UV-irradiated embryos: (a) extremely microcephalic; (b) normal (nonirradiated control); (c) microcephalic; (d) acephalic. From Chung and Malacinski (1975). Reproduced with permission.

jected into normal fertilized eggs. Grant and Wacaster (1972) conclude that UV destroys a cytoplasmic factor essential for neural induction, but not for chordomesoderm differentiation. They point out, in their discussion, that this active substance might be related to the already mentioned (Section III) factor, present in the germinal vesicle, which produces hypercephaly after injection in fertilized eggs (Huff, 1962; Malacinski, 1974). As we pointed out in Section III, it is known that —SH-containing proteins, presumably originating from the germinal vesicle, accumulate in the marginal zone of *Triturus* eggs (Brachet, 1938, 1950a); it is also known now that, in *Discoglossus,* a mixture of nuclear sap from the germinal vesicle and of clear cytoplasm moves toward the future gray crescent (Klag and Ubbels, 1975) (Fig. 17). But, we do not know anything about the UV sensitivity of this material. Grant and Wacaster (1972) agree with the conclusion of Curtis (1962) that the properties of the gray crescent change during cleavage: sensitivity to UV is maximal 1½ hours after fertilization and drops afterward. This suggests that the active factor might move from the cortex to the inner cytoplasm during cleavage; this could lead, at the blastula stage, to the symmetrization of the endoderm demonstrated by Nieuwkoop (1973), as we suggested earlier in this review.

Unfortunately, the biochemical target for UV radiation remains unknown in frog eggs; nucleic acids are very good candidates, but there are many other possibilities: breakage of —SS-bonds, destruction of tryptophan, changes in permeability to ions or in the intracellular pH, inhibition of protein synthesis, as recently found by Murphy *et al.* (1975) for tobacco cells, etc.

Even the interpretation of the UV effects on development itself is not so easy as it seems at first sight: microcephaly could result from abnormal gastrulation. As shown by Grant and Youngdahl (1974), UV irradiation of vegetal halves of *R. pipiens* fertilized eggs delays the onset of gastrulation, and this is partially due to an inhibition of cell division in the irradiated hemisphere: studying the incorporation of injected [^{3}H]-thymidine into DNA, they found a 15–20% reduction of DNA synthesis in the irradiated vegetal half, but no changes in the animal half. Since a direct effect of UV on the nuclei is excluded by the transplantation experiments of Grant and Wacaster (1972), and since it is believed that UV does not penetrate more than 5–10 μm deep, Grant and Youngdahl suggest that retardation of development might be due to UV inactivation of a factor controlling DNA synthesis. This possibility will be considered in more detail in the next section.

Inhibition of cytokinesis by UV doses of 6,000–18,000 ergs/min/mm^2 (Grant and Wacaster, 1972) used 10^2–10^3 ergs/min/cm^2) was observed by Beal and Dixon (1975) and by Züst and Dixon (1975), who irradiated the vegetal pole of *Xenopus* fertilized eggs: irradiation resulted in the formation of a syncytium, which fragmented at the morula stage. Finally, gastrulation was delayed, abnormal, or even abortive. According to these authors, UV might affect intercellular adhesion and its effects (inhibition of cytokinesis without stopping karyokinesis) are comparable to those of cytochalasin. They rightly point out that, before ascribing the effects of UV to nucleic acid inactivation, one should not forget that UV irradiation is a classical method for softening the jelly that surrounds *Xenopus* eggs; in this case, it probably acts by breaking interglycosidic linkages in mucopolysaccharides.

It would be of some interest to know whether the "pseudogastrulation" movements that occur when unfertilized *R. pipiens* eggs are left in Ringer for a few hours (Holtfreter, 1943b; Smith and Ecker, 1970; Baltus *et al.,* 1973) are affected by UV: as already mentioned, in such uncleaved eggs, an invagination of vegetal material takes place after several hours; it mimics blastoporal lips and is probably a consequence of cortical contractility (Fig. 8). UV irradiation of eggs undergoing pseudogastrulation might throw some light on the possible relationships between UV sensitivity and cortical contractility.

The analysis of the UV sensitivity of the gray crescent cortex has made more progress thanks to the work of Malacinski *et al.* (1974, 1975). They first confirmed (Malacinski *et al.,* 1974) that, as found by Grant and Wacaster (1972), UV irradiation of the vegetal half of fertilized, still uncleaved, *R. pipiens* eggs produces characteristic defects on the morphogenesis of the nervous system (Fig. 21).

They paid particular attention to the various ways in which the UV lesion in neural morphogenesis could be corrected; they found that the UV effects can be prevented by either incubating the irradiated embryos at low temperature (10°C), microinjecting them with oocyte homogenate or replacing, at the early gastrula stage, the dorsal lip of the irradiated embryo by that of a normal one. The UV inhibitory effects, as one would expect, are dose-dependent: 7500 ergs/mm^2 lead to only slight abnormalities, 15,000 ergs/mm^2 arrest development prior to the completion of neurulation. With 10,000 ergs/mm^2, development of the neural structures is much better if the embryos are reared at 10°C rather than at 25°C (this effect has been called "cryoreversion" by the authors). Injection of an oocyte homogenate into the blastocoel of a UV-irradiated gastrula also reverses the UV syndrome, but less efficiently than culture at low temperature. The most efficient and dramatic correction was obtained when the dorsal lip of the UV-irradiated embryo was replaced by the dorsal lip of a normal embryo.

In their second paper (1975), Malacinski *et al.* describe experiments on eggs from both the axolotl (which has a recognizable gray crescent) and the frog *R. pipiens*. In the first case, various regions of the egg could be directly irradiated; in the second, the area of the UV-hit was compared with the location of the dorsal lip at gastrulation. These experiments, as well as others on albino axolotl eggs, have established an important point: the dorsal marginal zone (i.e., the gray crescent region) is the most UV-sensitive area in the eggs of the two species. Microinjection into the blastocoel, at the early blastula stage, of the supernatant from a homogenate of normal oocytes centrifuged at 30,000 *g* can overcome the effects of UV irradiation. As in the experiments of Grant and Wacaster (1972), the maximal sensitivity to UV is observed prior to the time at which the gray crescent becomes clearly visible; let us recall that A. Brachet (1906) had already found that by pricking the egg with a hot needle one can detect the existence of bilateral symmetry before the gray crescent can be seen. In the UV experiments of Malacinski *et al.* (1975), the greatest UV sensitivity occurs at the time of first cleavage, the gray crescent not being visible before 90–130 minutes after fertilization. Ultraviolet irradiation of the ventral marginal region—like pricking in the old experiments of A. Brachet (1906)—has no visible effect. It is worth mentioning that, in the embryos developing from eggs that have been irradiated on the dorsal side, the nervous system is very deficient, but the notochord is normal; this suggests that UV destroys a component required for *neural induction* (possibly competence of the ectoderm), but not for chordomesoderm differentiation. This situation is identical to the one we met when we treated amphibian gastrulae with —SS-reducing agents (mercaptoethanol, for instance) or lipoic acid (Brachet, 1963). This similarity in morphogenetic effects suggests that the effects of UV on the —SS-, —SH equilibrium of the egg constituents, in particular its contractile proteins and cytoskeleton, might be worth investigating.

Finally, Chung and Malacinski (1975) succeeded in demonstrating that localized UV irradiation destroys a cytoplasmic component that is required for neural induction; this was shown by the fact that the UV lesion can be completely repaired by substituting a dorsal lip taken from a normal donor to the dorsal lip of a gastrula that had been irradiated 90 minutes after fertilization. Grafting of a dorsal lip from a gastrula that had developed from an irradiated egg failed to repair the UV lesion; grafting from normal ventral tissue did not substantially improve the formation of neural structures in UV-irradiated embryos. In agreement with the already mentioned work of Dürken (1937) and Reith (1937, 1941), it was found that dorsal lips from UV-irradiated eggs are poor inducers. These experiments clearly show that the damage to the lip is sufficient to account for the defect in normal development. They further show that a UV-sensitive constituent is required for neural induction; this constituent is restricted to the dorsal half of the gastrula and is probably, in agreement with the work of Curtis (1960, 1962) restricted to the cortex of the recently fertilized egg.

Very recently, Malacinski *et al.* (1977) published the conclusions of an extensive series of similar experiments; UV irradiation exerts two different effects on the dorsal lip: it diminishes the invagination capacity of the lip and it decreases its inducing power.

In this respect, a gastrula arising from a UV-irradiated *R. pipiens* egg is very similar to a gastrula deriving from fertilizing a *R. pipiens* egg with *R. sylvatica* sperm: development of the hybrid is blocked at the gastrula stage, because invagination of the dorsal lip stops; the inducing power of this dorsal lip is inferior to that of a lip taken from a control embryo (Moore, 1948). In both cases, the surface properties, as evidenced by the capacity for the cells to make aggregates, are decreased. It looks as though the UV-sensitive component(s) necessary for gastrulation and induction could not be synthesized by lethal hybrids.

In conclusion, UV irradiation is a very convenient tool for the analysis of the gray crescent cortex potentialities; it has the advantage over pricking that it does not injure the nuclei, as shown by Grant and Wacaster's (1972) nuclear transplantation experiments. The fact that the UV-induced lesions can be corrected by injection of cytoplasm or of a centrifuged homogenate from normal eggs gives hope that it will be possible to identify the UV-sensitive morphogenetic substances; it would be interesting to know, in this respect, whether a UV-irradiated homogenate from normal frog eggs is still capable of correcting the UV cortical lesions in the irradiated eggs. The fact that a large number of eggs can easily be UV-irradiated should make biochemical studies (RNA, protein synthesis, etc.) possible. As we shall see now, there is a very unfortunate scarcity of information about the biochemical and biophysical properties of the amphibian egg cortex.

VIII. Biophysical and Biochemical Studies

Vital staining experiments with dyes such as Neutral Red and Nile Blue sulfate have led Dollander and Melnotte (1952) and Dollander (1957) to the conclusion that there are *permeability gradients* in the fertilized eggs of *Triturus*. Permeability to these dyes would vary in the following order: ventral marginal zone < animal pole < gray crescent (dorsal marginal zone) < vegetal pole. This means that there is a polarity gradient, decreasing from the vegetal to the animal pole, on which a dorsoventral gradient is superimposed. In the marginal zone, the permeability of the gray crescent region is thus higher than that of the corresponding ventral side. Unfortunately, we do not know much about the molecular mechanisms of permeability to vital dyes; in experiments on isolated fragments of gastrulae, we observed (J. Brachet, 1950b) that neutral red penetrates better in cells from the interior of the embryo than in the superficial ones; the dye accumulates in the pigment granules and in the cortical layer of the yolk platelets.

We have already seen that the permeability to water of the cell surface is very low in frog eggs (Prescott and Zeuthen, 1953) and that it temporarily increases when the cortex contracts toward the animal pole (Løvtrup, 1962); water permeability falls back to the low initial level when the contraction wave relaxes, thus shortly before the gray

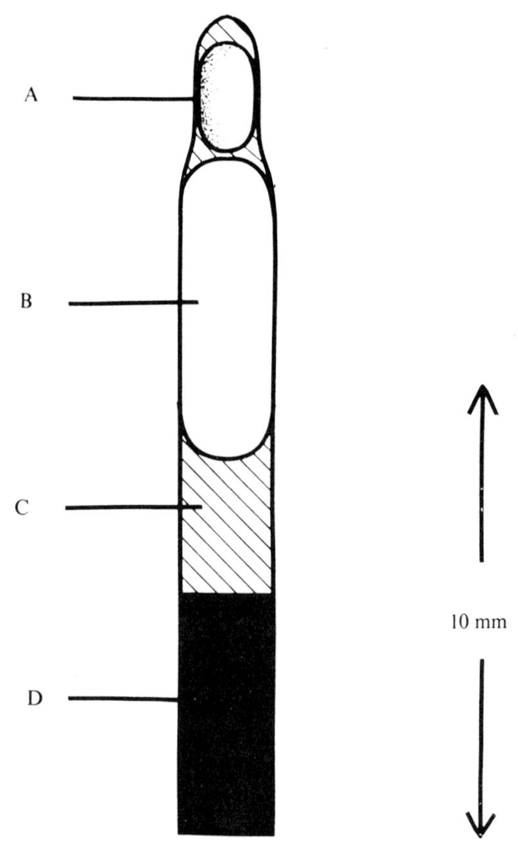

FIG. 22. Diver respiration chamber used by Landström and Løvtrup (1975) for reversal of the dorsoventral polarity. A, top part with embryo; B, air bubble; C, flotation medium; D, black varnish containing carbonyliron. Reproduced with permission.

crescent becomes visible in *R. temporaria* eggs. Løvtrup (1962) has suggested that the permeability to water and even to oxygen might be higher in the gray crescent than in other parts of the fertilized egg. This remains, for the time being, purely hypothetical and new investigations of the question, with the elegant microelectrode techniques applied to amphibian eggs by de Laat *et al.* (1974, 1975), would be extremely welcome: they should show whether permeability to water and ions is indeed higher in the gray crescent area than in the ventral marginal zone.

Løvtrup and Pigon (1958) and more recently Landström and Løvtrup (1975) have tested the idea that dorsoventral polarity might be linked to differences in permeability to oxygen; the basic principle of the two sets of experiments is the same: to place an amphibian egg, at the 2- or 4-cell stage, in a tightly fitting tube, in order to decrease the oxygen content of the surrounding water by the respiration of the egg itself. The apparatus used by Landström and Løvtrup (1975), based on the Cartesian diver principle (Fig. 22), should certainly be more efficient than the very simple system previously used by Løvtrup and Pigon (1958). The new experiments are also much more satisfactory from the biological viewpoint: Løvtrup and Pigon (1958) could not orientate axolotl eggs in the glass tube according to the position of the gray crescent; they did it according to the cleavage plane; but we have seen that, at least in *Rana temporaria,* cleavage plane and bilateral symmetry plane coincide in only 70% of the eggs. In the more recent experiments of Landström and Løvtrup (1975), which were performed on *Xenopus laevis* eggs at the 4 cell-stage, orientation of the egg was under better control: it is known that, at this stage, the two dorsal blastomeres are generally smaller than the two ventral ones (Fig. 23); thus the two small blastomeres could be placed on the aerobic or anaerobic side of the diver at will.

Both Løvtrup and Pigon (1958) and Landström and Løvtrup (1975) claim to have succeeded in reversing dorsoventral polarity by restricting the oxygen supply to the dorsal side: the posterior end will always appear at the aerobic side, while the development of the anterior end, oriented toward the anaerobic side, is partly suppressed. Development is retarded in the treated embryos and, as one would expect, their oxygen consumption is lower than that of the controls.

Landström and Løvtrup (1975) conclude that dorsoventrality is associated with a gradient in oxygen consumption. The effect of dorsoventral polarity would be quantitative rather than qualitative and "it may be futile to search for cortical or cytoplasmic inductors, evocators or regulators in the embryo."

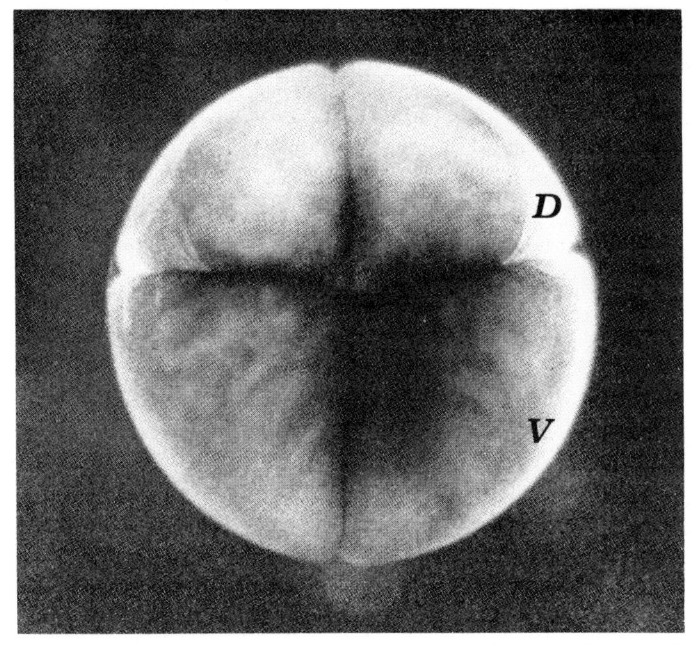

FIG. 23. *Xenopus laevis* egg at the 4-cell stage. The size difference between the dorsal and the ventral blastomeres can readily be seen. After Landström and Løvtrup (1975). Reproduced with permission.

This is a rather discouraging conclusion; in fact, it sets us back to the old physiological gradients theory of C. M. Child (discussed in detail for amphibian eggs, by Needham in 1930 and 1942). After much discussion (see J. Brachet, 1960, for details), it is now generally accepted that, at the gastrula stage, the dorsal half has a slightly higher oxygen consumption than the ventral one. This has been recently confirmed by Landström and Løvtrup (1974). But it is very doubtful that this dorsoventral difference in respiratory rate is due to a better permeability to oxygen of the dorsal half: reduction of the oxygen partial tension has little effect—during a few hours at least—on the rate of oxygen consumption in amphibian eggs. In fact, we found it very difficult to completely inhibit respiration of frog eggs by flushing purified nitrogen through Warburg flasks (J. Brachet, 1934): this shows that amphibian eggs are capable of utilizing efficiently traces of oxygen. This fact certainly complicates the interpretation of the results obtained by Løvtrup and Pigon (1958) and Landström and Løvtrup (1975): the inhibition of development in the "anaerobic" half of the egg is not necessarily due to a decrease of oxygen consumption, but might as well be ascribed to CO_2 (and possibly other acids) accumulating in the confined end of the diver (Brachet, 1935). Changes in the pH of the very small amount of medium that surrounds the egg are unavoidable, and one can regret that a pH indicator has not been added to the 1.5 μl of medium which was in contact with the embryo. Indeed, in a very recent paper which was published after completion of the present review, Landström *et al.* (1976) conclude from new experiments that the effect of anaerobiosis on dorsoventral organization is probably due to lactic acid accumulation. It is also well known that anaerobiosis and KCN treatment stop development at the end of cleavage in amphibian eggs (J. Brachet, 1934): gastrulation does not take place under these conditions, and this might well be the main reason for the "reversal of dorso-ventral polarity" observed by Løvtrup and Pigon (1958) and Landström and Løvtrup (1975). Prolonged decrease in the O_2 supply will necessarily inhibit, sooner or later, macromolecule (DNA, RNA, proteins) synthesis; if such an inhibition occurs on one side only of the developing egg, it is not surprising that this side will be underdeveloped. Finally, the eggs (as shown in Fig. 22) are strongly stretched; this might impede the morphogenetic movements, and the experiments should thus be repeated with eggs marked with vital stains in order to follow these movements.

In conclusion, I think that the experiments of Landström and Løvtrup (1975) are interesting and well worth continuing, but they have, of course, no bearing on the *initial* establishment of dorsoventral polarity and bilateral symmetry. The results of Landström and Løvtrup (1975) are similar to those of Gilchrist (1928) and Glade *et al.* (1967), who showed that, when a temperature gradient is applied over an amphibian gastrula, the dorsal side will be formed toward the warmest side. But the significance of these experiments is far from clear, since local heating affects the morphogenetic movements and, as a consequence, axis formation. There is really nothing very surprising in the fact that cooling down, reducing the oxygen supply, or lowering the pH of the surrounding medium have adverse effects upon the development of the exposed dorsal half of an amphibian egg or gastrula.

It has been suggested by Løvtrup (1965), and more explicitly by Grant and Youngdahl (1974), that the gray crescent might contain a factor that stimulates DNA synthesis and mitotic activity; it is a fact that, at the blastula stage, the size of the cells is smaller on the dorsal than on the ventral side; it is another fact that such a factor exists in amphibian eggs (Benbow and Ford, 1975): they found that extracts from early stages of *Xenopus* contain an initiation factor (FI) which induces DNA synthesis in nuclei isolated from adult livers of *Xenopus*.

FI is a protein; its content increases during maturation; it is abundant in fertilized eggs, blastulae, and gastrulae and tends to disappear at later stages of development. It certainly would be very interesting to know whether it accumulates in the dorsal half of the egg and embryo, whether it is UV sensitive, etc. However, the smaller size of the dorsal cells, at the blastula stage, does not necessarily mean that they have undergone more mitoses than the ventral ones: it might be simply a consequence of the unequal furrowing between dorsal and ventral blastomeres, which often takes place already at the 4-cell stage (Fig. 23). Smaller dorsal blastomeres can be expected to give rise to smaller cells in the blastula without assuming necessarily a different rate of DNA synthesis. Special experiments should be done in order to establish whether the rate of DNA synthesis is really higher on the dorsal than the ventral side.

We have tried (Brachet and Hubert, 1972) to study, by autoradiography, the effects of localized injury of the dorsal and ventral cortex of *Xenopus* eggs on macromolecule synthesis. These experiments were designed in order to test a hypothesis that I proposed in 1967: we know that neural induction is the result of gene derepression (Brachet, 1967; Tiedemann, 1975, 1976); since injury of the gray crescent cortex in the fertilized egg prevents gastrulation and medullary plate formation, it is possible that this cortex exerts some remote control on RNA synthesis in the nuclei. Such a remote control exists in the eggs of the mollusk *Ilyanassa,* where removal of the polar lobe (which contains no nucleus) delays for many hours the onset of RNA (in particular HnRNA) synthesis (Davidson *et al.,* 1965; Koser and Collier, 1976). As already mentioned in this review, we came across an unexpected difficulty: slight injury of the cortex produces frequent abnormalities of the mitotic apparatus and the chromosomes. For this reason, the experiments had to be discontinued: it was of course not possible to test the initial hypothesis in a system where injury in the cortex induces changes in the nuclei, including aneuploidy. Few eggs were thoroughly analyzed, and only two conclusions could be drawn: destruction of the dorsal cortex seems to reduce RNA synthesis in the nuclei of the dorsal lip of the blastopore; there is a close correlation between morphogenesis and nuclear RNA synthesis: the latter is almost absent when development is blocked at the blastula stage.

The only paper where a serious biochemical analysis of the cortex of *Xenopus* eggs has so far been done is that of Tomkins and Rodman (1971): they have analyzed by polyacrylamide gel electrophoresis the proteins present in the cortex from the animal pole and the gray crescent of fertilized (1-cell) eggs and 8-cell stages. This was done by excising the various portions of the cortex with tungsten needles and pooling the samples in a centrifuge tube kept at −60°C; the samples were then thawed and centrifuged at 10,000 *g* for 10 minutes. Both the supernatant and pellets were submitted to gel electrophoresis. It was impossible to obtain detectable bands from the soluble fraction, but the electrophoretic patterns of insoluble proteins were unique for each type of cortex analyzed (animal pole at 1-cell stage; animal pole at 8-cell stage; gray crescent at 1-cell stage; gray crescent at 8-cell stage). These interesting results demonstrate that the composition of the cortex differs regionally and that it changes between the stages 1 and 8 blastomeres. It would of course be of great interest to test the proteins specific to the gray crescent cortex for biological (inducing) activity.

Recently, a method for analyzing the soluble proteins of *Xenopus* eggs has been described in abstract form by Namenwirth and Moen (1973); they state that the distribution of soluble proteins is different at the animal and vegetal pole of both uncleaved eggs and blastulae. It is to be hoped that this method will also be used for studying the distribution of the soluble proteins along the dorsoventral axis.

IX. Conclusions

The main purpose of this review is to draw the attention of today's embryologists to a very important, but too neglected, subject: the formation of dorsoventral polarity and bilateral symmetry. As pointed out at the beginning of this review, without the animal–vegetal polarity already present in the oocyte, we should have neither head, nor tail (i.e., a coccyx, in the case of man). Without the changes that lead to the establishment of a gray crescent (or its unseen equivalents), we would have neither back nor belly and the words right and left would not make any sense: in other words, we would be anidian monsters.

The story of the gray crescent is a long one: it started, more than a century ago, with the work of Newport (1854). In this long story, one meets the names of all the great experimental embryologists of the past: W. Roux, O. Schultze, G. Born, T. H. Morgan, A. Brachet, etc. When one rereads their classical papers, one can only respectfully admire their skill, ingenuity, and intelligence and hope that their work will be continued by new men, provided with new ideas and methods.

It is clear, from this review, that we are still very ignorant of the mechanisms that lead to the symmetrization of the fertilized egg: more accurate studies of its ultrastructure, not only by transmission and scanning electron microscopy, but also by freeze-etching, cytochemistry, and autoradiography at the ultrastructural level, are badly needed. In particular, we know nothing about the distribution of microfilaments, microtubules, contractile proteins in the dorsal and the ventral cortex; the effects of now classical drugs such as colchicin, vinblastin, cytochalasin on the formation of the gray crescent have not even been studied.

But it is in the biochemical, molecular field that our ignorance is most serious. Analysis of the nucleic acids and proteins present in the amphibian egg cortex has barely begun. We do not know the nature of the UV-sensitive constituent present in the gray crescent, which plays a morphogenetic role: Is it a stored, maternal messenger RNA as one would like to think, or something entirely different? Are the inducing substances isolated by Faulhaber and Lyra (1974) accumulated or synthesized in the dorsal cortex? Is there a localization, in the dorsal part of the egg, of the various factors that are required for DNA, RNA, and protein synthesis? Why does a gray crescent form so fast after a heat shock in axolotl eggs?

We have no answers to these and many other questions, primarily because embryologists working with amphibian eggs seldom look at the gray crescent: the latter, in species where it can be seen, is a very useful marker of the dorsal side; as shown by A. Brachet 70 years ago, it is a "germinal localization." But, we do not know, except for the interesting work of Whittaker (1973) on ascidian eggs, what a germinal localization really is. Is it an accumulation of preexisting, maternal messages? Does it contain substances, presumably nonhistone proteins, that will specifically derepress given genes in the nuclei that have colonized a particular cytoplasm? Answers to these questions should provide an answer, in molecular terms, to the great problem raised by the "naturalists" of the 18th century (Spallanzani, Buffon, Haller, Bonnet, Needham, etc.): preformation or epigenesis?

ACKNOWLEDGMENTS

I wish to thank Professor J. Signoret, Dr. M. Namenwirth, and Dr. M. Geuskens for providing me with original photographs and allowing me to reproduce them. My best thanks also go to Professors J. J. Pasteels, A. Ficq, and P. Van Gansen and to Dr. R. Tencer for help and advice in the preparation of the manuscript. Dr. C. Evans kindly corrected the English.

REFERENCES

Asashima, M. (1975). *Wilhelm Roux' Arch. Entwicklungsmech. Org.* **177**, 301.
Ancel, P., and Vintemberger, P. (1948). *Bull. Biol.* **31**, Suppl., 1.
Anservin, R. D., and Williams, B. J. (1974). *J. Exp. Zool.* **190**, 373.
Baker, P. C. (1965). *J. Cell Biol.* **24**, 95.
Balinsky, B. L. (1960). *In* "Germ Cells and Development," p. 550. Baselli, Pavia.
Baltus, E., Brachet, J., Hanocq-Quertier, J., and Hubert, E. (1973). *Differentiation* **1**, 127.
Banki, O. (1929). *Proc. Int. Congr. Zool., 10th, 1927,* p. 375.

Beal, C. M., and Dixon, K. E. (1975). *J. Exp. Zool.* **192**, 277.
Benbow, R. M., and Ford, C. C. (1975). *Proc. Natl. Acad. Sci. U.S.A.* **72**, 2437.
Benford, H. H., and Namenwirth, M. (1974). *Dev. Biol.* **39**, 168.
Bluemink, J. G. (1970). *J. Ultrastruct. Res.* **82**, 142.
Bluemink, J. G. (1972). *J. Ultrastruct. Res.* **41**, 95.
Bluemink, J. G., and de Laat, S. W. (1973). *J. Cell Biol.* **59**, 89.
Bluemink, J. G., and de Laat, S. W. (1974). *J. Cell Biol.* **60**, 529.
Bluemink, J. G., and Hoperskaya, O. A. (1975). *Wilhelm Roux' Arch. Entwicklungsmech. Org.* **177**, 75.
Bluemink, J. G., Tertoolen, L. G. J., Ververgaert, P. H. J., and Verkleij, A. J. (1976). *Biochim. Biophys. Acta* **443**, 143.
Born, G. (1885). *Arch. Mikrosk. Anat.* **24**, 475.
Brachet, A. (1904). *Arch. Biol.* **21**, 103.
Brachet, A. (1906). *Wilhelm Roux' Arch. Entwicklungsmech. Org.* **22**, 326.
Brachet, A. (1911). *Arch. Biol.* **26**, 337.
Brachet, A. (1931). "L'oeuf et les facteurs de l'Ontogénèse." Doin, Paris.
Brachet, J. (1934). *Arch. Biol.* **45**, 611.
Brachet, J. (1935). *Arch. Biol.* **46**, 1.
Brachet, J. (1938). *Bull. Acad. Roy. Sci. Belg.* **6**, 449.
Brachet, J. (1948a). *Experientia* **4**, 353.
Brachet, J. (1948b). "Unités biologiques douées de continuité génétique," p. 145. CNRS, Paris.
Brachet, J. (1950a). "Chemical Embryology," p. 358. Wiley (Interscience), New York.
Brachet, J. (1950b). *Experientia* **6**, 56.
Brachet, J. (1960). "Biochemistry of Development." Pergamon, Oxford.
Brachet, J. (1963). *Dev. Biol.* **7**, 348.
Brachet, J. (1967). "De l'Embryologie expérimentale à l'Embryologie moléculaire" (E. Wolff, ed.), p. 1. Dunod, Paris.
Brachet, J. (1972). *Arch. Biol.* **83**, 243.
Brachet, J. (1975). "Introduction à l'Embryologie moléculaire." Masson, Paris.
Brachet, J., and Hubert, E. (1972). *J. Embryol. Exp. Morphol.* **27**, 131.
Brandes, J. (1940). *Arch. Biol.* **51**, 219.
Brandes, J. (1941). *Arch. Biol.* **53**, 149.
Briggs, R. W., and Cassens, G. (1966). *Proc. Natl. Acad. Sci. U.S.A.* **55**, 1103.
Brothers, A. J. (1976). *Nature (London)* **260**, 112.
Brummett, A. R., and Dumont, J. W. (1976). *J. Ultrastruct. Res.* **55**, 4.
Chung, H. M., and Malacinski, G. M. (1975). *Proc. Natl. Acad. Sci. U.S.A.* **72**, 1235.
Clavert, J. (1962). *Adv. Morphog.* **2**, 27.
Curtis, A. S. G. (1960). *J. Embryol. Exp. Morphol.* **8**, 163.
Curtis, A. S. G. (1962). *J. Embryol. Exp. Morphol.* **10**, 410.
Curtis, A. S. G. (1965). *Arch. Biol.* **76**, 523.
Dalcq, A., and Pasteels, J. (1938). *Bull. Acad. R. Med. Belg.* **3**, 261.
Davidson, E., Haslett, G. W., Finney, R. J., Allfrey, V. G., and Mirsky, A. E. (1965). *Proc. Natl. Acad. Sci. U.S.A.* **54**, 696.
de Laat, S. W., Luchtel, D., and Bluemink, J. G. (1973). *Dev. Biol.* **31**, 163.
de Laat, S. W., Buwalda, R. J. A., and Habets, A. M. (1974). *Exp. Cell Res.* **89**, 1.
de Laat, S. W., Wouters, W., Marques da Silva Guarda, M., and da Silva Guarda, M. A. (1975). *Exp. Cell Res.* **91**, 15.
Denis-Donini, S., Baccetti, B., and Monroy, A. (1976). *J. Ultrastruct. Res.* **57**, 104.
Dollander, A. (1957). *C.R. Seances Soc. Biol. Ses Fil.* **151**, 977.

Dollander, A. (1961). *Arch. Anat. Histol. Embryol.* **44**, Suppl., 93.
Dollander, A., and Melnotte, P. J. (1952). *C.R. Seances Soc. Biol. Ses Fil.* **146**, 1614.
Dürken, B. (1937). *Z. Wiss. Zool.* **147**, 295.
Elinson, R. P. (1975). *Dev. Biol.* **47**, 257.
Epel, D. (1975). *Am. Zool.* **15**, 507.
Fankhauser, G. (1934). *J. Exp. Zool.* **67**, 349.
Faulhaber, J. (1972). *Wilhelm Roux' Arch. Entwicklungsmech. Org.* **171**, 87.
Faulhaber, J., and Lyra, L. (1974). *Wilhelm Roux' Arch. Entwicklungsmech. Org.* **175**, 151.
Franke, W., Rathke, P. C., Seib, E., Tredelenburg, M. F., Osborn, M., and Weber, K. (1976). *Cytobiologie* **14**, 111.
Gilchrist, F. G. (1928). *Physiol. Zool.* **1**, 231.
Gingell, D. (1970). *J. Embryol. Exp. Morphol.* **23**, 583.
Glade, R. W., Burrill, E. M., and Falk, R. J. (1967). *Growth* **31**, 231.
Grant, P., and Wacaster, J. F. (1972). *Dev. Biol.* **28**, 454.
Grant, P., and Youngdahl, P. (1974). *J. Exp. Zool.* **190**, 289.
Grey, R. D., Wolf, D. P., and Hedrick, J. L. (1974). *Dev. Biol.* **36**, 44.
Grey, R. D., Working, P. K., and Hedrick, J. L. (1976). *Dev. Biol.* **54**, 52.
Hanocq, J., Baltus, E., and Steinert, G. (1974). *C.R. Hebd. Seances Acad. Sci.* **279**, 211.
Hebard, C. N., and Herold, R. C. (1967). *Exp. Cell Res.* **16**, 553.
Holtfreter, J. (1943a). *J. Exp. Zool.* **93**, 251.
Holtfreter, J. (1943b). *J. Exp. Zool.* **94**, 261.
Holtfreter, J. (1948). *Ann. N.Y. Acad. Sci.* **49**, 709.
Holtfreter, J., and Hamburger, V. (1955). *In* "Analysis of Development" (B. Willier, P. Weiss, and V. Hamburger, eds), p. 230. Saunders, Philadelphia, Pennsylvania.
Hoperskaya, O. A. (1975). *J. Embryol. Exp. Morphol.* **34**, 253.
Huff, R. (1962). *Dev. Biol.* **4**, 389.
Ikushima, N., and Maruyama, S. (1971). *J. Embryol. Exp. Morphol.* **25**, 263.
Kalt, M. R. (1971). *J. Embryol. Exp. Morphol.* **26**, 51.
Klag, J. J., and Ubbels, G. A. (1975). *Differentiation* **3**, 15.
Koser, R. B., and Collier, J. R. (1976). *Differentiation* **6**, 47.
Kubota, T. (1967). *J. Embryol. Exp. Morphol.* **17**, 331.
Landström, U., and Løvtrup, S. (1974). *Wilhelm Roux' Arch. Entwicklungsmech. Org.* **176**, 1.
Landström, U., and Løvtrup, S. (1975). *J. Embryol. Exp. Morphol.* **33**, 879.
Landström, U., Løvtrup-Rein, H., and Løvtrup, S. (1976). *J. Embryol. Exp. Morphol.* **36**, 343.
Løvtrup, S. (1962). *J. Exp. Zool.* **151**, 79.
Løvtrup, S. (1965). *Acta Zool. (Stockholm)* **46**, 119.
Løvtrup, S., and Pigon, A. (1958). *J. Embryol. Exp. Morphol.* **6**, 486.
Luckenbill, L. M. (1971). *Exp. Cell Res.* **66**, 263.
Malacinski, G. M. (1974). *Cell Differ.* **3**, 31.
Malacinski, G. M., Alles, C. D., and Chung, H. M. (1974). *J. Exp. Zool.* **189**, 249.
Malacinski, G. M., Benford, H., and Chung, H. M. (1975). *J. Exp. Zool.* **191**, 97.
Malacinski, G. M., Brothers, A. J., and Chung, H. K. (1977). *Dev. Biol.* **56**, 24.
Manes, M. E., and Barbieri, F. D. (1976). *Dev. Biol.* **53**, 138.
Markert, C. L., and Ursprung, H. (1963). *Dev. Biol.* **7**, 560.
Masui, Y. (1974). *J. Exp. Zool.* **187**, 141.
Masui, Y., and Markert, C. L. (1971). *J. Exp. Zool.* **177**, 129.
Melton, C. G. (1965). *Dev. Biol.* **12**, 387.
Monroy, A., and Baccetti, B. (1975). *J. Ultrastruct. Res.* **50**, 131.

Moore, J. A. (1948). *J. Exp. Zool.* **108**, 127.
Morrill, G. A., and Murphy, J. B. (1972). *Nature (London)* **238**, 282.
Morrill, G. A., Kostellow, A. B., and Murphy, J. B. (1971). *Exp. Cell Res.* **66**, 289.
Murphy, T. M., Wright, L. A., and Murphy, J. B. (1975). *Photochem. Photobiol.* **21**, 219.
Namenwirth, P., and Moen, T. L. (1973). *J. Cell Biol.* **67**, 302a.
Namur, P. (1974). *C.R. Hebd. Seances Acad. Sci.* **278**, 1103.
Needham, J. (1930). "Chemical Embryology." Cambridge Univ. Press, London and New York.
Needham, J. (1942). "Biochemistry and Morphogenesis." Cambridge Univ. Press, London and New York.
Newport, G. (1854). *Philos. Trans. R. Soc. London* **144**, 219.
Nieuwkoop, P. D. (1973). *Adv. Morphog.* **10**, 2.
O'Dell, D. S., Tencer, R., Monroy, A., and Brachet, J. (1974). *Cell Differ.* **3**, 193.
Pasteels, J. (1932). C.R. Assoc. Anat. Congr. Nancy, Abstr.
Pasteels, J. (1938). *Arch. Biol.* **49**, 629.
Pasteels, J. (1939). *Arch. Biol.* **50**, 292.
Pasteels, J. (1940). *Arch. Biol.* **51**, 335.
Pasteels, J. (1953). *J. Embryol. Exp. Morphol.* **1**, 5.
Pasteels, J. (1964). *Adv. Morphog.* **3**, 363.
Penners, A., and Schleip, W. (1928a). *Z. Wiss. Biol.* **130**, 305.
Penners, A., and Schleip, W. (1928b). *Z. Wiss. Biol.* **131**, 1.
Perry, M. M. (1975). *J. Embryol. Exp. Morphol.* **13**, 127.
Perry, M. M., John, H. A., and Thomas, N. S. (1971). *Exp. Cell Res.* **65**, 249.
Prescott, D. M., and Zeuthen, E. (1953). *Acta Physiol. Scand.* **28**, 77.
Reith, F. (1937). *Z. Wiss. Zool.* **150**, 179.
Reith, F. (1941). *Biol. Gen.* **15**, 394.
Roux, W. (1887). *Arch. Mikrosk. Anat.* **29**, 344.
Roux, W. (1903a). *Anat. Anz.* **23**, 65.
Roux, W. (1903b). *Anat. Anz.* **23**, 113.
Roux, W. (1903c). *Anat. Anz.* **23**, 161.
Sanders, E. J., and Zalik, S. E. (1972). *Wilhelm Roux' Arch. Entwicklungsmech. Org.* **171**, 181.
Schroeder, T. E., and Strickland, D. L. (1974). *Exp. Cell Res.* **83**, 139.
Schultze, O. (1894). *Arch. Entwicklungsmech. Org.* **1**, 269.
Selman, G. C., and Perry, M. M. (1970). *J. Cell Sci.* **6**, 207.
Selman, G. C., Jacob, J., and Perry, M. M. (1976). *J. Embryol. Exp. Morphol.* **36**, 321.
Slaughter, D., and Triplett, E. (1976). *Cell Differ.* **4**, 429.
Smith, L. D., and Ecker, R. E. (1970). *Dev. Biol.* **22**, 622.
Smith, L. D., and Ecker, R. E. (1970). *Curr. Top. Dev. Biol.* **5**, 1.
Steinhardt, R. A., and Epel, D. (1974). *Proc. Natl. Acad. Sci. U.S.A.* **71**, 1915.
Tiedemann, H. (1975). *In* "The Biochemistry of Animal Development" (R. Weber, ed.), Vol. 3, p. 25. Academic Press, New York.
Tiedemann, H. (1976). *J. Embryol. Exp. Morphol.* **35**, 437.
Tomkins, R., and Rodman, W. P. (1971). *Proc. Natl. Acad. Sci. U.S.A.* **68**, 2921.
Tung, T. C. (1933). *Arch. Biol.* **44**, 809.
Van Gansen, P., and Weber, A. (1972). *Arch. Biol.* **83**, 215.
Waddington, C. H. (1938). *J. Exp. Biol.* **15**, 371.
Wall, R., and Faulhaber, I. (1976). *Wilhelm Roux' Arch. Entwicklungsmech. Org.* **180**, 207.
Wallace, R. A., Jared, D. W., Dumont, J. N., and Sega, N. W. (1973). *J. Exp. Zool.* **184**, 321.

Wartenberg, H., and Schmidt, W. (1961). *Z. Zellforsch. Mikrosk. Anat.* **58**, 118.
Wasserman, W. J., and Masui, Y. (1976). *Science* **191**, 1266.
Weigmann, R. (1927). *Z. Wiss. Zool.* **129**, 48.
Whittaker, J. R. (1973). *Proc. Natl. Acad. Sci. U.S.A.* **70**, 2096.
Wolf, D. P. (1974a). *Dev. Biol.* **36**, 62.
Wolf, D. P. (1974b). *Dev. Biol.* **38**, 14.
Wolf, D. P. (1974c). *Dev. Biol.* **40**, 102.
Wolf, D. P., Nishihara, T., West, D. M., Wyrick, R. E., and Hedrich, J. L. (1976). *Biochemistry* **15**, 3671.
Wyrick, R. E., Nishihara, T., and Hedrich, J. L. (1974). *Proc. Natl. Acad. Sci. U.S.A.* **71**, 2067.
Züst, B., and Dixon, K. E. (1975). *J. Embryol. Exp. Morphol.* **34**, 209.

CHAPTER 6

CONTROL OF PLANT CELL ENLARGEMENT BY HYDROGEN IONS

David L. Rayle and Robert Cleland

DEPARTMENT OF BOTANY
SAN DIEGO STATE UNIVERSITY
SAN DIEGO, CALIFORNIA, *and*
DEPARTMENT OF BOTANY
UNIVERSITY OF WASHINGTON
SEATTLE, WASHINGTON

I. Introduction

A. General Remarks about Plant Cell Enlargement

Few aspects of plant development have attracted as much attention as the process of cell enlargement. The reasons for this are not hard to discern. In the first place we have the sheer magnitude and importance of the phenomenon; the size and shape of a plant are to a large extent determined by the amount and direction of cell enlargement. For example, we calculate that if the cells in a redwood tree behaved like typical liver cells and only enlarged to 20 μm, the redwood would have a maximum height of less than 2 feet. Second, cell enlargement in many plant cells is under tight hormonal control; it can be made to start or stop simply by adding or removing from the tissue the hormone auxin. Finally, this hormone-induced cell enlargement is one of the few responses in plants in which the effects of the hormone are detectable in minutes rather than hours, days, or weeks.

Before discussing the mechanism by which cell enlargement is controlled, let us recall a few salient characteristics of plants in general and the process of cell enlargement in particular. As a model let us consider a pea stem. Cell enlargement is restricted to only a small region of the stem, a zone extending at most 2–3 cm below the tip. The cells within this zone may elongate manyfold, their final size being determined primarily by two factors: the hydrostatic or turgor pressure generated by the cell contents, and the extensibility of the cell wall. Most cells possess a high turgor pressure (5–20 atm) and therefore must have a wall with sufficient strength to yield to this pressure in a controlled way. The cells within the elongating region are organized into tissues which in some cases are themselves a mixture of dissimilar types of cells. Each cell is held in position within the stem and connected to its neighbors by the walls which they share in common. A result of this kind of organization is that the enlargement of all the cells may be controlled by only a fraction of the cells. Surrounding the outside of the pea stem is a cuticle, a waxy noncellular layer, which provides an effective barrier to the entry or release from the tissue of ions or organic compounds. A consequence of this relatively impermeable barrier, the cuticle, is that the solution within the cell walls adjacent to the intercellular spaces but outside the plasma membrane is isolated and may differ from the outside environment in many ways, including pH and concentrations of dissolved chemicals. This becomes an important experimental consideration because when sections taken from plant stems are placed in a bathing solution only a small fraction of the chemicals in that solution may ever penetrate the stem and reach the cell surface.

When a plant cell enlarges, most of the increase in volume is due to the uptake of water into an expanding, centrally located vacuole. The direction of the cell expansion depends on the molecular architecture of the wall (Preston, 1974) and can be primarily in one direction (cell elongation) or equally in all directions. Cell enlargement can be initiated in one of two ways: by an increase in the osmotic concentration of the cell or by an increase in cell wall extensibility (cell wall loosening) (Lockhart, 1965). In most systems cell enlargement is initiated by wall loosening (Cleland, 1971). This wall loosening then leads to a transient decrease in cell water potential, water enters the cell stretching the existing cell wall (Ray *et al.,* 1972). Meanwhile synthesis of new cell wall has been occurring, "fixing" the expanded wall into its stretched state and "repairing" the wall so that further loosening can occur.

If a section is removed from the elongation zone of a pea stem and placed in water, the cells enlarge, but only at a slow rate. Rapid enlargement can be induced by only four agents: the group of hormones called auxins, hydrogen ions, CO_2 (possibly via acidification), and the phytotoxin fusicoccin (FC), which is produced by the fungus *Fusicoccum amygdali* Del. (Rayle and Cleland, 1970; Marré *et al.,* 1973). Let us initially focus our attention on the mode of action of the naturally occurring auxin, indoleacetic acid (IAA). IAA initiates rapid cell elongation by causing cell wall loosening to take place (Cleland, 1971). But the site at which this auxin acts is not the cell wall, where the loosening occurs, but either in the cytoplasm or at the plasma membrane. This is indicated by three pieces of evidence. First, binding sites for auxin have been found at the plasma membrane (Lembi *et al.,* 1971; Hertel *et al.,* 1972), in the endoplasmic reticulum (P. M. Ray, personal communication, 1975), and in the nucleoplasm (Mondal *et al.,* 1972), but never in the cell wall. Second, auxin is unable to cause cell wall loosening of isolated walls, but is effective only if intact, functional cells are present (Rayle *et al.,* 1970). Finally, the action of auxin appears to require the continued synthesis of ATP and proteins, as indicated by numerous inhibitor studies (e.g., Bonner, 1949).

B. The Wall-Loosening Concept

Since the initial site of auxin action is located somewhere in the cell rather than in the cell wall, it follows that there must be some form of communication between cytoplasm and wall (Fig. 1). This communication may be accomplished by the secretion from auxin-treated cells of some substance which causes the walls to undergo loosening. For lack of a better name, we have called this factor a "wall-loosening factor," or WLF (Cleland, 1971). In the past many candidates have been suggested as the WLF. These include polysaccharide hydrolases, such as

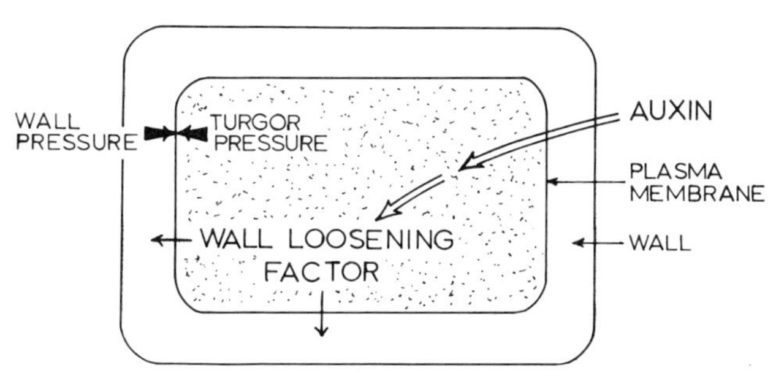

FIG. 1. Simplified scheme illustrating auxin's role in cell extension and the concept of the wall-loosening factor.

cellulase and β-1,3-glucanase, wall polysaccharides, and agents which might modify hydroxyproline-rich wall proteins (for references, see Cleland, 1971). In no case has it been shown that addition of any of these factors to isolated wall matrices would cause significant cell wall loosening of a type which mimicked the *in vivo* situation.

A new candidate for the WLF arose when Rayle and Cleland (1970) and Hager *et al.* (1971) independently proposed that the WLF was simply hydrogen ions, and formulated the "acid-growth" theory. This theory states that auxin initiates an active acidification mechanism, possibly a membrane-bound proton pump, with the result that the pH of the wall solution decreases. As a consequence of the lowered pH, some still hypothetical enzymes responsible for wall loosening are activated, the wall is loosened, and cell enlargement takes place.

Using data obtained primarily from work with the oat coleoptile (*Avena sativa* L.), we shall now summarize some of the evidence which has accumulated during the intervening 6 years concerning the validity of this theory. Additional information can be found in reviews by Davies (1973) and Evans (1974a).

II. Evidence for H^+ as the Wall-Loosening Factor

A. The Acid-Growth Response

If the WLF is indeed H^+ as we have proposed, certain criteria must be met. One is that a tissue which can undergo auxin-induced elongation must show a similar growth response to added H^+. In *Avena* coleoptiles there are striking parallels between the elongation responses to auxin and to H^+ (Rayle and Cleland, 1970, 1972). Sections begin to elongate rapidly about 10 minutes after addition of auxin, and reach a maximum rate of about 5%/hour in another 10–15 minutes. The same maximal rate of elongation is obtained by an optimal hydrogen ion concentration (pH 3), but the lag is only about 1 minute (Fig. 2). Both auxin and H^+ initiate similar increases in wall extensibility. Both agents are effective only when the cell's turgor pressure is nearly maximal, and both show the same unusual temperature dependence for elongation: a Q_{10} of about 5 between 15° and 25°C but a Q_{10} close to 1 between 25° and 35°C.

In addition, as predicted by the theory there are also differences between the two growth responses (Rayle and Cleland, 1970, 1972). Metabolic inhibitors, such as cyanide and dinitrophenol, which would be expected to block the secretion of the WLF but not its subsequent ability to cause wall loosening, prevent auxin-induced elongation but are without effect on the acid-induced growth response. Moreover, one

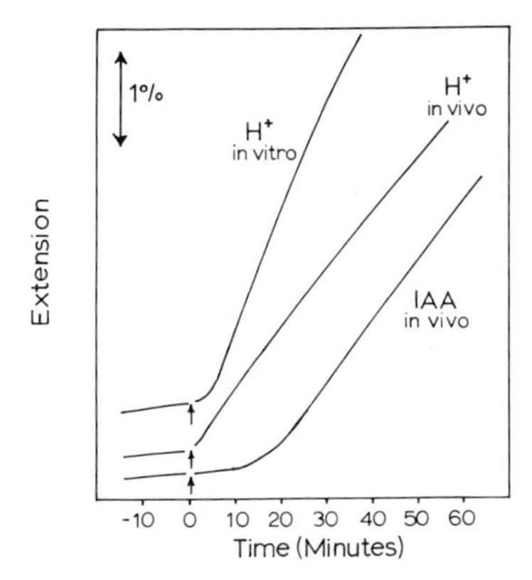

FIG. 2. Kinetics of auxin- and H^+-induced cell elongation. Living *(in vivo)* or frozen-thawed *(in vitro) Avena* coleoptile sections were initially incubated in 10 m*M* phosphate buffer at pH 6.5. At the arrow the incubation solutions were changed to either pH 6.5 buffer + 10^{-5} indoleacetic acid (IAA) or to 10 m*M* citrate buffer pH 3.0. For the *in vivo* records, growth was monitored via a continuous shadowgraphic technique (see Evans and Ray, 1969). The *in vitro* record was obtained using a constant-stress apparatus (force 20 *g*) which detects elongation via displacement of a core within a position transducer (see Rayle and Cleland, 1972). In both the *in vivo* and *in vitro* tests, the cuticle was intact.

would predict that if hydrogen ions are the WLF, then acidic solutions but not auxin should cause wall loosening if added to isolated cell wall matrices. We have tested this (Rayle *et al.*, 1970) by disrupting the cells in *Avena* coleoptile sections by repeated freezing and thawing, and then subjecting the flaccid wall matrices to a constant force of 20 g (to replace the turgor pressure which was eliminated by the disruption of the cell's contents) and recording their subsequent rate of extension. When in a pH 7 buffer the sections undergo a limited amount of viscoelastic extension and then cease elongating. Addition of auxin to the sections is without effect. But if an acidic buffer is given, the sections will continue to elongate for hours. This *in vitro* acid-growth response resembles the two *in vivo* growth responses in Q_{10} and in the fact that the hydrogen ions increase the capacity of the walls for extension *only* if given while the walls are under tension (Cleland and Rayle, 1972).

What concentration of protons is necessary in order to initiate cell wall loosening and extension growth? The answer to this question depends upon whether or not the cuticle is intact. If the cuticle is intact, live or frozen-thawed sections extend only if the pH of the external solution is below 4.5, and a maximum response requires a pH of 3 (Rayle and Cleland, 1970). However, if the cuticle is removed or abraded the situation changes dramatically (Fig. 3). Now cell wall loosening is induced whenever the pH is below about 5.8, and a maxi-

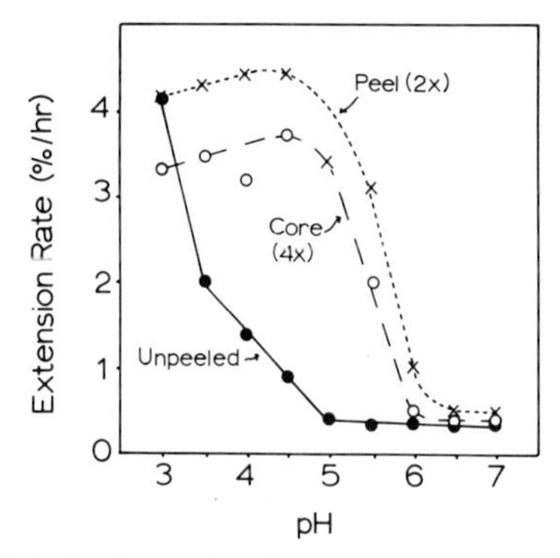

FIG. 3. Comparison of the hydrogen ion dose-response curve in *Avena* coleoptile tissue with (unpeeled) and without (peel or core) an intact cuticle. Peeling was accomplished using fine forceps to mechanically remove the cuticle and epidermal layer (peel) from the sections (cores) before freezing and thawing. Extension was then monitored under constant stress at various hydrogen ion concentrations. Similar results can be obtained with tissue which has not been freeze-thawed (see Rayle, 1973).

mum response is induced by pH 4.8 or below (Rayle, 1973). Thus the pH of *Avena* coleoptile walls need drop only one pH unit below 5.8 to change an inextensible wall into one that can undergo maximal cell wall loosening.

In conclusion, then, we can say with certainty that *if* hydrogen ions are excreted from auxin-treated *Avena* coleoptile cells, and if the pH of the wall region falls below 5.8, the walls would undergo cell wall loosening and growth would occur. We shall now examine the evidence that this is indeed the case, and in so doing satisfy the second major criterion establishing the validity of the acid-growth theory.

B. AUXIN-INDUCED HYDROGEN ION EXTRUSION

In 1973 four groups, using three different plant materials, demonstrated that auxin could induce hydrogen ion excretion (Cleland, 1973; Ilan, 1973; Marré *et al.*, 1973; Rayle, 1973). The experimental system is straightforward, but does require mechanical removal or abrasion of the cuticle as this waxy layer is a barrier to the efflux of protons as well as to their entry. The "peeled" sections are floated on 2–5 ml of a weakly buffered solution (e.g., 1 mM K-P_i, pH 6.0) or in distilled water fortified with certain salts, and the pH of the incubation solution is monitored with time. Using such a system, auxin-induced acidification can be detected in approximately 20 minutes (Fig. 4) although it takes nearly 180 minutes for the pH to fall to its minimum value (Cleland, 1973; Rayle, 1973). It can be demonstrated that the rather long time interval required for this phenomenon is an artifact of the relatively large volume of the incubation solution compared with the volume of the cell wall fluid via the use of an alternative procedure. Eight peeled coleoptiles are placed on a slide moistened with a drop of dilute salt solution, and a flat-surface combination pH electrode is then rested on the upper surface of the sections. Using this technique, auxin-initiated acidification begins after a lag of 11–15 minutes (Fig. 4) and proceeds at a rate of about −0.5 pH unit/10 minutes before leveling off at a pH of approximately 4.5–4.7 (Cleland, 1976a). Using a technique in which a microelectrode is placed directly in pea stem tissue, Jacobs and Ray (1976) have reported similarly short latent times for auxin-enhanced acidification. Thus the rapidity of the acidification response to auxin coincides closely with the speed of the growth induction as one begins to maximize conditions for the detection of acidification; presumably if one could place a pH electrode directly in the wall solution, one would be able to detect hydrogen ion excretion even more rapidly. To date, however, this has not been technically possible.

In addition to the above-mentioned correlation between the speed of auxin-induced acidification and growth, there are other similarities which greatly strengthen the notion that hydrogen ions are the WLF. For example, all agents so far tested which inhibit cell extension nonosmotically also inhibit acidification. These include KCN, 2,4-dinitrophenol, carbonyl cyanide *m*-chlorophenyl hydrazone (CCCP), valinomycin, abscisic acid, and cycloheximide (Rayle, 1973). Further-

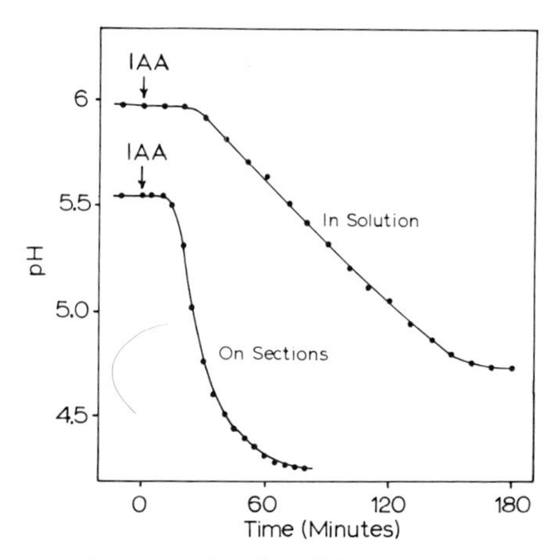

FIG. 4. Demonstration of auxin-induced acidification using two different assay procedures. When the pH of the solution surrounding peeled coleoptiles (upper curve) is monitored, auxin-induced acidification is relatively slow. Using a flat surface electrode placed directly on *Avena* sections (lower curve), acidification can be more rapidly detected. IAA, indoleacetic acid.

more, growth-active synthetic auxins such as 2,4-dichlorophenoxyacetic acid induce hydrogen ion excretion while growth-inactive analogs, such as 3,5-dichlorophenoxyacetic acid are without effect (Rayle, 1973; Marré *et al.,* 1973). Finally, if the growth rate is manipulated by varying the concentration of auxin or the age of the tissue, or by addition of metabolic inhibitors, and the rate of hydrogen ion excretion is measured, a close correlation is found between growth rate and the degree of proton extrusion (Cleland, 1975).

One possible initial objection to the notion that H^+ are the wall-loosening factor stems from the fact that plant cells are often fairly sensitive to protons and can be killed by excessively acidic conditions. Therefore, if auxin causes elongating cells to extrude protons, and if the protons are trapped within the tissue by the cuticle, one might ask how the tissue deals with the real or potential hazards of "overacidification." A possible answer can be seen from experiments in which *Avena* coleoptile sections were incubated in dilute buffers varying in pH between 4 and 7.5, and the initial pH was maintained by titration with HCl or KOH (Cleland, 1975). In the absence of auxin the sections take up protons when the pH of the incubation solution is below 5.7 and extrude protons into solutions of pH 5.7 and above (Fig. 5). By including CCCP in the solutions in order to block active acidification, it is possible to show that the apparent uptake of protons at low pH is not due to active pumping. The passive uptake and active extrusion are at equilibrium in the absence of auxin at a pH of about 5.7. At such a

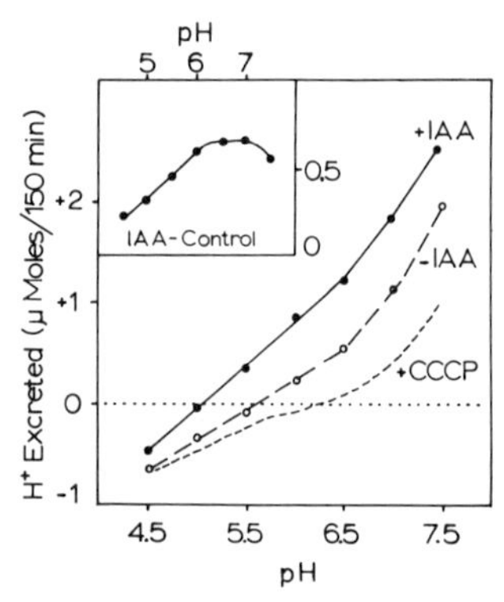

FIG. 5. Proton extrusion as a function of the pH of the external medium. Peeled *Avena* sections (10) were incubated (± IAA) in 2 ml of medium at the pHs indicated. The initial pH was maintained by titration at frequent intervals until 150 minutes, and the total moles of H^+ extruded or taken up were tabulated. The dashed line represents typical data obtained in the presence of 10^{-5} *M* CCCP. Inset (top left) is the difference in hydrogen ions extruded from sections ± IAA. From Cleland (1975), with permission.

proton concentration only a slight amount of acid-induced cell wall loosening occurs, which of course is consistent with the low rate of cell elongation that takes place in the absence of auxin. But when sections are treated with auxin, they excrete protons at an enhanced rate, and the pH of the external solution drops. This increased proton level has two consequences; the lowered pH increases the rate of passive H^+ uptake and inhibits the rate of active extrusion. The net result is that a new equilibrium is reached at a pH of 4.8–5.0. At such a proton concentration the increased auxin-induced rate of proton excretion is matched by the increased passive proton reabsorption by the tissue. This equilibrium pH is sufficient to cause nearly maximum cell wall loosening and thus rapid cell elongation, but is not so low as to cause detectable damage to the cells. If auxin is removed from the tissue, or if the active extrusion phenomenon is blocked by metabolic inhibitors, passive uptake then results in a rapid increase in the external pH and cell wall loosening returns to the low basal level seen in nonauxin-treated tissues. It should be noted that the passive-uptake phenomenon may not reflect uptake into the cells, but could result directly from the buffering capacity of the walls themselves; this matter has not yet been settled.

Is the proton excretion which takes place in the absence of auxin mediated by the same mechanism as the auxin-induced proton excretion? Probably not, as the auxin-induced excretion is blocked by the protein synthesis inhibitor cycloheximide while the basal level of excretion is unaffected (Cleland, 1975). It would appear, then, that auxin sets into action an extrusion process which is inactive in its absence, and the resulting acidification supplements the auxin-insensitive basal extrusion.

C. Fusicoccin-Induced Hydrogen Ion Extrusion

Additional evidence for the role of H^+ as the WLF comes from the studies with the fungal toxin fusicoccin (FC) (Lado *et al.*, 1973). Previously, FC had received some attention as an agent which caused dark-opening of stomates, apparently by stimulating K^+ uptake into the guard cells (Turner and Graniti, 1969), but in 1973 Marré *et al.* reported that FC could act as a "super-auxin" causing pea stem sections to grow and excrete hydrogen ions at rates greater than those obtained with maximal auxin. A similar situation exists in *Avena* coleoptiles. Upon addition of 10 μM FC growth begins after a lag of about 1 minute and proceeds at a rate approaching 12%/hour (Cleland, 1976b). However, this rapid rate of cell elongation persists for only a short time, and within 4–6 hours has fallen to the control level. Consistent with the acid growth theory, FC-enhanced acidification can be detected within the first minute after application (Cleland, 1976a) and proceeds at a rate in excess of 1 pH unit/10 minutes, until a new equilibrium pH is reached at 3.8–4.0 (Fig. 6). Thus two structurally unrelated growth active agents initiate acidification with kinetics which closely approximate their relative speed of action with respect to extension growth.

Interestingly, the molecular mode of action of FC and IAA with respect to acidification seems to be different. While both mechanisms require respiratory energy as evidenced by the inhibitory action of KCN and DNP, their sensitivity to cycloheximide and to osmoregulatory agents is quite different. Cycloheximide rapidly (within 2–5 minutes) terminates IAA-induced acidification but is virtually without effect on the FC-induced growth or proton extrusion (Rayle, 1973; Cleland, 1976a). Isotonic mannitol (0.4 *M*) completely blocks auxin-induced but not FC-induced hydrogen ion excretion (Cleland, 1976b). In addition, FC and IAA also differ in their tissue specificity. For example, as far as has been tested IAA initiates acidification only in actively growing tissues, while FC appears to be far less specific, initiating proton excretion in such differing tissue types as the tomato leaf disk, squash cotyledons (Lado *et al.,* 1972), and barley, maize, and pea roots (Pitman *et al.,* 1975a; Lado *et al.,* 1976) as well as in rapidly growing tissues. In addition, from the inhibitor data it would appear that FC stimulates the basal level proton excretion process discussed earlier rather than activating the auxin-sensitive system. But regardless of the precise mechanism involved our point is the same, and that is that H^+ extrusion occurs and appears to lead to wall loosening and thus to cell elongation.

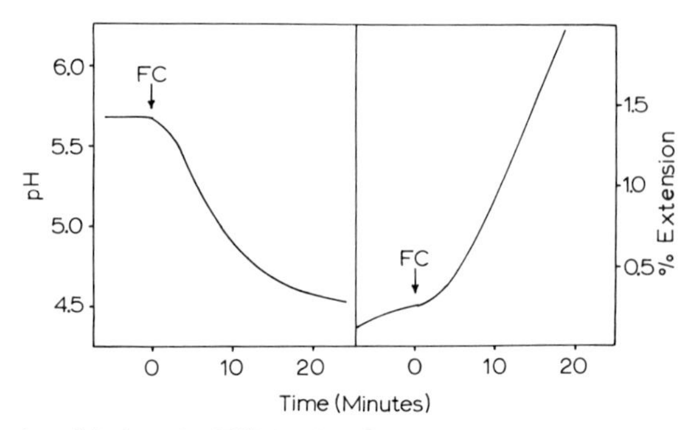

FIG. 6. Kinetics of fusicoccin (FC)-initiated proton excretion (left) and growth (right) in *Avena* coleoptile sections. Acidification was assayed with a flat surface electrode placed directly on peeled sections. Elongation was monitored via a continuous shadowgraphic technique (see Evans and Ray, 1969).

D. Potential Difficulties with the Acid-Growth Theory

The experimental data we have discussed thus far were obtained largely from investigations with *Avena* coleoptiles. But obviously if the acid growth theory is to be a general one, the two criteria mentioned above should also apply to other plants whose cells extend in response to auxin. That is, all tissues which elongate in response to auxin should also respond to hydrogen ions and, second, it should be possible to demonstrate auxin-induced acidification from all tissues whose growth is promoted by auxin.

The first criterion has, in general, been satisfied. A wide variety of auxin-sensitive tissues have been shown to respond to H^+: oat, rye, and wheat coleoptiles (D. L. Rayle, unpublished data), pea epicotyls (Marré *et al.,* 1973), lupine (Perley *et al.,* 1975), soybean (Vanderhoef and Stahl, 1975), cucumber, zucchini, morning glory, and *Helianthus* hypocotyls (D. L. Rayle, unpublished data) and corn roots (Edwards and Scott, 1974). The only exception reported in the literature was sections from green pea stems (Barkley and Leopold 1973). In this case we have reinvestigated the apparent paradox and demonstrated that the lack of response was due simply to failure of the protons to cross the cuticle, and that whenever the cuticle was disrupted by peeling or with holes or by slits a good acid-growth response could be obtained (Cleland and Rayle, 1975). Perley *et al.* (1975) have claimed that while auxin-induced elongation of lupine hypocotyl cells was accompanied by transverse expansion, acid-induced elongation resulted in transverse contraction. However, since the osmolarity of the acid solution was 10 times greater than that of the control or auxin solution it is not certain that the contraction was really in response to the acid.

The second criterion necessary to validate the general nature of the acid growth theory has been harder to meet. Most of the reported studies on hormone-induced proton extrusion have utilized peeled *Avena* coleoptiles or pea epicotyl segments, and with such tissues a good correlation between rate of H^+ excretion and rate of growth has been relatively easy to demonstrate (Marré *et al.,* 1974c; Rayle, 1973; Cleland, 1975; Yamagata and Masuda, 1976). With other commonly used species (e.g., *Helianthus* or cucumber hypocotyls), physical removal of the cuticle and associated cell layers renders the tissue unresponsive to auxin with respect to both elongation and acidification (D. L. Rayle, unpublished data; Yamamoto *et al.,* 1974), and therefore, inoperative as an experimental system. The problem of rendering such tissues freely permeable to the flow of H^+ while retaining auxin sensitivity has only recently been solved (J. Mentze and D. L. Rayle, unpublished data). One successful technique involves gently stroking the cuticle with carborundum powder (Green and Cummins, 1974). When this technique for tissue preparation is combined with the flat surface electrode method for detection of H^+ secretion, a correlation similar to that reported for *Avena* has been found for all dicots tested—sunflowers, soybeans, cucumbers, zucchini, morning glory, and bean (J. Mentze and D. L. Rayle, unpublished data). Thus auxin-induced wall acidification as well as hydrogen ion-induced growth appears to be a general phenomenon occurring in both auxin-sensitive monocots and dicots. It must be noted, however, that there have been reports of auxin-induced growth occurring without a parallel excretion of protons (Ilan, 1973; Ilan and Shapira, 1976; Pope *et al.*, 1975; Penny *et al.*, 1975), but in each case questions can be raised as to whether the pH measured is that of the walls of the growing cells or only that of some remote area.

Another concern with respect to the acid growth theory centers on the duration of the acid-growth response. Tissues will grow for many hours in response to auxin, but the response to hydrogen ions is usually only of 1–2 hours duration (Rayle and Cleland, 1972; Rayle, 1973). If a constant tension of 20 g is imposed on these sections, however, the H^+-induced elongation persists for 4–8 hours, instead (R. Cleland and D. L. Rayle, unpublished data). These results can be explained by assuming that prolonged cell elongation not only requires auxin-induced H^+-excretion but also requires the participation of a second auxin-enhanced process such as osmoregulation or wall repair (Rayle, 1973; Vanderhoef and Stahl, 1975; Cleland, 1977). The two auxin-sensitive processes may operate through separate mechanisms. On the other hand, one could also maintain that the auxin-enhanced H^+ pump drives other intracellular events necessary for long-term growth by virtue of an increase in cytoplasmic pH. For example, changes in cytoplasmic pH might give rise to the uptake and/or synthesis of osmotic solutes (Johnson and Rayle, 1976), changes in ion uptake, or activation of enzymes such as glucan synthetase (Ray, 1973). In short, regardless of the view one takes regarding auxin action, there appears to be logical reasons why experimental application of protons alone (Perley *et al.*, 1975) might not precisely mimick the growth response to auxin.

III. Mechanism of Active Acidification

The reduction of cell wall pH must come about either by a net efflux from the cytoplasm of an acidic substance(s) or acid-generating substance(s), or by a net influx from the wall of some basic substance(s). We can sort out some of the alternatives (Fig. 7) straight

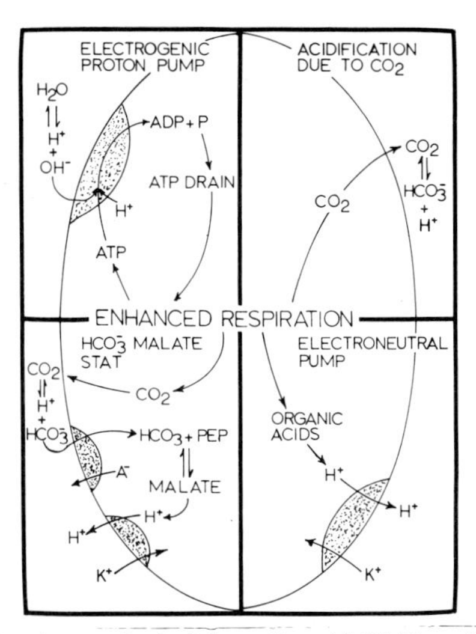

FIG. 7. Four possible schemes for indoleacetic acid (IAA)- or fusicoccin (FC)-enhanced acidification. Note that the enhancement of respiration common to all schemes could be a direct effect of the regulator or due to a feedback mechanism. In all cases the stippled areas represent ATP-requiring pumps located at the cell surface.

away. For example, it can be readily shown by titration that neither FC nor IAA causes the leakage of substantial amounts of bufferable materials or organic acids from the cytoplasm, and thus mechanisms based solely on leakage or transport of large organic molecules can be eliminated (Marré *et al.*, 1973; D. L. Rayle and K. D. Johnson, unpublished). Likewise, it can be readily shown that IAA- or FC-initiated acidification is not due to the passive release of respiratory CO_2 into the medium and its subsequent equilibration with H_2O to produce H^+ and HCO_3^- as suggested by Sloane and Sadava (1975). The evidence is simply that in *Avena* sections acidification occurs in beakers open to equilibration with the atmosphere and the acidity so generated cannot be bubbled away with vigorous N_2 gassing (D. L. Rayle and K. D. Johnson, unpublished data). This point is relatively important because it is well known that both growth regulators stimulate respiration (Commoner and Thimann, 1941; Kelly, 1947; Christiansen and Thimann, 1950; Johnson and Rayle, 1976) and hence could give rise to "extra" CO_2, which in theory could lead to acidification under certain conditions.

Of the remaining alternatives, the simplest and therefore perhaps most attractive wall acidification mechanism would be a direct enhancement of an electrogenic proton pump in the plasma membrane. Electrogenic proton pumps have been demonstrated in the algae

Nitella (Kitasato, 1968), *Chara* (Smith, 1972), and the fungus *Neurospora* (Slayman, 1970), and although the evidence for their existence in higher plants is less rigorous it has been strongly inferred (see Higinbotham and Anderson, 1974; Poole, 1974; MacRobbie, 1971). Such pumps are usually envisioned to initiate acidification via an ATPase which cleaves ATP, producing a proton on one side of the membrane and a hydroxyl on the other. The change separation thus produced is then partially neutralized by the passive flux of either cations or anions across the membrane.

As early as 1971 Hager *et al.* proposed that the auxin-induced proton extrusion could be mediated by a mechanism similar to that described above. This notion seemed consistent with, but far from proved by, data demonstrating that auxin-induced elongation of coleoptiles could be induced under anaerobic conditions by addition of either ATP or related nucleotides. Additional circumstantial evidence has surfaced from the electrophysiological measurements showing that hyperpolarization of the transmembrane potential occurs in response to both auxin (Etherton, 1970; Cleland *et al.*, 1977) or fusicoccin (Marrè *et al.*, 1974a; Pitman *et al.*, 1975a,b; Cleland *et al.*, 1977). The hyperpolarizations induced by auxin and fusicoccin begin simultaneously with the onset of H^+-excretion and are blocked by inhibitors of H^+-excretion (Marrè *et al.*, 1974a; Cleland *et al.*, 1977). In addition, the ATPase inhibitor *N,N'*-dicyclohexylcarbodiimide (DCCD) prevents proton extrusion and the fusicoccin-induced hyperpolarization of the membrane potential (Marrè *et al.*, 1974a). We are forced to conclude that both auxin- and fusicoccin-induced proton excretion involve some electrogenic component.

A variety of ATPases have been shown to exist in plant cells, and some have been localized at the plasma membrane (Lai and Thompson, 1971; Hodges *et al.*, 1972). Kasami and Yamaki (1974) reported that auxin, given either before or after homogenization, could activate ATPases from mung beans, but we have been unable to repeat these observations. Furthermore, attempts to demonstrate either auxin or FC activation of *Avena* coleoptile ATPases have not yielded positive results (M. Tepfer and R. Cleland, unpublished). Thus, a dilemma exists; indirect evidence favors the idea of a hormone-activated, ATPase-mediated electrogenic pump which could give rise to acidification, but the pump has not yet been demonstrated.

An alternative possibility exists which in theory could also explain active acidification, and that is a mechanism involving active bicarbonate uptake. HCO_3^- will arise from the equilibration of respiratory CO_2 with the aqueous wall environment, and a proton would be left behind in the wall if the HCO_3^- is then reabsorbed. The HCO_3^- taken up could then be fixed into malate via PEP-carboxylase (Raven and Smith, 1974) and the proton of the newly synthesized malate might then be exported in exchange for potassium ions by an ATP-driven antiport mechanism to give additional external acidification. Auxin and FC might enhance the acidification by stimulating the reabsorption of HCO_3^-, its fixation into malate, or the subsequent H^+-K^+ exchange process.

Both auxin and FC are known to enhance the uptake of label from HCO_3^- into malate (Haschke and Lüttge, 1975; Johnson and Rayle, 1976), but for both hormones the evidence indicates that reabsorption of bicarbonate is not a factor in the acidification process. With auxin the increased uptake of HCO_3^- did not begin until well after the start of the acidification (Johnson and Rayle, 1976). FC stimulated the uptake of label from HCO_3^- into *Avena* coleoptiles by approximately 3-fold after a lag of not more than 1 minute, but since kinetic disequilibrium experiments (Johnson and Rayle, 1976) indicated that most of the uptake occurred as CO_2 rather than HCO_3^-, it is unlikely that bicarbonate reabsorption plays any major role in the FC-induced acidification. In addition, both auxin and FC-induced acidification occur at a maximum rate at an external pH of 7.0 (Cleland, 1975, 1976b), a pH at which little acidification could arise even if the bicarbonate is reabsorbed. Auxin and FC may enhance malate synthesis by a mechanism that is independent of the acidification. Alternatively, the enhanced CO_2 uptake and malate synthesis may be a secondary response to alteration in the cytoplasmic conditions that accompany the acidification process (such as in increase in cytoplasmic pH). Further evidence will be needed to distinguish between these possibilities.

Finally, FC and auxin may activate a H^+-K^+ exchange process. K^+ uptake into a variety of tissues is enhanced by both auxin and FC (e.g., Higinbotham *et al.*, 1953; Haschke and Lüttge, 1975; Cleland, 1976c; Pitman, *et al.*, 1975a; Marrè *et al.*, 1974b; Cocucci *et al.*, 1976), but this enhancement could be due to increased passive uptake of K^+ in response to the hyperpolarization of the membrane potential, or it could be due to a specific, one-to-one exchange of K^+ for H^+. Haschke and Luttge (1973) noted that over periods greater than 4 hours K^+ uptake into auxin-treated coleoptiles equalled H^+ excretion, and proposed that auxin activates such a K^+-H^+ exchange. But more detailed studies on the timing and stoicheometry of H^+ excretion and K^+ uptake (Cleland, 1976c; Cleland and Lomax, 1977; Stout *et al.*, 1977) have shown that the auxin-induced increase in K^+ uptake does not begin until well after the onset of the H^+ excretion, and that the ratio of K^+ uptake to H^+

excretion (the K/H ratio) is well below 1 for at least the first 2 hours. It seems more likely that the enhanced uptake of K^+ is a secondary response to auxin.

Marrè and coworkers, in an elegant series of experiments (Cocucci *et al.*, 1976; Lado *et al.*, 1976; Marrè, 1977), have shown that FC-induced H^+ excretion and K^+ uptake must be coupled in pea epicotyl and corn root tissues. In each case the K/H ratio was 1 or close to it, and in each case it appeared that H^+ excretion could not occur in the absence of external K^+. The time course and sensitivity to inhibitors was similar for the 2 responses. Since FC does cause a hyperpolarization of the membrane potential, the K^+–H^+ exchange in these tissues cannot be exactly one-to-one, but Marrè (1977) has argued that it cannot ever be far from one-to-one.

We have made a similar analysis for the *Avena* coleoptile (Cleland, 1976c; Cleland and Lomax, 1977; Stout *et al.*, 1977). Again, FC-induced H^+ excretion and K^+ uptake appear to be linked, but in this tissue the K/H ratio varies from about 0.9 at 10 m*M* KCl down to a value as low as 0.01 at 1 μM KCl (exact K/H ratios cannot be obtained because some K^+ may be taken up from the cell walls). We cannot say whether FC-induced H^+ excretion can ever occur in the oat coleoptile in the absence of K^+ uptake, but it would appear that its transport system does not normally involve a strict one-to-one antiport of K^+ and H^+.

It should be clear, then, that we are still a long way from understanding the actual mechanisms of hormone-induced proton excretion in plants. But our present knowledge has provided us with theories that can be tested, and experimental approaches that can be taken, with some hope that our understanding of these mechanisms can be obtained in the foreseeable future.

IV. Mechanism of Acid-Induced Cell Wall Loosening

A. Measurement and Structural Considerations

Thus far we have attempted to acquaint the reader with some of the data and reasoning behind the acid growth theory by stressing the actual acidification process. Let us now turn our attention to the physical ramifications of proton extrusion by examining the wall-loosening process itself.

The primary cell wall is composed of two basic structural components: cellulose and a series of noncellulosic polysaccharides. The long chains of cellulose are arranged in bundles called microfibrils; the microfibrils are in turn oriented in the wall in specific patterns which are believed to determine the direction in which a cell can enlarge. The noncellulosic polysaccharides consist of a limited number of compounds of fairly short length, which are interconnected both with each other and with the cellulose (Keegstra *et al.*, 1973). The strength of the wall is provided by intertwining of the cellulose microfibrils themselves as well as by covalent connections between adjacent microfibrils provided by the other polysaccharides.

When subjected to stress, plant cell walls can extend a small amount viscoelastically. After the cessation of this purely physical phenomenon, further extension is minimal until some biochemical modification of the wall occurs, such as cleavage of bonds linking the polysaccharides, whereupon an additional amount of viscoelastic-like extension is then possible. Therefore, under conditions in which the wall is under constant stress, the limiting factor for wall extension is the rate at which these biochemical modifications or wall-loosening events take place (see Cleland, 1971). These facts make it possible to directly measure the capacity of the wall to undergo loosening by the simple expedient of applying a constant external force to live coleoptiles or young stem sections and monitoring the rate at which the tissue elongates. Using such a technique we have shown that FC, IAA, and H^+ greatly enhance the rate at which wall-loosening events take place. This general technique can also be modified to eliminate the potential complications of simultaneous changes in the wall-loosening capacity brought about by wall synthesis, protein synthesis, or release of degradative factors by utilizing frozen-thawed tissue and solutions of variable acidity to manipulate the rate of extension (Rayle *et al.*, 1970; Rayle and Cleland, 1972). It has been possible through the use of such a model system, made freely permeable to outside solutions through removal of the cuticle, to study in some detail how hydrogen ions initiate wall loosening.

In theory there are at least three possible ways by which hydrogen ions could lead to wall loosening: nonenzymic cleavage of acid-labile polymeric linkages, the direct disruption of noncovalent bonds in the wall, and the activation of wall-bound hydrolases. All of these possibilities have received some attention in the past, although most workers now favor an enzymic mechanism. The reasons for this preference, however, should be made clear.

The first idea put forward concerning H^+ loosening was that there existed within the cell wall acid-labile, alkali-stable polymeric linkages which became susceptible to hydrolysis as the wall became acidified. There are a few types of glycosidic linkages known to occur in plant cell walls which may be relatively labile under mildly acidic conditions (e.g., glycosyluronide bonds), and others which may be rendered labile when subjected to a critical yield stress—a force which must be above a certain threshold value before acid-induced increases in wall extensibility can occur (see Cleland, 1971; also Rayle and Cleland, 1972; Cleland and Rayle, 1972). When the "acid-labile bond" theory was first proposed, however, the observed pH optimum for acid-induced elongation was 3.0. Since we now know that the cell wall compartment pH need only drop to 4.8 or so for optimum cell elongation (work with peeled coleoptiles), and since this concentration of H^+ is probably too low to catalyze the hydrolysis of acid-labile covalent linkages, the acid-labile bond theory has become less popular. In addition, work with inhibitors (see below) does not readily fit such a model.

The second possibility, the disruption of noncovalent bonds, arose from recent progress made in Albersheim's lab (Talmadge *et al.,* 1973; Bauer *et al.,* 1973; Keegstra *et al.,* 1973) concerning the architecture of higher plant cell walls and has led this group to propose a structural model describing the precise arrangement of the various polymeric components of the cell wall. One of the most interesting features of this model is the existence of a hemicellulosic xyloglucan which forms hydrogen bonds to cellulose microfibrils and covalent linkages to the pectic fraction of the wall. Because of its strategic position within the wall linking the rigid microfibrils with the amorphous hemicellulose and pectic components, and since its attachment to cellulose represents the only major noncovalent bonding within the wall, the xyloglucan fraction seemed to be a logical site for the control of wall loosening. Keegstra *et al.* (1973) proposed that H^+ released into the cell wall could reversibly disrupt hydrogen bonds between cellulose and xyloglucan, thereby allowing slippage of the cellulose microfibrils relative to the noncellulosic components. Such a model can find indirect support from the observation by Labavitch and Ray (1974) that auxin causes a rapid turnover of xyloglucan in pea stems; an effect of low pH on this turnover of xyloglucan also has recently been reported (Jacobs and Ray, 1975). However, Valet and Albersheim (1974) tested the "low pH disruption of hydrogen bonds" theory directly by assaying the effect of increasing H^+ concentration on the *in vitro* binding of xyloglucan oligomers to isolated cellulose. Although the rate and percentage of binding was sensitive to temperature and amount of nonaqueous solvent, H^+ concentration did not influence the binding properties. Additional evidence against such a mechanism arises from studies of frozen-thawed coleoptiles, where cell wall loosening is not induced to any significant extent by agents which rupture hydrogen bonds, such as urea or guanidinium-HCl (R. Cleland, unpublished data).

B. Involvement of Proteins

A third possibility is that acidification of the wall solution activates some wall-associated enzyme, with an acidic pH optimum, so that the enzyme can cleave load-bearing bonds in the wall. Indirect evidence for the involvement of such an enzyme comes from the fact that treatment of peeled coleoptile sections or epidermal strips with either pronase or trypsin renders the walls incapable of undergoing acid-induced cell wall loosening (R. Cleland and D. L. Rayle, unpublished data). (Our earlier conclusion (Rayle and Cleland, 1974) that pronase-treated walls were still able to undergo acid-induced extension was in error because the pronase apparently could not reach the wall proteins due to the presence of an intact cuticle on the sections). But what enzyme is involved? One possibility is that it is a polysaccharide hydrolase. Many reports have appeared (Fan and Maclachlan, 1967; Katz and Ordin, 1967; Datko and Maclachlan, 1968; Tanimoto and Masuda, 1968; Wada *et al.,* 1968) which show that increases in measurable polysaccharide hydrolase activities are correlated with auxin-induced growth responses, but most of these enzyme activity enhancements do not become manifest until long after growth has been maximally stimulated by auxin. A notable exception has been the claim by Masuda and co-workers that β-1,3-glucanase of oat coleoptiles is stimulated by auxin treatment within 15 minutes after hormone application, and that treatment of coleoptile segments with a fungal β-1, 3-glucanase causes a rapid increase in cell elongation (Masuda and Wada, 1967; Tanimoto and Masuda, 1968). Other investigators, however, have had difficulty in repeating these observations (Cleland, 1968; Ruesink, 1969).

Nevertheless, over the last 5 years evidence has been accumulating that wall acidification caused by auxin enhances some form of cell wall hydrolase activity. Hager *et al.* (1971) were the first to propose that extruded H^+ operated through an enzymic mechanism leading to cell elongation, as they showed that Cu^{2+}, presumably by inactivating enzymes, inhibited H^+-induced growth in *Helianthus* hypocotyl segments. If such an enzyme model were to be operative in the wall-loosening process, certain predictions could be made and tested: polysaccharide hydrolases would have to be present in the cell wall; their pH optima should be in the acidic range, with comparatively little activity above pH 6.0; and treatments which inhibit the H^+ growth response (excluding treatments that would affect turgor pressures in fresh segments) should similarly affect enzyme activities, and vice versa.

Although certain polysaccharide hydrolases have been shown to be associated with cell wall fractions from a number of plant tissues (Lee *et al.*, 1967; Katz and Ordin, 1967; Nevins, 1970; Buchala and Meier, 1973; Johnson *et al.*, 1974), attempts to demonstrate unequivocally this localization *in situ* have been unconvincing. Katz and Ordin (1967) and Lee *et al.* (1967) have shown that incubation of isolated and washed oat and corn coleoptile cell walls resulted in a limited amount of self-autolysis which yielded a variety of free sugars and oligosaccharides. The extent of this degradative process in cell walls has been correlated with extension growth of young cells (Maclachlan and Young, 1962; Maclachlan and Duda, 1965). Kivilaan *et al.* (1961) were particularly concerned with the possibility of cytoplasmic contamination of the isolated walls with hydrolases during cell disruption and wall preparation. Using a glycerol washing procedure to reduce the level of such contamination, they reported the existence of a firmly bound complement of cell wall enzymes. On the other hand, Nevins (1970) showed that the yield of soluble bean hypocotyl glucosidase activity could be vastly improved by extraction of the tissue with high buffer strengths (50–500 m*M* Na-citrate buffer). However, since the same ionic strengths remove up to 60% of each of several glycosidase activities from isolated cell walls of oat coleoptiles (J. D. Cohen and K. D. Johnson, unpublished results), it would be difficult to differentiate between the two alternatives: (1) the salt-extractable enzyme fraction represents cytoplasmic contamination, or (2) there exists *in situ* a fraction of ionically bound glycosidases in the wall. Such results do indicate that the cell wall represents a strong ionic matrix for enzyme binding, but the extent of nonspecific vs. specific glycosidase binding to the wall cannot be ascertained through extraction techniques. For now, we will operate under the assumption that hydrolases are indeed present in the cell walls of growing tissues, but although this assumption is supported by available indirect evidence, it is not proved.

A search through the literature confirms that most plant carbohydrases exhibit acidic pH optima, and many function at an optimal rate between pH 4.5–5.5 (Agrawal and Bahl, 1968; Keegstra and Albersheim, 1970; Buchala and Meier, 1973). Based on earlier reports (Katz and Ordin, 1967; Loescher and Nevins, 1970) that oat coleoptile cell walls were equipped with a complement of glycosidases, Johnson *et al.* (1974) investigated the pH-activity profiles of these wall-bound glycosidases, enzymes which have hydrolytic activity toward *p*-nitrophenyl glycosides. Although such substrates are artificial, their employment enabled these investigators to monitor cell wall hydrolase activity *in situ* using while coleoptiles (peeled or nonpeeled) or isolated walls. Such an *in situ* assay was important in order to correlate an auxin-induced increase in cell wall hydrolase activity with extension growth and acidification. Several glycosidase activities found to be associated with coleoptile cell walls exhibited pH optima between 4.5 and 5.5: β-galactosidase, β-glucosidase, α-mannosidase, and β-xylosidase. The corresponding α-linked p-nitrophenylglycosidases and β-mannoside were not appreciably hydrolyzed by intact coleoptile tissue or cell wall preparations.

Since the β-galactosidase activity of isolated cell walls typically exhibited a 3- to 4-fold increase when the pH was lowered from 7.0 to 5.0, this enzyme was chosen as a "marker" for further tests relating to the hypothesis that the activity of certain cell wall hydrolases was positively correlated with cell elongation. One of the first tests run was based on the prediction that IAA treatment, through its effect on cell wall acidification, should enhance the measurable β-galactosidase activity of intact coleoptiles. When coleoptiles were pretreated with 0.1 m*M* IAA for 60 minutes in 1 m*M* phosphate–citrate buffer, pH 6.0, then assayed for β-galactosidase activity, the average hormonal stimulation of this enzyme's activity was 36% over control. In addition, as one would predict, a larger enhancement is induced by FC (Fig. 8). By comparing the level of β-galactosidase activity induced by IAA with a curve relating the effect of reduced pH on β-galactosidase activity assayed in a similar manner (using coleoptile segments), the hormonal stimulation would correspond to an average drop in cell wall pH from 6.0 to 5.0, at least in that part of the coleoptile where β-galactosidase is assayable. The auxin effect on β-galactosidase activity can be pre-

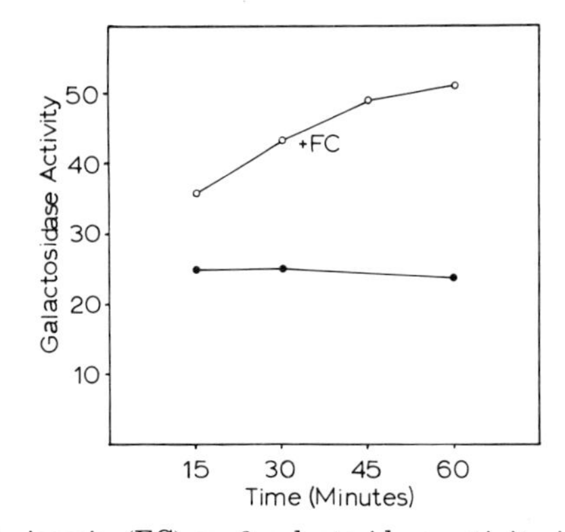

FIG. 8. Effect of fusicoccin (FC) on β-galactosidase activity in intact coleoptile segments. Segments were pretreated for the times indicated at 30°C in 1.5 ml of 1 m*M* phosphate–citrate buffer (pH 6.0) with or without FC, then assayed by the addition of 0.5 ml of 40 m*M* p-nitrophenyl-β-D-galactopyranoside.

vented with simultaneous inclusion of 10 μg/ml cycloheximide or 20 μM abscisic acid in the surrounding medium, inhibitors which are known to prevent auxin-stimulated cell elongation and H^+ extrusion. Furthermore, by progressively increasing the pH 6.0 buffer strength of the treatment medium from 1 to 18 m*M*, the auxin effect on β-galactosidase activity was progressively diminished; a similar finding has been reported for the effect of pH 6.0 buffer strength on auxin-induced cell elongation in peeled oat coleoptile segments (Durand and Rayle, 1973). These results certainly imply that the same bufferable agent (H^+) is required for cell elongation and activation of wall β-galactosidase.

If cell wall hydrolases are directly involved in wall loosening, then reagents or treatments which in a general way alter protein structure, or specifically inhibit wall-loosening enzyme activity, should also interfere with H^+-induced cell elongation. A few of the correlations which have been found (Cohen, 1974) are indicated in Table I.

Can specific inhibitors of glycosidase activity reduce cell elongation? Nevins (1975) recently reported that nojirimycin (5-amino-5-deoxy-D-glucopyranose), a potent inhibitor of β-glucosidase, inhibits in parallel IAA-induced growth and IAA-enhanced release of glucose from noncellulosic polysaccharides of oat coleoptiles and pea stem segments. The activity of β-glucosidase, but not β-1,3-glucanase, parallels these events. The corresponding aldonolactones of D-glucose and D-galactose are known to be potent inhibitors of β-glucosidase and β-galactosidase activities, respectively (Conchie *et al.*, 1967). Evans

TABLE I

CORRELATION OF β-GLUCOSIDASE ACTIVITY WITH H^+-INDUCED CELL ELONGATION

Treatment	% Inhibition glucosidase	% Inhibition H^+ extension[a]
High salt, 0.5*M* NaCl, 1 hr; 4°	50	50
Pronase, 0.1% 3.5 hr; 23°	90	70
Alkylating sulfhydryl agents: iodoacetate, *N*-ethylmaleimide, shadowmycin	<10	<10
Heavy metals: Ag; Hg.	70; 80	70; 98

[a] Extension was determined on frozen-thawed tissue (15 g force) at pH 4.5.

(1974) has recently reported that although the corresponding lactones (5 m*M*) can inhibit β-glucosidase (75% inhibition) and β-galactosidase (43% inhibition) activities of oat coleoptile segments, they have no effect on either IAA- or H^+-induced cell elongation. Unfortunately, any data generated with respect to an aldonolactone effect on IAA-induced growth are subject to trivial artifacts. If nonpeeled coleoptiles are assayed, penetration of the lactones will be nil due to the cuticular barrier. If peeled coleoptiles are used, which necessitates the employment of weak (1 m*M*) buffers so that wall acidification can take place, then spontaneous, rapid hydrolysis of the lactones will artificially reduce the pH of the surrounding medium, giving rise to acid growth. Our laboratory has tried to sidestep these problems by monitoring the effects of these aldonolactones on the low pH (100 m*M* buffer strengths) response of frozen-thawed, peeled coleoptiles (Cohen *et al.,* 1974). No effect of the lactones on acid growth could be observed unless the segments were first vacuum-infiltrated in the presence of the lactones. Under these conditions, a 10 m*M* concentration of both lactones together reduced the potential for pH 4.5-induced extension by an average of 30%. Our results essentially corroborate those of Evans (1974) but should further serve to emphasize the possibility that not all the cells in a given plant tissue are exposed to the same external environment provided by the experimenter.

The above results notwithstanding, it seems unlikely that glycosidases could play a direct role in wall loosening. A more logical candidate would be an enzyme or enzymes which break internal polysaccharide linkages, particularly when one considers the polymeric structure of the cell wall as proposed by Albersheim's group (Talmadge *et al.,* 1973; Bauer *et al.,* 1973; Keegstra *et al.,* 1973). But are the cell wall enzymes which split *p*-nitrophenyl glycosides highly specific for di- and possibly trisaccharides, or do these same enzymes exhibit activity toward polysaccharides as well? Greve and Ordin (C. Greve, personal communication) have recently purified an α-mannosidase from oat coleoptiles which not only splits *p*-nitrophenyl α-mannoside, but also exhibits endo-splitting activity toward commercial α-mannan (measured viscometrically). If this endomannanase displays a pH-activity profile similar to that of the pH-growth rate, it may be the (or one of the) elusive wall loosening factor(s). Much work lies ahead in determining the complement of endo- and exoglycanases present in cell walls of growing tissues, how their activities are affected by pH, and whether or not their activities parallel cell extension under the various conditions which affect H^+-induced cell extension. By knowing which enzyme(s) is (are) involved in wall loosening leading to growth, we may be able to deduce the growth-limiting chemical bond(s) in the cell wall.

V. Concluding Remarks

We have summarized the evidence that in *Avena* coleoptiles and pea stem tissues the hormone auxin induces cell enlargement by activating proton extrusion and that the resulting acidification of the wall leads to enzymic cell wall loosening and thus cell enlargement. In our opinion the data supporting this concept are strong. Nevertheless, there are a number of details which remain unknown. For example, we have emphasized the point that auxin itself does not act directly on the wall but acts at the cell surface or within the cytoplasm. If this is so, one would like to demonstrate an interaction (binding) of auxin with a cellular component which initiated some physiological or biochemical manifestation related to the acidification phenomenon. A potentially important step in this direction has been the recent refinement of auxin binding studies by P. M. Ray (personal communication, 1975). These studies indicate a rapid and reversible binding of natural and synthetic auxins to membrane fractions (largely the ER) with a specificity similar to that expected if such binding was related to auxin-enhanced growth. Unfortunately, at the present time it has not been possible to detect any biochemical ramifications of auxin binding to vesicles, thus pointing to an important area for further investigation.

Clearly we also need more information on the precise mechanism of active acidification. Most of the evidence available seems to point to an electrogenic coupling between FC-stimulated H^+ efflux and cation uptake. But how is this pump activated? Are ATPases involved? Do auxin and fusicoccin really activate different mechanisms as it would presently appear, or are there simply different steps leading to the activation of a single H^+ pumping system? It is our view these questions will not be resolved quickly, but possible clues may be obtained through more precise measurements of the stoichiometry of K^+–H^+–malate levels after brief exposure to growth-regulating agents.

Viewing the other extreme of the acid-growth theory, namely the detailed mechanism involved in wall loosening, the situation is approachable in theory but in practice quite difficult. We are relatively certain that H^+ ions activate the enzymic cleavage of wall bonds, but what is their chemical nature? We simply do not know. In addition, there is no reliable method for calculating how many such bonds need to be cleaved to produce a given increment of extension, nor do we know how fast such potential breaks in the wall matrix may be repaired. As a result of these uncertainties, it is our view that the most successful entry into this problem is via identification and characterization of the enzymes involved in wall loosening. In practice this approach centers on our ability to isolate an enzyme or enzymes which can be added back to a deproteinized wall matrix and initiate extension which mimics the native extension response. To date this has been impossible—a circumstance perhaps not unexpected considering difficulties in such an approach but one in which the potential rewards could be considerable.

Last, it is interesting to speculate briefly on the origin of hormone-induced acidification. It is now recognized that proton extrusion across the plasma membrane is necessary in most cells for the maintenance of internal pH (Raven and Smith, 1974). This is particularly true for photosynthetic plant cells where fixation of CO_2 into carbohydrates results in the production of H^+ which must be extruded in exchange for K^+ or other cations. Indeed, the ATPase-driven proton excretion mechanism may have evolved simply to handle the problem of the cell's internal pH. However, even if this were true the same mechanism seems to participate in a variety of other processes. Mitchell (1970) on the other hand has proposed that the proton pump arose as a means of setting up H^+ gradients which could drive other transport processes coupled to the back diffusion of H^+. Extending this notion Mitchell further proposed that when redox-powered proton excretion systems developed they eventually were capable of setting up such a large H^+ gradient that the ATPases were forced to "run backward" and synthesize ATP. Whatever the overall evolutionary strategy in the past may have been it would appear that plant cells have simply made use of an already existing mechanism, adapting it by increasing its magnitude and providing for control by hormones, and used it to control the rate of cell enlargement.

ACKNOWLEDGMENTS

This work was supported by National Science Foundation and NATO Grants to D. L. R. and by E.R.D.A. contracts to R. C. We wish to thank Drs. K. D. Johnson and W. K. Purves for critically reading this manuscript.

REFERENCES

Agrawal, K. M. L., and Bahl, O. P. (1968). *J. Biol. Chem.* **243**, 103.

Barkley, G. M., and Leopold, A. C. (1973). *Plant Physiol.* **52**, 76.

Bauer, W. D., Talmadge, K. W., Keegstra, K., and Albersheim, P. (1973). *Plant Physiol.* **51**, 174.

Bonner, J. (1949). *Am. J. Bot.* **36**, 323.

Buchala, A. J., and Meier, H. (1973). *Planta* **111**, 245.

Christiansen, G. S., and Thimann, K. V. (1950). *Arch. Biochem. Biophys.* **26**, 248.
Cleland, R. (1968). *Science* **160**, 192.
Cleland, R. (1971). *Annu. Rev. Plant Physiol.* **22**, 197.
Cleland, R. (1973). *Proc. Natl. Acad. Sci. U.S.A.* **70**, 3092.
Cleland, R. E. (1975). *Planta* **127**, 139.
Cleland, R. E. (1976a). *Plant Physiol.* **58**, 210.
Cleland, R. E. (1976b). *Planta* **128**, 201.
Cleland, R. E. (1976c). *Biochem. Biophys. Res. Commun.* **69**, 333.
Cleland, R. E. (1977). In, "Integration of Activity in the Higher Plant" (D. H. Jennings, ed.). Soc. Exp. Biol. Symp. Vol. 31. Cambridge Univ. Press, London and New York (in press).
Cleland, R. E., and Lomax, T. (1977). In, "Regulation of Cell Membrane Activities in Plants" (E. Marre and O. Ciferri, eds.), pp. 161–171. North-Holland Publ., Amsterdam.
Cleland, R. E., and Rayle, D. L. (1972). *Planta* **106**, 61.
Cleland, R. E., and Rayle, D. L. (1975). *Plant Physiol.* **55**, 547.
Cleland, R. E., Prins, H. B. A., Harper, J. R., and Higinbotham, N. (1977). *Plant Physiol.* **59**, 395.
Cocucci, M., Marrè, E., Ballarin Denti, A., and Scacchi, A. (1976). *Plant Sci. Lett.* **6**, 143.
Cohen, J. D. (1974). Master's Thesis, San Diego State University, San Diego, California.
Cohen, J. D., Johnson, K. D., and Rayle, D. L. (1974). *Plant Physiol.* **53**, Suppl., 42.
Commoner, B., and Thimann, K. V. (1941). *J. Gen. Physiol.* **24**, 279.
Conchie, J., Gelman, A. L., and Levy, G. A. (1967). *Biochem. J.* **103**, 609.
Datko, A. H., and Maclachlan, G. A. (1968). *Plant Physiol.* **43**, 735.
Davies, P. J. (1973). *Bot. Rev.* **39**, 139.
Durand, H., and Rayle, D. L. (1973). *Planta* **114**, 63.
Edwards, K. L., and Scott, T. K. (1974). *Planta* **119**, 27.
Etherton, B. (1970). *Plant Physiol.* **45**, 527.
Evans, M. L. (1974a). *Plant Physiol.* **54**, 213.
Evans, M. L. (1974b). *Annu. Rev. Plant Physiol.* **25**, 195.
Evans, M. L., and Ray, P. M. (1969). *J. Gen. Physiol.* **53**, 1.
Fan, D. F., and Maclachlan, G. A. (1967). *Plant Physiol.* **42**, 1114.
Green, P. B., and Cummins, W. R. (1974). *Plant Physiol.* **54**, 863.
Hager, A., Menzel, H., and Krauss, A. (1971). *Planta* **100**, 47.
Haschke, H. P., and Lüttge, U. (1973). *Z. Naturforsch.* **28C**, 555.
Haschke, H. P., and Lüttge, U. (1975). *Plant Physiol.* **56**, 696.
Hertel, R., Thomson, K.-St., and Russo, V. E. A. (1972). *Planta* **107**, 325.
Hiatt, A. J. (1967). *Z. Pflanzenphysiol.* **56**, 233.
Higinbotham, N., and Anderson, W. P. (1974). *Can. J. Bot.* **52**, 1011.
Higinbotham, N., Latimer, H., and Eppley, R. (1953). *Science* **118**, 243.
Hodges, J. K., Leonard, R. T., Bracker, C. E., and Keenan, T. W. (1972). *Proc. Natl. Acad. Sci. U.S.A.* **69**, 3307.
Ilan, I. (1973). *Physiol. Plant.* **28**, 146.
Ilan, I., and Shapira, S. (1976). *Physiol. Plantarum* **38**, 243.
Jacobs, M., and Ray, P. M. (1975). *Plant Physiol.* **56**, 695.
Jacobs, M., and Ray, P. M. (1976). *Plant Physiol.* **58**, 203.
Johnson, K. D. and Rayle, D. L. (1976). *Plant Physiol.* **57**, 806.
Johnson, K. D., Daniels, D., Dowler, M. J., and Rayle, D. L. (1974). *Plant Physiol.* **53**, 224.
Kasami, K., and Yamaki, T. (1974). *Plant Cell Physiol.* **15**, 957.
Katz, M., and Ordin, L. (1967). *Biochem. Biophys. Acta* **141**, 126.

Keegstra, K., and Albersheim, P. (1970). *Plant Physiol.* **45**, 675.
Keegstra, K., Talmadge, K. W., Bauer, W. D., and Albersheim, P. (1973). *Plant Physiol.* **51**, 188.
Kelly, S. (1947). *Am. J. Bot.* **34**, 521.
Kitasato, H. (1968). *J. Gen. Physiol.* **52**, 60.
Kivilaan, A., Beaman, T. C., and Bandurski, R. S. (1961). *Plant Physiol.* **36**, 605.
Labavitch, J. M., and Ray, P. M. (1974). *Plant Physiol.* **53**, 669.
Lado, P., Pennachioni, A., Caldogni, F., Russi, S., and Silano, V. (1972). *Physiol. Plant Pathol.* **2**, 75.
Lado, P., Caldogno, F., Pennachioni, A., and Marrè, E. (1973). *Planta* **110**, 311.
Lado, P., De Michelis, M. I., Cerano, R., and Marrè, E. (1976). *Plant Sci. Lett.* **6**, 5.
Lai, Y. F., and Thompson, J. E. (1971). *Biochim. Biophys. Acta* **233**, 84.
Lee, S., Kivilaan, A., and Bandurski, R. S. (1967). *Plant Physiol.* **42**, 968.
Lembi, C. A., Morré, D. J., Thomson, K.-St., and Hertel, R. (1971). *Planta* **99**, 37.
Lockhart, J. A. (1965). *J. Theor. Biol.* **8**, 264.
Loescher, W. H., and Nevins, D. J. (1970). *Plant Physiol.* **46**, Suppl., 14.
Maclachlan, G. A., and Duda, C. T. (1965). *Biochim. Biophys. Acta* **97**, 288.
Maclachlan, G. A., and Young, M. (1962). *Nature (London)* **194**, 1319.
MacRobbie, E. A. C. (1971). *Philos. Trans. R. Soc. London* **262**, 333.
Marrè, E., Lado, P., Caldogno, F., and Colombo, R. (1973). *Plant Sci. Lett.* **1**, 179.
Marrè, E., Lado, P., Ferroni, A., and Denti, A. B. (1974a). *Plant Sci. Lett.* **2**, 257.
Marrè, E., Lado, R., Caldogno, F. R., Colombo, R., and DeMichelis, M. I. (1974b). *Plant Sci. Lett.* **3**, 365.
Marrè, E., Colombo, R., Lado, P., and Rasi-Caldogno, F. (1974c). *Plant Sci. Lett.* **2**, 139.
Marrè, E. (1977). In "Regulation of Cell Membrane Activities in Plants" (E. Marrè and O. Ciferri, eds), pp. 185–202. North-Holland Publ., Amsterdam.
Masuda, Y., and Wada, S. (1967). *Bot. Mag.* **80**, 100.
Mitchell, P. (1970). *Symp. Soc. Gen. Microbiol.* **20**, 121.
Mondal, H., Mandel, R. K., and Biswas, B. B. (1972). *Nature (London), New Biol.* **240**, 111.
Nevins, D. J. (1970). *Plant Physiol.* **46**, 458.
Nevins, D. J. (1975). *Plant Cell Physiol.* **16**, 347.
Penny, P., Dunlop, J, Perley, J. E., and Penny, D. (1975). *Plant Sci. Lett.* **4**, 35.
Perley, J. E., Penny, D., and Penny, P. (1975). *Plant Sci. Lett.* **4**, 133.
Pitman, M. G., Schaefer, N., and Wildes, R. A. (1975a). *Plant Sci. Lett.* **4**, 323.
Pitman, M. G., Schaefer, N., and Wildes, R. A. (1975b). *Planta* **126**, 61.
Poole, R. J. (1974). *Can. J. Bot.* **52**, 1011.
Pope, D. G., Osborne, M., and Abroms, J. (1975). *Plant Physiol.* **56**, S2.
Preston, R. D. (1974). "The Physical Biology of Plant Cell Walls," 491. Chapman & Hall, London.
Raven, J. A., and Smith, F. A. (1974). *Can. J. Bot.* **52**, 1035.
Ray, P. M. (1973). *Plant Physiol.* **51**, 601.
Ray, P. M., Green, P. B., and Cleland, R. (1972). *Nature (London)* **239**, 163.
Rayle, D. L. (1973). *Planta* **114**, 63.
Rayle, D. L., and Cleland, R. (1970). *Plant Physiol.* **46**, 250.
Rayle, D. L., and Cleland, R. (1972). *Planta* **104**, 282.
Rayle, D. L., and Cleland, R. E. (1974). *Planta* **104**, 282.
Rayle, D. L., Haughton, P. M., and Cleland, R. (1970). *Proc. Natl. Acad. Sci. U.S.A.* **67**, 1814.
Ruesink, A. W. (1969). *Planta* **89**, 95.

Slayman, C. L. (1970). *Am. Zool.* **10**, 377.
Sloane, M., and Sadava, D. (1975). *Nature (London)* **257**, 68.
Smith, F. A. (1972). *New Physiol.* **71**, 595.
Squire, G. R., and Mansfield, T. A. (1974). *New Physiol.* **73**, 433.
Stout, R., Johnson, K. D., and Rayle, D. L. (1977). *Plant Physiol.* (in press.)
Talmadge, K. W., Keegstra, K., Baucr, W. D., and Albersheim, P. (1973). *Plant Physiol.* **51**, 158.
Tanimoto, E., and Masuda, Y. (1968). *Physiol. Plant.* **21**, 820.
Turner, N. C. (1972). *Nature (London)* **235**, 341.
Turner, N. C., and Graniti, A. (1969). *Nature (London)* **223**, 1070.
Valent, B. S., and Albersheim, P. (1974). *Plant Physiol.* **54**, 105.
Vanderhoef, L. N., and Stahl, C. A. (1975). *Proc. Natl. Acad. Sci. U.S.A.* **72**, 1822.
Wada, S., Tanimoto, E., and Masuda, Y. (1968). *Plant Cell Physiol.* **9**, 369.
Yamagata, Y., and Masuda, Y. (1976). *Plant Cell Physiol.* **17**, 1235.
Yamamoto, R., Maki, K., Yamagata, Y., and Masuda, Y. (1974). *Plant Cell Physiol.* **15**, 823.

SUBJECT INDEX

E

F

G

H

I

L

CONTENTS OF PREVIOUS VOLUMES

Volume 3

Volume 4

Volume 5

Volume 6

Volume 7

Volume 8

Volume 9

Volume 10

A 7
B 8
C 9
D 0
E 1
F 2
G 3
H 4
I 5
J 6